MAMMALS AS "VERMIN"

COUGAR
DOG
COYOTE
LYNX
FOX
WEASEL
MINK
MARTEN
FISHER
CAT
SKUNK
WEASEL
BADGER
SKUNK
WEASEL
CAT
OTTER
MINK
RACCOON
SHREW
BAT
FOX
FOX
BEAR

How increases in populations of
fish, insects, birds, and mammals
are kept in some sort of control
by activities of specific mammals

PALMER'S

Fieldbook of Mammals

A UNIT IN A SERIES OF
AIDS TO CONSERVATION

By
E. Laurence Palmer

A Dutton Nature Fieldbook

NEW YORK

E. P. DUTTON & COMPANY, INC.

1957

LIBRARY OF CONGRESS CATALOG CARD NO.: 57-8974

Introduction

UNLIKE most other books on mammals, this fieldbook devotes approximately one third of its space to a consideration of mammals that are domesticated or semi-domesticated. This is done in the conviction that more persons learn about the food habits, locomotion, reproductive behavior, and economic importance of mammals through observing domesticated ones than through observing those that are wild. The information that the average person needs about his dog, horse, or pig is not to be found in the average mammal book, and the knowledge needed about mice in the attic, squirrels in the trees, bats in the air, and minks in the brook is not to be found in books on domestic mammals. It is one of the purposes of this volume to help the average person in both areas.

For the technical zoologist, the book provides illustrations and information regarding representatives of each of the orders of living mammals, and facts concerning life habits and economics not common in zoology texts. The illustrations point out some of the important differences between closely related species not easily differentiated, and data are given on age variations, as shown by teeth and other characters, that are not usually readily available in the laboratory or library.

For the outdoor naturalist and conservationist, information on how to recognize the local presence of mammals by tracks and scats is included. Supplementing this are pertinent facts on the ecological problems of the mammal and of its associates.

It is hoped that the junior and amateur naturalist in town or country will find in the book ready information about the mammals he has the opportunity to see, written in a language that is not too difficult, while technically true. The farmer may be helped to understand his stock, and the vermin with which he has to contend, the housewife her pets and the household pests, the trapper his fur-bearers, and the tourist the strange animals he may see for the first time in new territory.

It is hoped that teachers charged with teaching the generalizations of conservation and of biology will find material which will be helpful in applying these generalizations to specific animals available for study locally, either wild or in confinement.

My hope is, too, that the book will serve as a field companion for the family on a summer vacation and as a guide for the parent telling a short bedtime story, the youth in a summer or winter camp, or the businessman off on his annual vacation in the wilds. Its size permits it to be carried readily in the pocket, or in the glove compartment of the family car, and its range of coverage has been planned to guarantee its usefulness almost anywhere. It is designed to supplement, not to compete with, other books dealing with mammals on a popular and professional basis.

Acknowledgments

ALL books probably represent the efforts, sacrifices, and co-operation of others besides the author. This one is no exception, and to all who have figured in its production acknowledgment is gratefully given.

Since the preparation of the book called for activities while I was otherwise employed, permission had to be given by my employers to take on the project. In this connection thanks go to Cornell University, *Nature Magazine,* the McGraw-Hill Book Company, and the National Wildlife Federation. All of these contributed to the development of the idea. Particularly useful and appreciated was the cooperation of *Nature Magazine* and the McGraw-Hill Book Company, who, over the years, have published, respectively, feature articles and the *Fieldbook of Natural History,* in which some of the original material on which this book is based first appeared. Permission to reuse some of this material, including illustrations, was most helpful. It is believed that this book will not compete with these earlier publications of mine, because of differences in scope, approach, and objective.

Of course, obligation is recognized to the literature of the field, and particularly to the governmental and professional organizations interested in advancing the understanding of mammalogy. Complete files of the *Journal of Mammalogy* and of the *Journal of Wildlife Management* were used·to enrich the material available from other sources, including my personal experience. I have seen living representatives in the field of approximately 80% of the kinds of animals described herein, and an additional 10% in captivity in zoos or elsewhere, leaving only about 10% known to me through literature. I have also been lucky enough to have traveled in every state of the United States as well as a dozen foreign countries, to have met professional groups in every state but two, and to have taught in Hawaii and New Zealand. Experiences during most of these travels have contributed to the preparation of this book.

The skull collection in the laboratory of Dr. William J. Hamilton, Jr., at Cornell University was used freely when needed, and Dr. Hamilton gave helpful suggestions during the preparation of the manuscript.

The artists employed included Hope Sawyer, Louis Fuertes, Stephen Collins, Edward Reilly, Jr., Elizabeth Burckmyer, Clara Garret, Carolyn Powers, and Frances McKittrick, as well as myself.

Special appreciation goes to Dr. Katherine VanWinkle Palmer, to whom the book is dedicated, whose patience, consideration, and encouragement were necessary when discouragement set in, and to whom I have been long and happily married.

E. LAURENCE PALMER

About This Book

IT MAY be true that "where ignorance is bliss, 'tis folly to be wise." It may with equal justice be said that when judgments are passed and actions are determined, it is dangerous to be ignorant. The fortunes of the world are influenced by specialists in the fields of science, politics, and economics. But highly important decisions in the affairs of mice and mares and men are also made by the engineer who upsets the ecology of a watershed, the farmer who grazes or burns over the "back forty" acres of his farm, the housewife who harbors a destructive pet, or the child who affectionately picks up an injured kitten.

This book, like some others, aims to assist in the identification and classification of mammals. It goes beyond that, however, giving also such data as body temperatures, which may be important to a physician; food, which is important in a farmer's economy; habits, which are meaningful to the conservationist; and behavior, which may help to mold our souls. Other books ably carry these specialties further. But it is hoped that this one will give help to the average person, who is in a position most frequently to help or hinder the relationships that exist between man and other mammals. These are the people who in the long run make the broad decisions.

The beginning of the book, therefore, attempts to establish a general understanding of how mammals live, move, and interpret their environment. In the major portion of the book, a single page is usually devoted to the attributes of each of the different animals discussed, and perhaps its relatives. In some sections of the book, such as those on dogs, cats, cattle, horses, and swine, discussions of more general aspects of the particular group of mammals—for example, their ancestry, services to man, reproduction, or care—are included on right-hand pages. The illustrations will aid in recognition, and the discussions will help to provide data on weight, length, and other specific facts of importance. When there are significant differences in weight or size between the sexes, this information is given.

Respiration rate is given as the number of cubic centimeters of air breathed per kilogram of the animal's weight per hour. It varies from 13,700 in some shrews to 14 in a hibernating woodchuck. The figures given do not refer to the number of breaths per unit of time.

This combination of general and specific information about mammals should help to bridge the gap caused by misunderstanding in our relationships with our hairy and furry fellow inhabitants of the earth.

Synopsis of Orders and Table of Contents

8

What Is a Mammal?

A MAMMAL may be described as a warm-blooded vertebrate whose skin bears hair that is usually molted periodically and glands of various types that produce sweat, scent, milk, or hair.

Above all, a mammal has a highly organized nervous system, which contributes to the fact that as a group mammals can just about master the earth. In this realm, it seems evident that man is superior to other mammals. We are asked the question whether mammals can reason, and since man is a mammal, and man can reason if any mammal can, we must answer that some mammals, at least, can reason, just as some can fly, some hibernate, and some lay eggs, and so on. Whether this ability to reason is shared by other mammals may be questioned, but it cannot be said honestly that man alone is aware of his environment, has curiosity, fear, and affection. Neither can it be said that man alone is able to make sacrifices for the happiness and safety of others or to act in preparation for a situation that is to develop in the future. Where reason comes into a consideration of all of these things may well depend on a strict definition of what is meant by reason.

The classification of mammals varies with different authors and depends on the characters used. If we use the reproductive system, it seems appropriate that the egg-layers and the pouch-bearers should be classed as more primitive than other mammals. It seems reasonable to assume that giving birth to helpless young is a more primitive character than giving birth to young able quickly to care for themselves. If we rely on the bony structure, it is usually recognized that the possession of many kinds of teeth, such as incisors, canines, premolars and molars, and many of each kind, is more primitive than to have fewer kinds of teeth, or fewer teeth of each kind. The dentition of man, who has incisors, canines, and so on, is obviously more generalized than that of a squirrel or a horse, which usually lack canines. Similarly, our hands and feet with their 5 units are more generalized and therefore more primitive than the single toe of the horse or the 2 toes of the cow.

In this book and in others I have tried to rationalize the order of presentation, partly in keeping with the apparent specialization of fundamental parts. Specifically, I have used where pertinent the classification as used in Miller's and Kellogg's *List of North American Recent Mammals*, referred to in detail on page 25.

Many writers in the past have jumped to conclusions freely in their interpretations of animal behavior, but when we get down to the facts of the case we know relatively little about the fundamental senses of mammals and probably much less about their emotional life. Obviously all mammals engage in activities that are defensive. On occasion they may become aggressive and offensive, particularly in defense of their young.

What Sight Means to Mammals

UNLESS an animal can see, it has difficulty in moving about safely, in finding its food and friends and avoiding its foes.

Seeing implies the presence of a suitably lighted object that activates a sensitive organ of sight. The light must be proportionate in luminance and color to the sensitivity of the animal.

We give a luminance intensity of 10,000 to the brilliant light of snow under a clear noonday sun; 1,000 to that of a hazy day; 10 to an average living-room wall; 6 to television; .019 to vanishing color; .01 to moonlight; and .0001 to a hazy, moonless, starlight night. Mammals vary greatly in their sensitivity to the whole range of luminance, some being blind at either end of the range.

Color is important to some animals. It varies from violet through blue, green, yellow, and orange to red. Among mammals, men and cats are most acutely sensitive to yellows. Insects may be blind to the red end of the spectrum and birds to the blue end. Color blindness may be inherited. Some believe deer to be color blind.

Size, shape, color, position, and movement are significant in sight. Mammals such as cattle, with wide pupils in the eye, have a wide horizontal range of vision, while cats, with vertical pupils, have greater vertical range.

Sight from two separated eyes provides a useful third-dimensional effect of importance in getting information on terrain, friends, and foes. Eye position may be important. A rabbit, with eyes on the sides of the head, can see forward and backward without making movements which might disclose its presence. Mammals may be significantly farsighted or nearsighted. They detect lateral movements more easily than differences in distance caused by moving along the line of vision.

Sometimes animals must avoid being seen. This may be done by moving in light to which enemies are not sensitive, by using concealing cover, by using deceiving camouflage, or by controlling movements to avoid erratic actions. A slow, sustained motion is less conspicuous than a fast, irregular motion.

Many mammals are not handicapped by limitations in vision because they have superior development of other senses, such as those of hearing, smell, or feeling. An animal blessed with a superior sense of smell can safely roam at night, when it cannot be seen by its enemies. Within a group, mammals may vary greatly in the reliance they place on different senses. A greyhound follows its prey by sight, a beagle follows its by scent, a hound may stay with the pack with the help of sound, and some dogs, by intense speed and courage, may be assured of full stomachs though they have little ability in most of the senses. Sight is of tremendous importance to mammals, but it is not the only valuable sense which they use effectively in surviving.

Sounds Affect Mammals

SOUNDS influence the health, survival, happiness, and general well-being of mammals, communicating intelligence, warning, and invitation from one to another, and being otherwise useful.

Ignoring philosophical discussions, we can say that sounds are caused by vibrations communicated through a medium to an organ receptive to the intensity and pitch of the vibrations received. Some low-pitched sounds can be felt as well as heard, and high-pitched sounds may produce effects of varying natures.

Sounds ranging from 15 to 20,000 cycles per second may be heard by man, individuals varying, in part with age, in their receptivity of the extremes of this range. Bats hear sounds ranging from 20 to 98,000 c.p.s.; cats, from 30 to 45,000; dolphins, from 100 to 130,000; opossums, from 100 to 19,000 or possibly 30,000; deer mice, from 500 to 95,000. Chimpanzees may hear sounds up to 33,000; and dogs, guinea pigs, and rats, up to 40,000, meaning that these mammals may hear sounds not heard by man with his 20,000 maximum. And bats, cats, dolphins, and deer mice are capable of hearing sounds not heard by rats, dogs, and guinea pigs. Katydids are sensitive to sounds ranging from 430 to 45,000 c.p.s.; pigeons, from 100 to 12,000. Goldfish can hear sounds of 2,700 c.p.s. and alligators, of 340 c.p.s. All of these figures assume sounds of suitable volume or intensity, and it is sometimes difficult to recognize the threshold between hearing and feeling.

To say that one creature can hear better than another, one must specify the sound involved.

Intentionally or otherwise, mammals produce significant sounds with the vocal cords; by violent expulsion of the breath; by striking the water, earth, or other part of the environment; and, in the case of man, by constructing and using involved machines powered by different kinds of variously used energy. Men produce sounds by clapping their hands; beaver by hitting the water with their tails; many other animals by beating the ground with their feet, possibly in excitement; and otherwise. Bats produce high-pitched sounds whose echoes advise them in flight of the imminence of food or obstructions.

Sounds are received usually by the ears, which must be receptive to be effective. The ears of many mammals are movable. This increases their receptivity of sounds. Commonly plant-eating animals, such as horses, cattle, and rabbits, have more movable ears than do the animal-eaters, thus permitting them to be informed of the approach of enemies with a minimum of dangerous movement.

Location of the direction of sources of sound is made easy by the possession of two separated hearing organs.

Since vibrations in the bones of one's own head affect the nature of sounds one produces, a recording of one's own voice may not sound natural because the record is restricted to airborne sounds. Health, age, and atmospheric conditions all modify sound reception.

Odors Have Meaning to Mammals

MANY mammals, such as deer, rely more heavily on their sense of smell for their safety than on their ears or eyes, thus making it possible to locate their food supply and mates through their ability to smell, or, for that matter, to give off scent.

Odors are commonly produced by the freeing into the air of some substance which, when moistened, produces a chemical effect to which certain nerves are sensitive. Here again there are three factors involved: a stimulating substance, a medium of transfer, and a suitable receptive structure.

The statement that polar bears can smell food 20 miles away has been questioned, but there is no doubt that animals vary greatly in their ability to use scent to their advantage. Bloodhounds have a remarkable ability to find significance in obviously faint scent, and man uses the bloodhound's ability to aid him in finding lost persons or running down criminals. Hunters know that their scent will be carried downwind to deer and other game, therefore they know how important it is to do their stalking upwind.

Man can detect oil of peppermint by smell at a concentration of .024 milligrams per liter of air and artificial musk at a concentration of .0004 m.p.l. In man, the sense of smell is concentrated in the wet mucous membrane of the nose. Mammals excelling in ability to know their environment through odor commonly have noses whose tips are moist and thus capable of moistening material in the air which may be used in scenting. Watch a dog at work using its nose and see how it moves the sensitive nose tip as an exploratory organ and how, by inhaling and expelling air, it increases the amount of air used in its work.

Mammals intentionally or otherwise give off scent for many reasons. Urine is a common medium used in scent trails, and some deer urinate on the scent glands on their legs, thus increasing the scent given off and helping keep a herd or family together. Many other grazing animals, such as horses, have scent glands on their legs which give a significant odor to plants as a signal to fellow members of the herd. Newly born fawns are protected by the fact that these animals do not give off scent, as they will when sufficiently mature to get safety by other means.

Members of the weasel group, particularly the skunks, also use scent in defense. It definitely is given off by female dogs in heat, attracting prospective mates from far and wide. Some squirrels have remarkable ability in scenting food buried under earth or snow.

We know so little about the getting and giving of scent by mammals that it is dangerous for us to draw conclusions about their behavior on the assumption that their actions are governed by stimuli more significant to us.

The Importance of Taste to Mammals

THE ability of mammals to taste their environment makes it possible for them to control to some extent the content of their alimentary tracts and to accept or reject foods available for consumption. Obviously this is highly important to their well-being.

To be useful, the sense of taste requires the presence of suitable receptive or rejective structures where the taste contact is made. The substance must be put into solution and brought to the taste organs or taste buds. These are normally inside the mouth and concentrated on the tongue. In the case of fishes and some amphibia, the taste organs may be over the outside of the body as well as in the mouth. A catfish can taste food in the mud with the underside of its body, but mammals, of course, cannot do this.

Through the sense of taste man can detect cane sugar in solution in water in a concentration of 1 part to 200; table salt, at 1 to 400; hydrochloric acid, at 1 to 15,000, and strychnine, at 1 to 2,500,000 parts. A rat will accept water and a salt concentration of .06%. A cat will sense the presence of salt in water at a concentration of .1 to .3%, and a rabbit will reject water with a salt content of 1.4%.

The sense of taste and the sense of smell are closely associated, and a person with a bad cold may not enjoy food because the sense of smell associated with the sense of taste is not functioning. The reason for this is that the mucous membrane involved in the sense of smell may be too inflamed to function.

Flavors are divided into those that are sweet, sour, bitter, and salty. Special parts of the tongue vary in their ability to sense each of these. Many mammals commonly explore the nature of prospective food and of associated animals by licking with the tongue. This may at times be of importance in learning of the condition of prospective mates in their breeding cycles. Since the sense of taste functions through materials in solution, it is normal that licking other animals for the sake of learning about them, by dogs, for example, commonly centers on areas where the mucous membrane is exposed.

Mammals vary considerably in the range of acceptance of substances tasted. Dogs will drink water not acceptable to horses, and horses can and will drink water not safe for human consumption. Unfortunately, taste is not wholly adequate in determining what is good or bad for the intestinal tract.

The Sense of Touch in Mammals

THROUGH the sense of touch, many mammals may learn of their environment without tasting, smelling, seeing, or hearing it. This may be important in locating food, in avoiding danger, or in seeking better environment, and it may produce pleasure or pain, as is the case with sound, light, odor, and flavor.

Contact between the subject being touched and suitable sensory areas of the receiver is essential in learning through the sense of touch. Raccoons explore mud for food with their sensitive "fingers." Star-nosed moles use the sense of touch through the unique structures at their noses. Touch plays an important part at times in moving from place to place, as when the footing under a stream is explored with the feet. It is also important in reproduction, in food getting, and in other activities. (See, for example, page 22.)

Feelings communicated by touch have been classified as including those that are painful, those that vary with temperature, those that vary with pressure, and those that move or are stationary. Some of these sensations are definitely measurable. Pressure pain is measured in the number of grams per square millimeter necessary for the production of pain. It varies in different parts of the human body, as follows: abdomen, 15; front of forearm, 20; calf and back of forearm, 30; back of hand, 100; sole of foot, 200; and finger tip, 300.

Pricking pain differs from pressure pain in different parts of the body, in the following order of intensity: forehead, check, nose, lips, chest, abdomen, groin, thigh, calf, shin, heel, shoulder, nape of neck, upper arm, back of hand, finger pad, and fingernail.

Temperature differences apparently are felt only by warm-blooded animals, but variously by them, by individuals of a kind, and by parts of the individuals. Man's face has relatively few cold receptors and many warmth receptors. The mucous lining of the mouth has relatively few warmth receptors. Man seems to be most sensitive to touch through his face and through the surface of the fingers.

Sensitivity to movement through touch is important to many eaters of small animals, who by this means can locate the presence of living food in areas where they cannot see, hear, smell, or taste.

Comparatively little is actually known about the sensitivity of most mammals to touch. At least, what is known is seldom known so well that it can be recorded in data significant in understanding the mammals. So many factors, such as age, health, fatigue, temperature, humidity, light, and chemical nature, are involved that studies in this field offer tremendous opportunities for those interested in advancing knowledge of mammals.

15

Mammals and Man's Major Problems

MAN'S major problems include those of food, shelter, health, work, and happiness. In all of these, other mammals play a role.

From mammals man gets food in the form of dairy products and flesh. Through selection, man has been able to get a maximum of these foods, as regards both quantity and quality, with a minimum of labor and time. Research increases effectiveness here.

Shelters and clothing made of hides, hair, and fur from mammals have made it possible for man to survive at times and in places in which he could not otherwise exist. Sheep, goats, and the fur bearers have been the most helpful here, but technical developments are making us decreasingly dependent on raw animal products. Eventually coal tar or cellulose may give us the raiment which we now get from cattle, sheep, goats, or minks, and from plant sources.

Man uses other mammals effectively in studying his own diseases and those of his associated animals. Serums useful in fighting disease are produced in horses. The development of disease patterns are observed in mice, dogs, monkeys, and other laboratory animals, and the findings are used in interpreting effectively man's disease and nutrition problems. This is particularly important with animals whose problems are similar to man's but whose life cycle is shorter. Mammals also help man to be healthy by encouraging him to get exercise through riding and other sports. Materials processed from the glands of mammals are effective in correcting deficiencies in the glands of man, and a great variety of unique substances found in the carcasses of mammals are useful in the arts developed by man.

Some mammals carry diseases which may be communicable to man, and may thus form a threat to man's health and wellbeing. Rabies and tuberculosis have been involved in this story.

Man must work, and he has found that other mammals can often be used to increase the amount of work done. Draft animals, such as horses, oxen, and dogs; pack animals, such as camels, horses, burros, and dogs; riding animals, such as horses, mules, camels, and elephants, have helped man in his labors. In some cases, as with race horses, they have also added to man's joy in living and have sometimes contributed to his downfall economically.

Mammals such as domestic dogs, cats, and horses have also given men welcome companionship. Many men find a purpose in life in trying to understand domestic mammals, possibly as a means of understanding themselves, and certainly as a means of helping other men live happily and well.

Mammals have contributed to man's everyday customs, to his religion, and his folklore, and in spite of technological developments man will continue to find happiness and help in his associations with other mammals.

Independence and Interdependence

TOPOGRAPHY and climate are important factors for mammals in maintaining independence. Whales and mountain goats are not competitors for breeding territory, and polar bears and yaguarundis do not fight with one another over fish. Man, who has mastered the art of roaming at will over and under the ocean, over mountaintops and through the sky at any season and climate, has been the arch competitor with all other mammals for food and other necessities and luxuries of life.

Lesser ecological units, like a hole in the ground, a spring, or a dense tree, frequently provide effective isolation, helping animals to remain independent of others. Faunas of varying degrees of simplicity are to be found in the depths of the ocean and at its surface, in its shallows, and on its shores. Lakes and streams of varying stability and chemical content, wet border-lands, grasslands, woodlands, deserts, sand dunes—each has a degree of entity so far as its mammal populations are concerned, and this makes independence relatively simple. Man, who can control the wanderings and breeding habits of many animals, has been very active in using isolation to develop breeds of other mammals, superior in the qualities man recognizes as worth while.

The interdependence of man and other mammals, of mammals and plants, and of mammals and other animals, is often as important to understand as is independence, and it is frequently disastrously misunderstood.

Competition for territory in which to raise a family, and for food with which to satisfy hunger, is modified by the needs of different animals. Plants compete with each other for a place in the sun and for water and elbow room. Plant-eaters, such as sheep and gophers, compete with one another for plants which they can eat; and coyotes, wolves, and foxes compete with one another for the gophers that satisfy their hunger. Families of coyotes compete with other coyote families for food, and mastery of territory is important for the survival of the young of a new generation. The young pups of a family compete with one another for food and mates, making emigration important, not only to prevent inbreeding but also to assure some use of suitable unused territory.

The role of predation must be recognized as important and valuable in controlling populations which might otherwise compete disastrously with their own kind. Cougars keep down the deer population, lynxes control rabbits, and foxes decimate mouse populations to mutual advantage. Man does not always recognize the niceties of these interrelationships, and frequently uses observed isolated predations as an excuse for wholesale depredation through unwarranted vermin campaigns. It is hoped that this book may be helpful in rationalizing man's behavior in this area, at least.

Home and Sanitation Problems

THE survival of mammals may depend on opportunity to construct and defend a home or to control a home territory. Such defense may be of an individual, family, or herd nature, but in all these cases it is important. Often success in controlling desirable territory depends on ability in combat, this ability being either mental or physical. However, the meek may inherit the earth, and animals capable of rapid multiplication frequently compete successfully with more powerful creatures.

Owing to seasonal conditions and the varying abundance of food, the home range of many mammals may cover thousands of miles. Seasonal migrations vary with the food needs of animals and their ability to move through the air, as do bats, over the ground, like elk, or through the water, like seals and whales. Denial of access to parts of the natural range may at times lead to the extermination of a species. Many mammals avoid long surface migrations by being able to migrate vertically, finding sanctuary from severe winter by moving a few inches or feet underground, where survival is possible. For example, cottontails, which do not dig burrows, use the burrows of woodchucks for this purpose. Thus one species may be dependent for its existence on the activities of another.

The elements of a home usually include shelter, food, and water, light and opportunity for waste disposal also being variously involved.

Shelter may be simply a bed in natural cover, or it may involve the gathering of suitable material and fashioning it into structures varying from a mouse nest to a skyscraper. How widely mammal shelters vary is suggested in the subsequent treatment of different species. Frequently comfort for helpless young is required, and this is forthcoming in countless forms, ranging from the grass linings of nests to electric blankets.

Wastes must be disposed of efficiently, since no organism can live in an environment clogged with its own waste products. Wastes such as urine, dung, and carrion are disposed of carelessly or meticulously in the different species. The presence of urine deposits is often obvious to animals with well-developed senses of smell, and may play interesting roles, as suggested on page 13. Not only is presence thus indicated, but also sometimes sexual condition, and this serves to bring mates together. A fleeing tapir may urinate backward between its legs and thus leave a sign that may have significance.

Dung may be allowed to accumulate, left at random, or meticulously buried. The dung is variously spoken of as "chips" for bison, "scats" generally, or particularly for dogs and cats, "droppings" generally, and of course "manure" for cattle. In some cases, as in rabbits, droppings including undigested food may be eaten and used a second time by the animal responsible. Many scats are illustrated in this book. They are usually significant in revealing the food eaten by the animal and, as such, are important in food studies and in general research.

Reproduction in Mammals

ONE cannot appreciate the whole story of mammals, judge their potentialities, or manage them without reasonable understanding relative to their reproductive story, which involves the winning of mates, breeding, gestation, and birth; juvenile, mature, and senescent life; and even the factors involved in the evolution of breeds and the improvement, by controlled selection, of the mammals of the future.

In the early pages of this book I give brief examples of mammals with primitive methods of reproduction, including the laying of eggs from which the young hatch after an incubation period much like that found in some birds. At the end of the book animals are discussed whose young may move about freely within hours of the time they are born. In between are the mammals that spend their early days in a brood sac in the mother's body and those in which the young in early stages are practically helpless and wholly dependent on parental care for most essentials of life. Mammals, of course, are unique in the care given the young by nursing through mammary glands.

In general, the number of young is greater in those species in which the hazards of early life are the greatest, and may decrease as the available protection from the parent generation increases.

The mating story varies widely. Some mammals are promiscuous; the males may mate with many females, or the females mate with many males, as opportunity presents itself. Polygamy and polyandry appear when, as in deer, a single male maintains for himself as large a harem of females as possible, or when a female accepts a number of males as mates. Monogamy, in which an individual male and female mate with each other, may last for a breeding period or for life. Examples of all these types of behavior appear in the specific descriptions later in the book. Important in the breeding story is the span of life during which this is possible, and particularly the age at which it begins. Shrews, with a total life span of a year or two, must breed earlier than man, with a life span to roughly a century. In this story the age of each sex is important to complete understanding.

The gestation period between the mating act and birth varies in time, in season, and in type. Its duration is given where possible. Usually the mating period precedes actual birth by enough time to permit birth at a time of year when the young can have an adequate season of good conditions in which to develop through critical early stages. In bats, some weasels, and some other animals, there may be a delayed period after mating in which the sperm do not fertilize the egg, followed by a relatively short period of embryo development. Control of breeding is effected in cattle and some other mammals by artificial insemination. One bull of domestic cattle of proven quality may be involved in the fertilization of 200 cows at one service and father 6,000 calves a year, as contrasted with a more normal 30 calves a year.

Tracks, Trails, and Signs

MAMMALS are highly secretive in much that they do, and their presence is often unsuspected if we depend wholly on the daylight hours for observation. An understanding of the tracks, trails, and signs left by mammals in their wanderings is revealing and important to all interested in them. Books have been written on the subject by such authors as Jaeger, Murie, and Seton, as listed on pages 24 and 25. There is much room for further careful recording of track and sign data.

In this book I have tried to reduce reports on tracks and trails to formulas which cannot be complete, but which give a maximum of information in a minimum of space. Like any track representation, the formulas are primarily suggestive. Briefly, the track formulas given in this book may be interpreted as follows:

F 1 x 2, 5 means that each front foot leaves a track measuring 1 by 2 inches, and possibly shows 5 toes. The number of toes present and shown may not be the same, and often no toes will be indicated in the track, so the formula is merely a suggestive approximation. *H 2 x 5, 5* would refer similarly to the measurements and toes of each hind foot track. *Sp* refers to the lateral measurement between the tracks that are normally side by side or in pairs, as in rabbits. We call it the spread. It may or may not be significant in interpreting the width of the mammal making the tracks. A cautiously moving fox makes tracks in a single line, while a wandering woodchuck, of approximately similar width, would not leave the same kind of tracks. *L* refers to the leaping distance. The term *pug* may properly be used to describe any track or footprint, and since the tail often leaves a significant record, we include it in the sketches of those tracks or pugs. I use the term *trail* to indicate a series of tracks defined by a repetition of the track of a given foot or other structure.

The recognition of proper direction is important if one does not wish to backtrack a creature he is trying to follow. It may be observed that normally the profile of a single track is more nearly vertical in the direction in which the animal was moving. In other words, mammals tend to slide into their tracks and step out of them more neatly. In snow, the sun may melt this profile and distort it, and rain may cause confusing changes, as may wind, but the generalization may well be kept in mind by trackers.

Knowledge of tracks is of great importance in making studies of population counts to determine the abundance of different species in specific areas—a knowledge which may be essential to proper management and control measures. Knowledge of tracks and other signs is also of importance in the proper placing of responsibility for damages caused by mammals.

There is significance in the movements of mammals through the air, up and down trees, over and under the ground, and through the water.

What Mammal Skulls Tell Us

THE most durable part of a mammal is the enamel on the teeth. There is significance in the order of appearance and disappearance of the different teeth. Their nature indicates, for example, the food habits of animals that may have become extinct before man appeared on the earth. Age is indicated by the degree and nature of the wearing of the grinding surfaces of different teeth.

Since teeth and the associated skulls are not easily digested, they commonly appear in the parts discarded by predators and in the droppings left by them. Teeth also leave significant markings on bark, wood, and other foodstuffs which, if recognized, help us interpret situations which might otherwise be highly enigmatic. There is merit, then, in being able to recognize from a skull not only the animal that owned it, but also its age, food habits, and perhaps even some of its accidents. To help in this understanding, I have given a sketch of representative skulls of most groups, a tooth formula or formulas, and for most major groups, a sketch of the skeleton. With this help, a horse owner may have some idea of the age of his beast of burden. This also may be helpful to owners of dogs, cats, sheep, pigs, horses, goats, and cattle. All of this information should be particularly helpful to the field naturalist and practical conservationist. Bryan P. Glass has given us a useful paper on the skulls of some American mammals. It is listed in the bibliography on page 24.

The tooth formula used refers to the number of each kind of tooth on one side of each jaw, with the number of teeth on the upper jaw given first and that on the lower jaw second. *I* refers to the front, incisor, or cutting teeth; *C* to the canine, piercing or biting teeth; *P* to the premolars, and *M* to the molars, or grinding teeth. It should be noted that in many of the grazing mammals there are no incisors on the upper jaw, and that in the mammals discussed early in the book, there tend to be more of each kind of teeth than is the case with the animals discussed later, many of which may have no representative of some of the teeth.

For example, the tooth formula for the gray wolf is: I 3/3; C 1/1; P 4/4; M 2/3. I interpret this as follows: I 3/3 means that there are 3 incisors on both the upper and lower jaws, on one side, or a total of 12 incisors in the head. C 1/1 means that there is one canine tooth on each side of each jaw, or a total of 4 canines. P 4/4 means that there are 4 premolars on each side of each jaw, and M 2/3 means that there are 2 molars on each side of the upper jaw and 3 molars on each side of the lower jaw.

Careful studies are being made of the appearance and wear of teeth of mammals of known age. This information is of importance in harvesting parts of populations to assure good management and sustained, rational abundance.

The Importance of the Fur, Hide, and Hair of Mammals

It may be said with considerable truth that the fortunes of mammals hang by a hair, or at least by many hairs. For the possession of true hair is one of the unique characteristics of mammals, all of which at some time in their lives have some hair on some part or parts of their bodies. In another sense, it is certainly true that the future of many mammals will be much affected by recent technological advances in the production of synthetic furs. These artificial furs not only match the beauty of natural furs, but also exceed them in durability, are not subject to moth damage, and can be produced at a fraction of the financial cost and labor, and without the atrocious suffering inflicted on animals by the use of the inhumane steel trap.

Should the production of artificial furs come up to present expectations, mammals now in danger of extermination by unwise trapping will no longer be threatened. Incidentally, many men in the low-income brackets and rural youths who have earned something from the trapping of furs will no longer find it worth their while. Some will have to find other occupations, possibly less appealing to their abilities and their temperaments. Fortunes invested in fur farms may well be lost, and city folk burdened by the high cost of furs primarily of ornamental value may seek other areas in which to impress and arouse the envy of their neighbors and associates.

The fur trade, the center of many labor troubles associated with the processing of furs, may encounter in artificial furs another factor to cause disturbance.

Furs are classified on the basis of their durability, with otter fur considered as the standard of highest excellence. Data on this point are provided subsequently where appropriate. Industry has given many trade names to inferior furs in an attempt to make common furs appear more attractive. Some of these names are also given in the discussions.

The story of furs and competitive synthetic products may be duplicated in the field of wool production, with far-flung implications. Time was when men interested in grazing land for their sheep fought to the death with men seeking to use the same land for the grazing of cattle that yielded flesh and hides. Animal fabrics from the hair of domestic animals have had major economic importance in some parts of the world. Skilled human beings have demonstrated exceptional ability in being able to grade goats' wool by touch, and to recognize 13 diameter differences between 0.003 and 0.0067 inch. Only one man in 10,000, after three years of training, can master this skill well enough to be able to grade 500 pounds of wool a day.

The hair and wool of mammals, and the hides that bear these substances, have great importance to man.

The Management of Mammals

MAN'S intelligence, coupled with his knowledge of mammals, has made it possible for man to manage many of them and direct their destinies to his advantage. Mammals that provided a threat to his physical safety have been eliminated over much of their natural ranges. Conditions in some areas have been modified so that mammals can move in and prosper in areas where they could not normally exist. The manner in which this management has been effected has varied widely, from damming a brook or draining a swamp to improving the conditions needed by different animals—changing the courses of great river systems, irrigating wide desert lands, or converting productive forest lands or orchard lands into cracker-box suburban developments. There seems to have been little intelligence used by man in some of these management procedures.

Management of mammals calls for a whole series of decisions before a wise pattern of action can be established. Here are a few factors in that series.

First, we must decide what is wanted from an area or facility to be managed. Is a suburban development needed more than an orchard or a forest? Next, what is the existing population of the area, and what exotic organisms might exist there with benefit to all? To manage a mammal population intelligently, information as to its quality may be as important as data as to its nature. For example, is the population healthy, vigorous, and composed of individuals that are developing, or is it too largely composed of those who have seen their best days? If a population is to be harvested, is it certain that it might not be more useful alive than dead? Can the harvest be made efficiently so that the reproductive capacity of the group remains high? Is the harvesting to be done at random, by means that injure the product? For example, a muskrat nursing young, if shot with a gun, is more than a complete loss, because the hide is injured by the bullet and the litter of young cannot survive.

Processing of the product must be done competently to avoid undue drain on the source of raw material. The product must be where it can be marketed, and the end product must be used wisely by the consumer to make the most of the resource. These are but a few of the angles that must be understood by those who would manage mammals, either wild or under domestication. The control of enemies and disease, the planning of breeding, the fair division of the rewards from the mammals to landowners, harvesters, and other members of society, all come into the picture and make the management of mammals a challenge and a potential source of superior rewards.

The methods involved in management vary greatly and call for a careful evaluation of such questions as whether management shall be effected by cover control or artificial husbandry, and whether harvesting shall be conducted for the benefit of the landowner or of society at large. This makes the whole subject interesting.

A Mammal Library

Obviously a book of this size cannot completely satisfy anyone's interest in mammals. A good library is most helpful. On page 183 I give specific references to good books on dogs, and here I list some of the books on mammals in general that can be recommended if one is building his own library or seeking help in the public library.

In addition to these books, a number of periodicals should be consulted for further help. Among these may well be the files of the following:

Animal Kingdom, published by the New York Zoological Society.

Journal of Mammalogy

Journal of Wildlife Management

Nature Magazine

Natural History Magazine

General books on mammals include:

Anthony, H. E., *Fieldbook of North American Mammals,* G. P. Putnam's Sons, New York. 1928. 625 pages.

Barker, Will, *Familiar Animals of America.* Harper and Brothers, New York. 1956. 300 pages.

Booth, Ernest S., *How to Know the Mammals.* William C. Brown, Dubuque, Iowa. 1950. 206 pages.

Bourlière, François, *The Natural History of Mammals.* Alfred A. Knopf, New York. 1954. 375 pages.

————, *Mammals of the World.* George G. Harrap and Company, Toronto, Canada. 1955. 223 pages.

Burns, Eugene, *The Sex Life of Wild Animals.* Rinehart and Company, New York. 1953. 290 pages.

Burt, W. H., and R. P. Grossenheider, *A Field Guide to the Mammals,* Houghton Mifflin Company, Boston, Massachusetts. 1952. 200 pages.

Burton, Maurice, *Animal Courtship.* Frederick A. Praeger, New York. 1954. 267 pages.

Cahalane, Victor H., *Mammals of North America.* The Macmillan Company, New York. 1947. 682 pages.

Camp, Raymond, ed., *The Hunter's Encyclopedia.* Stackpole and Heck, New York. 1948. 1,152 pages.

Drimmer, Frederick, ed., *The Animal Kingdom,* 3 volumes. Greystone Press, New York. 1954. 2,062 pages.

Glass, Bryon P., *A Key to the Skulls of North American Mammals.* Burgess Publishing Co., Minneapolis, Minn., 1951. 54 pp.

Hall, Raymond, *Handbook of the Mammals of Kansas.* Museum of Natural History and Biological Survey of Kansas, Lawrence, Kansas. 1955. 303 pages.

Hamilton, William J., Jr., *American Mammals.* McGraw-Hill Book Company, New York. 1939. 434 pages.

————, *The Mammals of the Eastern United States*. Comstock Publishing Company, Ithaca, New York. 1943. 432 pp.

Howell, A. Brazier, *Speed in Animals*. University of Chicago Press, Chicago, Illinois. 1944. 268 pages.

Ingles, Lloyd Glenn, *Mammals of California and Its Coastal Waters*. Stanford University Press, Palo Alto, California. 1954. 396 pages.

Jaeger, Elsworth, *Tracks and Trailcraft*. The Macmillan Company, New York. 1948. 380 pages.

————, *Land and Water Trails*. The Macmillan Company. New York. 1953. 223 pages.

Jennison, George, *Natural History: Animals*. The Macmillan Company, New York. 1925. 344 pages.

McCracken, Harold, and Henry Van Cleve. *Trapping*. A. S. Barnes and Company, New York. 1947. 196 pages.

McSpadden, J. Walker, ed., *Animals of the World*. Garden City Publishing Company, New York. 1917. 690 pages.

Miller, Gerrit S., and Remington Kellogg, *List of North American Recent Mammals*. Bulletin 205, United States National Museum, Washington, D.C. 1955. 954 pages.

Moore, Clifford B., *The Book of Wild Pets*. Charles T. Branford Company, Boston, Massachusetts. 1954. 55 pages.

Murie, Olaus, *Fieldbook of Animal Tracks*. Houghton Mifflin Company, Boston, Massachusetts. 1954. 374 pages.

National Sportsman, ed., *Hunting and Fishing Handbook*. National Sportsman, Boston, Massachusetts. 1944. 110 pp.

Noble, Ruth Crosbie. *The Nature of the Beast*. Hutchinson and Company, London. 176 pages. N. D.

Palmer, E. Laurence, *Fieldbook of Natural History*. McGraw-Hill Book Company, New York. 1949. 655 pages.

Palmer, Ralph S., *The Mammal Guide*. Doubleday and Company, Garden City, New York. 1954. 384 pages.

Peterson, Roger Tory, *Wildlife in Color*. Houghton Mifflin Company, Boston, Massachusetts. 1951. 191 pages.

Pike, Oliver G., *Wild Animals in Britain*. The Macmillan Company, New York. 1950. 231 pages.

Pratt, H. S., *Manual of the Vertebrates of the United States*. P. Blakiston's Sons and Company, Philadelphia, Pennsylvania. 1923. 422 pages.

Sanders, Edmund, *A Beast Book for the Pocket*. Oxford University Press, London. 1951. 378 pages.

Sanderson, Ivan J., *Living Mammals of the World*. Doubleday and Company, Garden City, New York. 1955. 303 pages.

Seton, Ernest Thompson, *Lives of Game Animals*. Doubleday, Doran Company, New York. 1928. 949 pages.

Spector, William S., ed., *Handbook of Biological Data*. W. B. Saunders Company, Philadelphia, Penn. 1956. 584 pp.

Tate, G. H. H., *Mammals of Eastern Asia*. The Macmillan Company, New York. 1947. 366 pages.

Zim, Herbert, and Donald Hoffmeister, *Mammals*. Simon and Schuster, Inc., New York. 1955. 160 pages.

ORDER MONOTREMATA (*Egg-laying Mammals*)

Duck-billed Platypus
Ornithorhynchus anatinus · Ornithorhynchidae

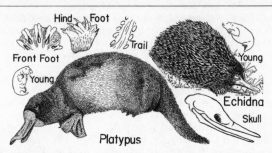

IMAGINE a brownish-gray animal with fur like that of a beaver, with a flattened furry tail, a flattened leathery beak like a duck's, and webbed feet, 2 of which may bear poisoned spurs as lethal as a snake's fangs. The duck-billed platypus, of streams in eastern Australia and Tasmania, is such an animal.

Male duckbills are 2 feet long, including tail, and may weigh more than 4 pounds; the 16-inch females, 2 pounds. Females, which lose poison spurs at 2 months, lay parchment-covered eggs like those of some reptiles. Forefeet have strong claws useful in digging and heavy webs adapted for swimming.

Nocturnal animals, powerful swimmers and burrowers, platypuses often live as a family in a wet-leaf-lined den built by female at end of burrow to 40 feet long, some 2½ inches high and 3½ inches wide, with underwater entrances, frequently plugged. Breed in midwinter (July to October). Females retire to dens where, 15 days after mating, they lay 1–3 parchment-shelled, 1-inch, connected eggs which dent after drying for a few minutes. Mothers lie on backs holding eggs against abdomens. Young nurse not from nipples but from milk-bearing areas on abdomen; are blind and helpless at first; do not see daylight until about 4 months old, 1 foot long, and able to get own food. Life span, to 15 years. Respiration rate, 460.* Temperature, 77°–95° F.

Spiny Echidna or Anteater · *Tachyglossus aculeatus* ·
Tachyglossidae

SPINY echidnas are land animals from Tasmania, New Guinea, and Australia, 1–2 feet long, with cylindrical, toothless mouths and extensile tongues. Covered with spines, they feed on worms and insects. Their 4-clawed feet can dig horizontally down into soil. Lay single, leathery eggs that are incubated for some days in brood sacs until young develop spines that cause discomfort to mothers. Respiration rate 1,100. Temperature, 90°–95° F. Life span, 15 years.

* See page 7.

ORDER MARSUPIALIA
(*Pouch-bearing Mammals*)

Virginia Opossum · *Didelphis marsupialis* · Didelphidae

FROM New England to Florida, west through Wisconsin, central Iowa, and central Mexico and in isolated parts of southern California, many persons are startled on dark nights by a white-faced, naked-tailed opossum staring into a flashlight from some tree, chicken coop, or bird feeding station and showing teeth. (Range is being extended to north.)

Opossums are trapped, shot, caught by hand for sport, as inferior greasy food, for fur (6% durability of otter, but among 6 leading U.S. fur bearers), and as vermin. May destroy fruit and vegetables or poultry, and may foul buildings badly. When disturbed, may play dead, fight, threaten with mouth, hang by tail, hide, or escape.

Length to 3 feet, including 15-inch tail. Weight to 5 pounds. Males the smaller. Ears and tail sparsely furred or naked. Most of pelt a fluffy, grayish to white fur. Eyes dark. Feet black; 5 toes on each foot, with 1 opposable. Tracks are: F 1¼ x 1½, 5; H 1¼ x 2½, 5; Sp. 6.* Teeth are: I 5/4; C 1/1; P 3/3; M 4/4.† Possum of 4½ pounds may go through 2¾ inch hole. Possums probably do not hibernate but may sleep in bad weather in filthy den in burrow or hollow tree.

Breed twice a year in South, beginning at 8 months; once in North, beginning at 1 year. Copulation lasts for only seconds. Egg fertilized 8 hours after mating. Twelve–13 days after the mating, bear up to 20 young, each smaller than honeybee, about ½ inch long, with 1½ inch tail; ¹⁄₂₇₀ oz. Young make way unassisted to brood sac, where first 11–13 become attached to teats. Others die. Weight increases 10 times first week. Show heads at 4 weeks; leave pouch briefly at 5 weeks; become independent at 8 weeks. Pulse, 120–240. Temperature, 90°–99° F. Life span, to 8 years.

Opossums and species covered on next two pages nurse young in brood sacs and are known as "pouched animals." Freely spoken of as marsupials, they are primitive animals, but less so than the egg-bearing monotremes discussed on page 26.

---

* For explanation of track formulas, see page 20.
† For interpretation of tooth formulas, see page 21.

Flying Phalanger · *Petaurus* sp. · Phalangeridae

Skull

Skull

Flying Phalanger

Bushtail

Skull
Wombat
Koala

AUSTRALIA and neighboring lands are the homes of many pouched mammals or marsupials. Some have worldwide fame, others are not well known. Of the 4 shown here, the flying phalanger is a master of the air, sailing from a high to a low point; the wombat is a superior burrower in the soil, and the koalas and bushtail tree kangaroos are at their best in treetops. On page 29 are shown wallabies and giant kangaroos that hop rapidly over the ground.

Flying phalangers, or sugar squirrels, vary in length from 15–30 inches, of which about half is tail. They are nocturnal, feed on insects, fruits, and leaves, breed in winter, and after a 3-week gestation bear 1 to 2 young that are furred at 2 months, remain in nests for 4 months. Expectancy, 7–10 years.

Koala · *Phascolarctos cinereus* · Phalangeridae

KOALAS, known affectionately as Teddy bears, feed mostly in treetops on eucalyptus leaves. They are to nearly 3 feet long, with a height of 1 foot, and weigh to 30 pounds. Their thick, ash-gray fur becomes yellowish beneath. Thumbs of all feet are opposable; 2nd and 3rd toes of hind feet are united. Young at birth are 1 inch long and of the diameter of a pencil, at 6 months are fully furred and have eyes open, but at 1 year are still helplessly riding on the mother's back. They are full grown at 4 years. Temperature, 95°–100° F. Expectancy, 20 years.

Wombat ("Badger") · *Phascolomis* sp. · Phascolomidae

WOMBATS make burrows to 100 feet long. They are gray fawn colored, to 4 feet long and to 80 pounds in weight. They feed almost wholly on vegetation, breed in April, and carry 1 young in pouch. Life expectancy, 30 years.

Bushtail, or Tree Kangaroo
Dendrolagus sp. · Macropodidae

TREE kangaroos are to 4 feet long, half being tail, which is slender and brush-tipped. They can jump safely to ground 50 feet below starting point. Food includes leaves and fruits, largely, woody plants. Two Australian, 4 New Guinea species.

Great Gray Kangaroo or Forester

Macropus gigantea · Macropodidae

A. A. MILNE'S stories of Pooh have introduced many of us to kangaroos through acquaintance with Kanga and her offspring Roo, who was carried in a pouch. Others meet them in zoos and circuses, but wild kangaroos are to be found in Australia and Tasmania. Kangaroos and related wallabies hop about fields and woodlands, feeding on vegetation in competition with domestic sheep and cattle. They are hunted as pests, for sport, for flesh, fur, and hides from which waterproof leather is made.

Male great gray kangaroos may measure to 9½ feet, including tail, weigh to 200 pounds, leap 10 yards at a bound and to 10 feet high. May be found in herds or "troops" of over 50 animals. Tail is used for balancing, not as a springboard. Kill such enemies as dogs or dingoes with a blow from hind feet or by holding them under water until drowned. Females are about ⅔ size of males and have conspicuous brood sacs. One 1 oz. young, born 30–40 days after mating of male "boomer" and female "flier," makes way alone in one half hour to brood sac, where it attaches itself to teat, and develops after several months into a "joey." At this time, when well developed, it leaves pouch; also does so earlier on warm days. It has a life span of to 15 years. Temperature, 94°–96° F.

Wallaby · *Petrogale* sp. · Macropodidae

WALLABIES, like tree kangaroos, are essentially little kangaroos. Some are as small as rabbits and others more than a yard long. Some are active only at night while others are most active in broad daylight. Some retreat to dens in rocks if disturbed; others rest in forms on the ground or escape to treetops, where they are perfectly at home. Possibly most primitive are musk kangaroos, *Hypsiprymnodon*, which measure to 18 inches, including 7-inch tail, are practically hairless, give off musky odor, breed February to May. They usually bear 2 young, which share brood sacs. Favor country well supplied with water. Pulse, 125. Temperature, 97°–99° F.

ORDER INSECTIVORA
(Hedgehogs, Shrews, Moles)

European Hedgehog · *Erinaceus europaeus* · Erinaceidae

FROM Cretaceous times to the present there has lived on the earth a group of animals almost invariably small, with rooted teeth that bear tubercles; usually with tapering snouts, and 5 toes on each foot. These Insectivora include the hedgehogs, shrews, and moles.

European hedgehogs, which have been introduced and established widely over the earth, are native from the British Isles east through Europe and Asia to Korea and Manchuria. Hedgehogs are characterized by having coarse spines in place of hair except on the face, under parts, and legs. In the closely related moonrats and gymnures, the covering is entirely of hair.

European hedgehogs are up to 10 inches long, including inch-long tails; males slightly larger than females. The sexes are superficially alike and are usually chocolate-colored, with the spine tips a pale yellow. The spines are not barbed, so the animal can be handled circumspectly with some degree of safety. Compare with spiny echidna (page 26) and porcupine (page 114).

European hedgehogs usually breed twice a year (March and September), and 35–49 days later from 5–7 young are born blind and naked in a leaf-lined nest in a burrow just under the surface of the ground. The young are blind at birth and bear soft, whitish spines which become hard and colored like those of the parents within 3 weeks. Within a month the young follow the mother, who is most active at night.

The food of hedgehogs is largely insects and similar small animals. Hedgehogs grow fat in late summer and fall, then, rolling themselves into a ball, they hibernate in a plant-lined hollow until spring, when they unroll themselves and start a family. They are useful destroyers of insects and may kill mice. The flesh is edible. They do not milk cows, as sometimes reputed to do. Pulse, 189–320. Temperature, 90°–97° F. Life expectancy, to 10 years.

30

Common or Masked Shrew · *Sorex cinereus* · Soricidae

Skull

Tracks

SHREWS are superficially mouselike, and most are small. The largest shrew lives in Borneo and is more than 2 feet long; the smallest, the Etruscan, of southern Europe, measures under 3 inches and is the smallest of all mammals. As is the case with all mammals considered later in this book, the young are developed within the body of the mother and remain attached to the uterus until birth. The hedgehogs, family Erinaceidae, are discussed on page 30. The shrews, Soricidae, are treated on pages 31–36, and the moles, Talpidae, on pages 37–41.

Most shrews are short-lived and aggressive, and they are generally useful. Some bear glands that secrete poison similar to that of cobras. Some produce a valuable perfume. There are superstitions associated with them.

The teeth of shrews are important in identification. The front teeth are hooked, with a supplementary prong. They are much longer than wide. Adjacent smaller teeth are red- or black-tipped. Three of the 34 listed North American shrews of the genus *Sorex* are considered on pages 31–33. In *Sorex* the tail is longer than 1⅛ inches, and more than half the length of the head and body. The ears are plainly visible. The 5 teeth behind the pronged teeth are visible from the side. The 3rd of these is not smaller than the 4th.

Common shrews are brown above and gray beneath. Length to 4 inches, including yellow-brown tail 1⅗ inches long; weight, to ⅕ ounce. They are found from salt marshes to mountaintops from New England to Alaska, but not in the Cascades, Sierras, or southern Rockies. The 4–9 young are born 3 weeks after the mating, at 1 day are hairless, ⅕ inch long, about ⅟₃₅ weight of mother. To 3 litters a year. Breed any time of year. Jump 5 inches standing, 6 inches running. Store food. Body wastes are not piled. When nursing, may eat twice weight in earthworms daily. Eat mice, oats, and other food. May gorge in morning and starve in afternoon. May damage pelts of trapped fur bearers. Pulse, 588–1,320.

Smoky Shrew · *Sorex fumeus* · Soricidae

Teeth

SMOKY shrews are confined to the northeastern United States, living in damp woodlands and moist areas where there is an abundance of old, moss-covered logs and ferns. Found mostly in runways of large shrews and of mice. Not common in dry areas or near salt water. Sometimes abundant in a given region and at other times practically nonexistent. One subspecies extends range into Quebec, New Brunswick, and Nova Scotia. More likely to be found in crowded populations than are other shrews. While the 5th teeth behind the front teeth are smaller in the common shrew and the 4th teeth behind are smaller in the water shrew, all 5 of these teeth are practically uniform in size in the smoky shrew, as shown in the illustrations.

Length of a smoky shrew is about 5 inches, of which about 2 are tail. Weight, to ⅖ ounce. Back and upper parts of body and tail are distinctly darker than the under parts, sometimes so conspicuously so as to permit quick identification. Color may be darker in winter. Ears rather well developed.

In breeding season in the spring the tail is swollen. Blind, naked, and helpless young, 4–7, are born in a nest of fine vegetable matter. Commonly have 2 and sometimes 3 litters a year. Activity is high day or night, summer or winter. Life expectancy is seldom over 2 years.

Smoky shrews are valuable destroyers of insects and of other animals, even though these shrews for the most part are found outside crop-growing areas.

Other shrews in the genus *Sorex* include the water shrew (page 33), the Pacific shrew, *S. bendirii,* of the Pacific Coast; the Trowbridge shrew, *S. trowbridgii,* of the same general area; the California long-tailed shrew, *S. ornatus;* the vagrant shrew, *S. vagrans,* the commonest Western shrew; the dusky shrew, *S. obscurus,* of the West; the dwarf shrew, *S. tenellus,* of the Nevada area; the Merriam shrew, *S. merriami,* of the Rocky Mountain area in the United States; the saddle-backed shrew, *S. arcticus,* of the north central United States and south-central Canada; and others. The long-tailed shrew, *S. dispar,* of the Rocky Mountains, has the high respiration rate of 13,700.

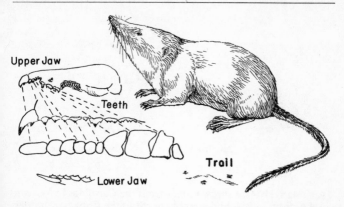

WATER shrews live most of life in water. Fur is water-repellent and keeps animals as dry as if they were on land. Hind legs are fringed, making effective swimming organs. It has been reported that these shrews can run on the water a distance of 5 feet. Naturally this statement is questioned.

As shown in the illustration, the 3rd, 4th, and 5th teeth behind the front teeth in the upper jaw, and particularly the 5th teeth, are smaller than the first 2. All 5 of these teeth are visible from the side, however.

Water shrews are 7 inches long, including 3-inch tails, with the sexes equal in size, and weight about ½ ounce. Upper parts are brownish gray, with some white-tipped hairs. Under parts of the body and tail are silvery white, the color differences being conspicuous on the tail. Little age or seasonal color change.

Water shrews range through colder North America and are represented by 10 North American species. These include the Northern, *S. palustris,* and Pacific, *S. benderii.* Collectively they range from Alaska to southern California east into southeastern Canada and the northeastern United States. Little is known of their life history. Probably 3 litters a year with 6 young to the litter. Sociable, with a number living in harmony in a single cavity in a log or tree hollow.

Food is largely snails and small insects and other small animals, some of which may be cached. Essentially useful to man's interests.

Water shrews swim well, using the flattened tail to supplement the admirably adapted feet. Bubbles on the hairs of the feet may provide sufficient buoyancy to sustain the animal on the water's surface for some distance.

The tracks are not usually found, but they show the weaving tail track matching the alternating foot tracks.

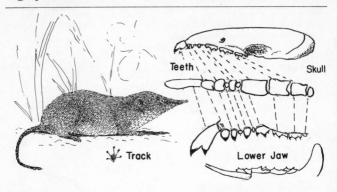

THIS relatively rare shrew ranges from the Carolinas to Wisconsin discontinuously, and roughly north to the Canadian border. There is but 1 species to the genus, but a half-dozen forms are recognized in the species, ranging from coast to coast.

Pigmy shrews are to 3¾ inches long, of which about 1 inch is tail. Weight, to 1 ounce. Color is reddish brown, with the under parts paler than the upper. Under parts may be smoky gray. The upper parts are darker in winter than in summer. The tail is obscurely two-colored above and below, but definitely not darker at the tip. Ears are inconspicuous. Eyes are small but distinct. There are 32 teeth, of which the 5 behind the conspicuous upper foreteeth are most important for identification purposes. Of these, the 3rd and 5th are notably smaller than the others, but may be seen distinctly from below, as shown in the illustration. They are not conspicuous.

Pigmy shrews' food is largely insects and earthworms. Their chief enemies include weasels, other shrews, and birds of prey. Little is known about their life history except that the mothers bear several litters a season, with from 5–6 in a litter. As is the case with most shrews, the life expectancy is undoubtedly short, but the animals maintain intense activity both day and night throughout the year.

These are among the smallest of the American shrews, being about the same size as the least shrews (page 36). The scent glands are excessively large when compared with those of the larger relatives. This may account for the fact that while a cat will kill the animals, it may prefer to bring them home rather than to eat them. The nose or snout is rather excessively long, and to these shrews scent may be a most important means of knowing the environment.

So far as man's interests are concerned, pigmy shrews are essentially useful. They destroy some small animals which harm man's crops, and are of interest to students as representing possibly the smallest neighborhood mammal.

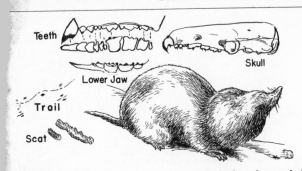

ort-tailed Shrew, Blarina, or Mole Shrew

Blarina brevicauda · Soricidae

Teeth

Skull

Lower Jaw

Trail

Scat

'o many farm folk, blarinas are the "moles" that the cat brings
.ome from its nightly prowls. Of course they are not actually
moles, and lack the mole's digging feet. More useful than some
cats; one record shows that blarinas killed more than 60% of
a year's crop of destructive larch sawflies in eastern Canada.
Food by bulk of 244 specimens proved to be nearly half insects
and the rest earthworms, molluscs, salamanders, and 125 types
of plants. The bite is reputed to be poisonous but apparently
has never harmed a human. The animals give off an offensive
scent. Enemies include owls, cats, foxes, and weasels. Known
to have at least 14 parasites. Respiration rate, 5,200. Pulse,
618–780. Temperature, 94°–100° F.

A half-dozen species or subspecies of *Blarina* range through
the eastern United States and southeastern Canada. They in-
habit trash in woodlands, fields, and buildings. They are 6
inches long, with 1-inch tails; weight to 1 ounce. The sexes are
superficially alike. Have small eyes, soft fur, and pointed noses,
and are dark slate gray above and lighter beneath; in summer,
entire coat is the lighter color. Have black tails. Shed hair in
March and October. The 1st and 2nd teeth behind the front
teeth are larger than the 3rd to 5th; the 5th is much the smallest
and is not easily seen from the side, if visible at all.

In captivity each animal needs to 100 square inches of floor
space. May be fed hamburger, ground liver, or good dog food.
Food may be stored by free or captive animals. Courting males
pursue females, giving unmusical clicks. Females repulse them
with loud squeaks and chatter. Copulation lasts from a few
seconds to 25 minutes, may be repeated 6 times an hour or
more than 20 times a day. Young, 3–8, are born 2½–3 weeks
after the mating, are like pink wrinkled honeybees, measuring
at 1 day, 1⅛ inches; at 1 week, 2⅜ inches; at 2 weeks, 3 inches;
at 3 weeks, 3⅘ inches. Then weaned. At 1 month they are half
grown; at 6 months, mature; at 16 months, aged, and at 30
months probably dead. Mating is for season and there are several litters a year. Sense of sight poor; of touch and smell, acute.

Least Shrew, Little Shrew, or Lesser Short-tailed Sh

Cryptotis parva · So

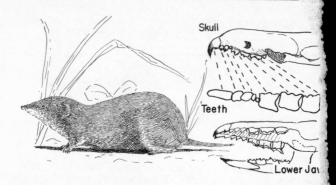

Skull

Teeth

Lower Jaw

USUALLY the least or little shrew is a rare animal. Of its 17 re lated species, most are tropical, only 2 being found within th United States. *Cryptotis parva* ranges from New York to Flor ida and through the Midwest.

This furry mite may exhibit a mighty fury, although it mea ures only 3½ inches long, including a ⅜ inch tail. Weight, to ounce. Looks like a small blarina. The eyes are hidden in t fur and almost invisible. The hair is short and close. Color almost uniform gray to slate or dark brown, with ashy gr beneath. The tail is conspicuously lighter beneath. The relat *Cryptotis floridana,* of Florida, is darker, grayer, and has a inch tail.

The nest is a ball of finely shredded vegetation up to 5 in in diameter. It may be occupied by 5 adults. Beginning March, several litters appear, each numbering about 6 yo Young are weaned in about 3 weeks, probably to make way the next litter. Life span, in captivity, to 2 years.

Enemies are many and include snakes, weasels, foxes, o and cats. Food may be wholly animal matter. The hard p of insects may pass through the shrew's alimentary cana 1½ hours, and food requirements are such that shrews do lend themselves ordinarily to conditions associated with c tivity.

Little is known about least shrews. They cannot be of gr economic importance, although their food of insects proba puts them in the category of animals useful to man.

Comparatively speaking, shrews have more slender bodi than do moles. Their forefeet are not modified for digging are the moles'. Shrews' eyes are more prominent than are those of moles, and shrews have external ears. Shrew moles may be smaller than blarinas, but usually shrews are smaller than are moles.

Lower Jaw

Skull

WHILE shrews find their living for the most part in the loose fresh and decaying plant materials at or near the surface of the ground, moles usually seek their food beneath the surface. Their strong forelimbs are most helpful. Their fur rubs smooth when brushed either forward or backward, as becomes necessary in burrow life. Usually moles push loose earth to the surface in a ring around the hole, while pocket gophers (page 91) may deposit it to one side. External ears are absent in moles, and while eyes are present they do not always appear through the skin. Nose or snout is a flexible organ useful in exploring loose soil. Tunnels are of two types, one near the surface and one going to depths of to 20 inches. Obviously moles are not speedsters, but European moles are believed to have a speed of 2½ miles an hour underground and can burrow in soft soil at a rate of 15 feet an hour.

Shrew moles have a length of to 4½ inches, including 1½ tail. Weight, to nearly ½ ounce. Female is slightly the larger. This is one of the smallest American moles. The snout long like that of a shrew, but naked tipped like that of a mole. The palm is longer than it is wide. There are 36 teeth.

Shrew moles are found along the Pacific Coast of northern California, Oregon, Washington, and southwest British Columbia in woody, marshy areas or along streams. They swim readily, climb low shrubs, move cautiously over the ground, and may be gregarious. Give off a faint, sweet twittering when frightened. They feed on most small animals which they can conquer. A nest is built in a cavity, and in it litters of 1–4 may be born a number of times in a year, about 2 weeks after mating. Newly-born young weigh 40 to the ounce and have 1-inch bodies. Adults probably do not survive 2 years. Little is really known about these animals, but they seem to be essentially useful creatures.

Western Mole · *Scapanus townsendii* · Talpidae

Skull · Lower Jaw · Upper Jaw

FROM northern Mexico to southwestern British Columbia, and east to central Oregon and Washington and western Nevada, is the range of a group of moles sometimes spoken of collectively as the Western moles. It is sometimes difficult for anyone except a specialist to tell one from another. The Townsend mole, however, occupies the range north of California; the California mole extends its range northward only into extreme southern Oregon; and the Pacific mole matches the range of the Townsend mole and covers the northern haunts of the California mole. Of these three, the Townsend mole is the largest and most beautiful. It is nearly 9 inches long, including 2-inch tail, is almost wholly black, and weighs to 6 ounces. The Pacific mole occasionally reaches a length of 6¾ inches, including ½-inch tail.

Male Townsend moles are longer than the females by nearly an inch. The fur is paler on the underside, with a brown tinge, and the animals are lighter in winter.

Western moles are rather solitary except in the breeding season, when a tunnel may be used by a number of them. The nest is in a cavern deep underground and is lined with dry grass and leaves. Mating is in late winter and the 2–4 young are born about a month later. Adult size and independence are reached in early summer or June. There is but 1 litter a year.

The food of Western moles is largely the larvae of insects, earthworms, and other soft-bodied animals to be found in the habitat. One record indicates that 1 Western mole in just over 2 months made more than 300 earth mounds in a field of ¼ acre. This definitely suggests the role moles play in aerating the soil. Probably most of the damage to crops charged against moles is really the work of mice, which run through the burrows to feed on exposed root crops. Of course a molehill on a golf putting green has its disadvantages, but it is possible that a golf putting green does not represent the best possible use of good agricultural soil. Control of moles is usually through trapping and the use of poison baits and poison gases.

38

Hairy-tailed Mole or Brewer's Mole

Parascalops breweri · Talpidae

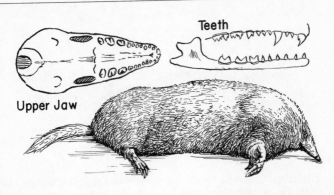

Teeth

Upper Jaw

AN area beginning with the Appalachian Highlands in northern Georgia and extending northeast into Ontario and New Brunswick represents the range of this husky mole. It is found at elevations of to 3,000 feet, and is often more abundant than is apparent.

Hairy-tailed moles are to 7 inches long, including a 1⅘ inch tail. Weight, to 3 ounces. The sexes are about equal in size and are similarly colored. The tail is smallest at the base, and hairy, and the snout is coarse and shorter than in the common mole (next page). There is but 1 species in the genus.

The fur is blackish, rather than gray as with common moles. Weight, to 3 ounces. Teeth are: I 3/3; C 1/1; P 4/4; M 3/3. The front feet are about as wide as they are long.

The food, of course, is largely insects and earthworms; a hairy mole may eat its weight in earthworms daily. The major food at some seasons may be the larvae of such beetles as the May beetle, which destroy so much plant material useful to man. Moles may leave their burrows and wander about on top of the ground in search of food. Under such circumstances they are ready prey for cats and other animals. They may also eat ants and other small animals, some of which are enemies of man.

Mating takes place in February or March. From 4–6 weeks later 4–5 young are born. These are blind, helpless, and naked except for a few whiskers, and each weighs about ⅓ ounce. At 4 weeks the young are weaned and become independent. Sexual maturity is reached at the first succeeding breeding season, and old age is reached within 4 years if the animals survive that long.

An individual probably will not know a home range in excess of 100 feet across, and 2 animals to the acre is considered a good population.

Common Mole · *Scalops aquaticus* · Talpidae

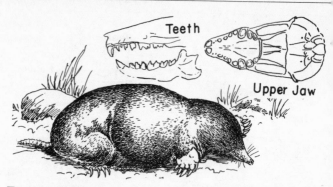

THE term "common" is always dangerous because what may be common in one place may be rare in another. This mole is common from southern Texas north almost to Montana and east to the Atlantic, except for the northern Dakota area, northern Minnesota, Wisconsin, New York, and New England. It varies in color over the range, being gray in the North and brown to copper in the Southwest. The young are usually gray.

Males may measure 9 inches, including a 1⅛ inch tail; females, 8 inches with a 1-inch tail. Weight, to 2 ounces. Tail is naked, or apparently so. There are no external ears, and the eyes are skin covered. The forefeet are broader than they are long, and the snout naked, with upward-pointing nostrils. Teeth are: I 3/2; C 1/0; P 3/3; M 3/3. The fur is finer and softer than that of the hairy-tailed mole.

These moles do not make molehills of excavated earth so commonly as do some of their relatives. They are active in tunnels at all seasons and times of the day, but in winter in the North the tunnels used are often deeper than those of the summer. One dug over 100 feet of tunnels in one day.

Common moles may dig 15 feet in an hour, eat at least half their weight in food daily. Normal population, about 2 or 3 to an acre in suitable territory. They rarely come to the surface, but when they do, they fall easy prey to many enemies. Because of their strong odor they are not commonly eaten by animals that kill them.

In the early spring breeding season 2 or more moles may be found in the same tunnel. Young are born probably 6 weeks after the mating takes place. The 2–6 young in the 1 annual litter are naked and helpless at birth. In 10 days they have a hair covering which is replaced a few weeks later with another coat. The young become independent when about 1 month old and breed at about 10 months of age. The nest is in a grass-lined, 5- to 8-inch den. Food is 50% insects, 30% earthworms, and some plants. Temperature, 94°–100° F.

40

Star-nosed Mole · *Condylura cristata* · Talpidae

Upper Jaw

Upper Jaw

Lower Jaw

STAR-NOSED moles are found in damp ground from southern Labrador to southeastern Manitoba and south to Georgia and Illinois. There is 1 species in the genus.

If you have ever explored the mud for something lost in it and have used all 5 fingers of your hand to help you, you have a slight idea of what star-nosed moles do much of the time. If you had all your fingers and toes on one hand to work with, you still would not be equipped as is the mole. The snout of a star-nosed mole has 22 fingerlike structures which it uses to explore the mud in which it finds most of its food of earthworms and insect larvae.

Male star-nosed moles are to 8¼ inches long, including a 3⅛ inch tail that is enlarged in the middle with stored fat, and constricted at the base. The tail swelling is greatest in winter. Weight, to 3 ounces. The eyes function, unlike those of most moles. The hind feet measure just over 1 inch, and there are 44 teeth. Teeth are: I 3/3; C 1/1; P 4/4; M 3/3. Both males and females are blackish-brown to black above and paler brown beneath. The legs are weak; the front feet, while wide, are not so large as those of common moles.

Star-nosed moles may live in the same area, and even in the same tunnels, that harbor other species of moles. They are active day or night throughout the year, sometimes in groups. Their hearing is excellent. Their sense of contact is superior, but of smell poor. Their food is about 50% earthworms and 33% insects, the rest of it being miscellaneous.

Mating may take place in the fall and wintering may be in pairs. Females breed when 10 months old. Height of breeding, however, is in January, and 3–6 young are born from mid-April to mid-June. At birth the young are pink, hairless, and helpless. First fur appears in 10 days and a full coat by 3 weeks, when the nest and parent are abandoned. These moles swim well, spend much time above ground, and can give a frightened squeak. About 2 star-nosed moles to an acre is normal, although there may be many more.

ORDER CHIROPTERA *(Bats)*

Vampire Bat · *Desmodus rotundus* · Desmodontidae

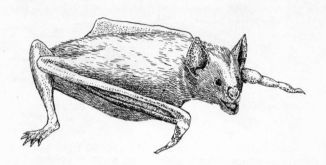

BATS are about the most misunderstood of animals, and at the same time the most interesting and sometimes the most useful. In general they fly as do the birds, and have some characteristics of mice. The German word for them is *Fledermaus,* literally "flying mouse," and the operetta *Die Fledermaus* gives them a somewhat ominous character not in keeping with that to which most bats are entitled. The mystery thriller play *The Bat* kept a generation of theater-goers on the edge of their seats. The name "vampire" refers in superstition to the bloodsucking ghost or reanimated body of a dead person imagined to return to earth to suck the blood of sleeping mortals until they, too, are dead. It's not an easy reputation to live down. Besides, bats are reputed to get into your hair—although the fact is that they are especially equipped by nature to avoid obstacles in flying—and they are alleged to harbor bedbugs.

The true vampire bat, however, is sinister enough: it is not known to eat anything but blood, which it extracts almost painlessly, often from a lightly sleeping person. Razor-sharp front teeth start the flow of blood, which the bat laps up as it stands on its victim. As unfortunately it may transmit germ diseases such as rabies in this act, it is in more ways than one a menace to men, horses, cattle, and other mammals.

Vampire bats are about 3 inches long, gray to brown, with short hair, short pointed ears, an ordinary-looking nose, and normal eyes. Weight, about 1 ounce. They can run along floors and up vertical walls with surprising speed, either walking, running, or hopping in a most unbatlike manner. In heat at 5 months; polygamous; 1 litter a year. Breed at any time of year.

Vampire bats range from Mexico to Brazil. The undesirable characteristics described above are not shared by any bats to be found free and wild in the United States or in Canada.

Little Brown Bat · *Myotis lucifugus* · Vespertilionidae

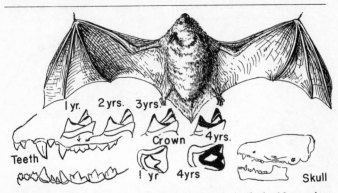

Teeth — 1 yr. 2 yrs. 3 yrs. 4 yrs. Crown — 1 yr 4 yrs — Skull

OUR little brown bats, of which we show 1, include 13 species ranging over all of the United States and most of Canada and Mexico, while all the vampires and false vampires are found south of the United States borders.

The great false vampire bats, *Vampyrum*, have a wingspread of to 30 inches and a length of to 6 inches. They are villainous looking but apparently wholly harmless.

Little brown bats are to 4½ inches long, including a 1½ inch tail, and have 1½ inch forearms. The ears laid forward reach to the end of the snout. Weight ¼–½ ounce. The sexes are colored alike and are dark brown above and lighter beneath. There are some 30 recognizable subspecies of little brown bats, out of a total of 2,000 species of bats in the world. Teeth are: I 2/3; C 1/1; P 3/3; M 3/3. See sketches for variations in teeth with age. Respiration rate, 1,500. Temperature, 97°–103° F.

Promiscuous mating takes place in the fall, but actual fertilization is delayed until spring. The young weigh about ¹⁄₂₀ ounce at birth, which takes about ½ hour. Gestation is about 56 days. Nursing lasts for 3 weeks and mature size is reached in 4 weeks. Flight begins at 3 weeks. Males may mate at 14 months and females at 10 months. The food is insects caught on the wing. An individual's home range extends for some 100 miles. An evening's flight or a foraging trip may cover 30 miles. Winter is spent resting in caves. Life expectancy, 10 years.

These bats give off sounds of 50,000–98,000 cycles per second while flying, and are guided by the echoes, as in radar. They call 25 times per second in open and 50 per second among trees. Thus equipped, they can miss obstacles to be avoided and find food to be eaten.

The greatest enemies of bats are their parasites, of which there are many. The little browns are valuable as destroyers of insects. One colony is said to have produced in its cave more than 2 tons of fertilizer, worth $200, in one year.

Silver-haired Bat

Lasionycteris noctivagans · Vespertilionidae

Skull

WHILE little brown bats are most active an hour before sunset, silver-haired bats are out and about for the hour just after sunset. When one leaves the skies the other takes over. Just as particular areas in space are favored by most mammals, in this case particular periods of time are significant.

Silver-haired bats favor waterways for their flights. While they range through most of North America north of Mexico, they rarely if ever breed in the southern part of the range. In the summer the males may range much farther north than do the females. There is but 1 species in the genus.

These bats are 4¼ inches long, including 1⅖ inch tail. They have 1⅖ inch forearms. Weight, to ½ ounce. The relatively large ears are ¾ inch from tip to base. The sexes are colored alike, with little seasonal or age variation. They are dark brown to chestnut above, with silver-tipped hairs, while the under parts are similarly colored but have fewer silver-tipped hairs. Teeth are: I 2/3; C 1/1; P 2/3; M 3/3. The wingspread is to 13 inches.

Silver-haired bats may confine their evening's range to an area 100 yards across. They do not fly high—for the most part not over 40 feet above the ground. The flight is most erratic, including glides, fluttering, and sudden dashes. Some have been found far out at sea where they have taken refuge on ships. In the summer the males stay for the most part by themselves, while the females may tend to flock together. Breeding takes place in early fall, but fertilization is probably delayed. The 1 or 2 young are black and wrinkled and are born in June or July. At first they are carried by the mother, clinging to her as she flies. By 3 weeks they may be weaned and take to wing on their own, although at first they are not strong fliers.

In winter this species may either hibernate in some cave or sheltered spot, or it may migrate to the South, returning to the North for the summer months. The food is probably wholly insects taken in flight.

Pipistrelle · *Pipistrellus subflavus* · Vespertilionidae

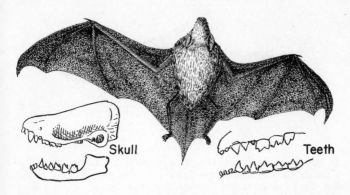

Skull

Teeth

THE Eastern pipistrelle is *P. subflavus;* the Western, *P. hesperus.* The Eastern ranges through the United States east of the Great Plains except for Maine and southern Florida. The Western ranges west from the beginning of the Rockies to the coast, except for areas in western Oregon, northern California, northern Washington, and eastern Idaho.

The pipistrelles are our smallest bats and are sometimes known as "pigmy bats." The length is to 3½ inches, including a 1½ inch tail. The forearms are 1⅛ inches long and the weight to ¼ ounce. The wingspread is to 6 inches.

The two sexes are colored alike and the bats show little seasonal or age variation. They are light yellow-brown above but paler beneath, with the hairs slaty black at the base. Teeth are: I 2/3; C 1/1; P 2/2; M 3/3. Temperature, 86°–92° F.

As a rule pipistrelles are poor fliers and except in the breeding season are not active through the night. They appear about dusk and again at sunrise, or just before sunset and just after sunrise. If the season is advanced, they may appear as early as March. During the time when the young are with the mother, the sexes remain segregated. In the summer, these bats rest in fairly exposed places, even among loose rocks, but in winter they take to caves, crowding in with other species and sleeping quietly and soundly.

There may be breeding seasons in the late summer and fall, and again in the spring, but there is only 1 litter of 1–3 young. The young are born from May through July, depending on the territory; are at first carried by the mother, develop rapidly, and in 3 weeks' time are on their own.

Because pipistrelles are so small and so slow in flight, they are frequently confused with large moths of similar size. However, their food is wholly insects, possibly including the moths.

45

Big Brown or House Bat

Eptesicus fuscus · Vespertilionidae

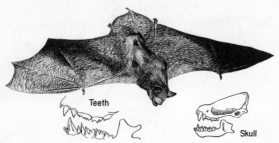

Teeth

Skull

IF you find a bat hibernating in a house in the United States or Canada, the chances are good that it is a big brown bat or house bat. This species ranges through southern Canada, the whole of the United States, and on into Mexico. It commonly finds itself lost in rooms, much to the distraction of misinformed humans, who use everything available either to kill or drive out the elusive intruder, who frequently seems only slightly disturbed by the attack.

House bats are to 5 inches long, including a 1½ inch tail. The wingspread is to nearly 12 inches and the weight to 1 ounce. Teeth are: I 2/3; C 1/1; P 1/2; M 3/3. The membrane between the hind limbs is not furred above. The thumb is large; the ears longer than broad, tapering to a rounded tip. The wing membranes are black and are not furred. The body is uniformly yellowish brown above.

These bats are most active for the hour beginning a half hour after sunset. The food is almost, if not exclusively, insects caught on the wing, about ⅓ by volume being beetles. They take relatively few moths in comparison with some other bats. Winter is spent in a cave or other shelter in a more or less torpid condition. These bats may remain active rather late in the fall. The males go into hibernation earlier in the fall than do the females. As many as 20 or even more may be found hibernating closely together.

Promiscuous mating takes place in the fall, but fertilization is probably delayed, since the young are not born until May in the South, or as late as the end of June in the North. Birth occurs 183–265 days after the mating. The usual 2 young are naked at birth and have closed eyes. They weigh about ¹⁄₁₀ ounce, are weaned at 3 weeks, and reach mature size in 2 months. Banded individuals have been known to live for 9 years.

Among the few enemies of the big brown bat are snakes, which may raid the roosts, and, more important, the parasites that may sometimes be so conspicuous. These bats, like other bats, use sound and echoes while in flight (see page 43). Respiration rate, 800. Temperature, 97°–104° F.

Red Bat · *Lasiurus borealis* · Vespertilionidae

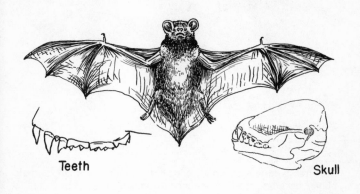

Teeth

Skull

IF any bat may be considered beautiful, it seems safe to say that it must be either the red bat or its close relative, the hoary bat (see next page). A mother red bat with a pair of twins hanging to her, when first seen, is hard to forget. Red bats range through most of the United States and southern Canada except for the Rocky Mountain area and southern Florida. Their close relatives, the Seminole bats, *L. seminolus*, are found in the southern parts of the Gulf States. Red bats are medium sized, to 4½ inches long, with a 14-inch wingspread, and weigh ⅓ ounce. The tail measures 2 inches; the forearms 1⅗ inches. The ears are low, broad, and well rounded. Teeth are: I 1/3; C 1/1; P 2/2; M 3/3. The males are orange red, females a dull, frosted chestnut. Under parts are less reddish and paler. Individuals vary slightly in color. The hair is relatively long and the upper surface of wing membranes is usually well furred.

Mating takes place in late summer for older females and in spring for the young of the preceding year. The young, numbering 1–4, are born in mid-June in the North and earlier in the South. A female may carry 4 young from her 4 nipples, their combined weight exceeding hers. The young grow rapidly and by 3 weeks are often ready to shift for themselves. They are full sized by 2 months. The females tend to congregate during the time they are with young; fall colonies are formed in October and summer colonies from May to September. They may migrate at a height of 400 feet, and have been found 240 miles at sea. They have a good homing instinct and make reasonably gentle pets. May be fed mixture of bread, banana, boiled egg, cottage and other cheese, clabbered milk, unsalted vegetables, and, to prevent diarrhea, broken beetles and grasshoppers.

Hoary Bat · *Lasiurus cinereus* · Vespertilionidae

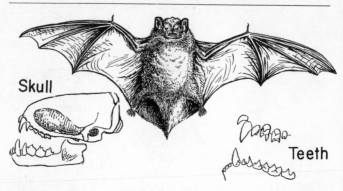

Skull

Teeth

MY first experience with a hoary bat was when a huge football player became greatly frightened at one and heroically killed it with an ice pick. The football player weighed more than 200 pounds, the bat some 1½ ounces. The bat was one of the most beautiful animals I remember ever seeing.

Hoary bats, or great northern bats, are 5½ inches long, including a tail to 1½ inches long. They have a wingspread of to 16 inches. The females are slightly heavier than the males. The ears are short and rounded, with naked black borders. The webs between the legs are well furred. The general color is mahogany brown, with grayish white all over the body. Teeth are: I 1/3; C 1/1; P 2/2; M 3/3. They resemble somewhat the much smaller silver-haired bat (page 44).

Hoary bats are most active during the second hour after sunset and the next to last hour before sunrise. They are essentially a woodland species, flying high, late, swiftly, and sometimes erratically. They range from the Gulf of St. Lawrence to Great Slave Lake and south to southern Mexico. They commonly summer north of Pennsylvania and winter to the south of it. They roost commonly in trees, and it was one of these roosting animals that my football player friend killed.

Mating takes place in late summer and though the females have 4 nipples, they usually bear but 2 young. These are born in mid-June, nearly a year after the mating. There is but 1 annual litter. During the nursing period the females may congregate, but the young develop rapidly and within a month are independent. They develop the hoary appearance at 3 weeks.

Under some circumstances, hoary bats may give a loud buzzing sound, but, as with most bats, most of the sounds they make are inaudible to humans. In the late summer months these bats may be found more often about settled areas. Their food is probably wholly insects, and usually rather large ones, although they are known also to eat mosquitoes. Like many other bats, they certainly deserve protection.

Lump-nosed Bat

Corynorhinus rafinesquii · Vespertilionidae

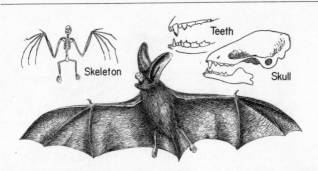

Teeth

Skeleton

Skull

THIS bat is also known as the Rafinesque bat, but whether the name was given it as a compliment to an early, eccentric, but able American naturalist, or because of an incident recorded about Constantine Rafinesque in one of Audubon's biographies, I do not know. The story is to the effect that Audubon found Rafinesque, who was a house guest, chasing a bat about the room with Audubon's choice violin, with no damage to the bat but total damage to the instrument.

The lump-nosed bat is about 4 inches long, including a tail of nearly 2 inches. Weight, ½ ounce. There is a conspicuous protuberance between the nostril and eye, from whence comes the name "lump-nosed." The ears are large and thin; bent backward, they reach to the middle of the body. The wingspread is to 13 inches; the wing and tail membranes are furless. There is little fur on the inner margins of the ears. The fur is soft, brown in color above and slaty beneath. Teeth are: I 2/3; C 1/1; P 2/3; M 3/3. The bat is also known as the "big-eared bat."

Some recognize 2 species of these bats, an Eastern and a Western, the dividing line being just west of the Mississippi River and north of the Ohio River. The Eastern species is found east and south of this line, extended to the Atlantic through Virginia except for the southern tip of Florida. The Western species extends west of the line to the Pacific in an area from southern British Columbia, northern Wyoming, and central Nebraska, Kansas, and Missouri, into Mexico.

Mating takes place in the fall, with fertilization delayed until spring. One young is born in May or June, 2–3 months after fertilization. The young is pink, hairless, with closed eyes, and weighs ¹⁄₁₀ ounce. In 4 days it has short hair, then the eyes open. At 2–3 weeks it can fly, and at 2 months it can do so at night, although it may continue nursing until 2 months old. The food probably is mostly soft-bodied insects taken close to foliage. Life expectancy known to be more than 10 years.

49

Yellow Bat · *Dasypterus floridanus* · Vespertilionidae

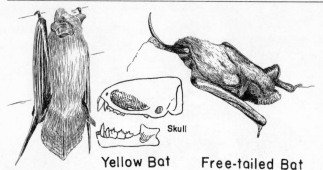

Yellow Bat   Free-tailed Bat

THREE species of related bats are to be found in this genus in the United States. They are essentially Southern, ranging from South Carolina to California. *Floridanus* is found only along the Gulf Coast from South Carolina to Texas. This species is about 5 inches long, grayish yellow to chestnut, with the membrane fur limited to the basal half of the upper surface. Teeth are: I 1/3; C 1/1; P 1/2; M 3/3.

Free-tailed Bat · *Tadarida mexicana* · Molossidae

OF the free-tailed bats, the variety known as the Mexican free-tailed bat is best known, as it maintains enormous roosts in Carlsbad Cavern, New Mexico. Here its guano or manure once covered an area nearly ¼ mile long, 100 feet wide, and nearly 100 feet in depth. The guano is built up at about 1 inch a year. It has been used as fertilizer in times of peace and in making explosives in time of war. It is reported that in World War II, Mexican free-tailed bats were chilled to 40° F., then freed to make their way into buildings carrying incendiary bombs with them.

Free-tailed bats are just over 4 inches long, with forearms nearly 2 inches long. They are brownish chocolate to almost black or smoky in color. The ears are broad and seem to be united at the base by a series of projections. The tail is long and its latter half extends beyond the membrane, giving the bat its common name. A closely related species, *T. cyanocephala,* is found along the southern coast of the United States, from South Carolina to Texas. Mexican free-tailed bats range from Texas to southern Oregon and south into Mexico. Another species, *T. molossa,* has brown hair that has a whitish base. These bats are to 5½ inches long.

All the bats described on these pages, save the vampire, are obviously usually of more value to man alive than dead, though unfortunately their services to man are little understood. This species may carry rabies.

ORDER DERMOPTERA *(Flying Lemurs)*

Flying Lemur · *Cyanocephalus variegatus* · Galeopithecidae

Flying Lemur

Potto

Tarsier

Marmoset

FEW who read these words will ever see alive the species shown on this page. Fewer will ever see wild any representative of the Order Dermoptera. Flying lemurs are probably basically members of the Insectivora. They also have some of the characteristics of bats, except that they do not fly in a true sense and each limb ends in 5 digits, all of which are connected by a membrane that extends between the arms, legs, and tail, and serves as a parachute. Can glide to 70 yards, losing little altitude. Unlike other mammals, their upper incisors and canines have 2 roots, and the lower incisors resemble combs. The illustrated flying lemur lives in the Philippines, the other in the Borneo, Malaya, and Java area. The flying lemur shown above hangs back down by all 4 feet when at rest. To 18 inches long, with a 10-inch prehensile tail, it is brown to gray above and reddish beneath. It bears 1 young that is poorly developed and hangs to mother a long time.

ORDER PRIMATES *(Monkeys, Apes, and Man)*

IN the Primates each limb ends in 5 digits, each of which is usually tipped by a curved or flattened nail. There is a bony ring around the eye, directed forward. Usually the thumb and the great toe are opposable, and there is a highly functional nervous system. There are 3 commonly recognized suborders, representatives of which are shown.

The suborder Lemuridea, represented by the Potto (see also *Potos,* p. 195), has claws on the 2nd toe and nails on the others. Its tail may be absent and, if long, is never prehensile. Its representatives live in the Africa–Southeast Asia area.

The suborder Tarsoidea, here represented by the tarsier, has claws on the 2nd and 3rd toes, protruding eyes, large ratlike ears, a non-prehensile tail, and pads on the digit tips. Squirrel sized. Family, Tarsiidae.

The suborder Anthropoidea includes man, Hominidae; the monkeys and apes (a number of families); and the marmosets, Callithricidae. These all have cupped nails on all digits. There are 5 families. Marmosets are squirrel sized, with non-prehensile tails. Squirrel marmosets, *Saimiri* sq., belong in the Cebidae.

Spider Monkey · *Ateles ater* · Cebidae

Howler Monkey

Skull

Spider Monkey

THE family Cebidae includes the New World monkeys, such as the spider monkeys, the howler monkeys, and the capuchins or sapajous. These and the marmosets (Callithricidae: weight, to 2 pounds; gestation, 146 days; to 2 young; respiration rate, 1,040), are sometimes grouped into a superfamily, the Ceboidea, all of which are New World animals. In the Cebidae, the tail may be prehensile. In the Callithricidae, it is not.

Spider monkeys, *Ateles ater,* have prehensile tails. They are to 4½ feet long, including 2½-foot tail. Weight, to 19 pounds. Height at shoulder is to 18 inches. There are 5 toes on each foot, 4 fingers on each hand, but the thumb is missing. They are black except for gray noses and cheeks. One 2-pound young is born after 140-day gestation period. The young is gray for a year. Independent at five months. Often live in clans, a typical one including 2 males, 4 females, 4 juveniles, and 2 dependent young. Can leap across 30 feet of space.

Howler Monkey · *Alouatta palliata* · Cebidae

HOWLER monkeys are to 58 inches long, including a 30-inch tail. Height at shoulder is 26 inches. Weight, to 16½ pounds. Face is oblique, body thick, tail hairy and prehensile, with bare spot under the tip. Fur is golden brown on back and deep chestnut beneath, except in young, which are brown or gray, changing at 2 years to adult coloration.

Initiative in mating is taken by either sex. Breeding takes place at any time of year and is promiscuous. Young weighs 3½ pounds at birth. The mother carries her young, at first beneath her body, but later it rides on her back.

Male howler monkeys have heavy beards hanging from below bare faces. The howling begins in the early morning or evening, and may be frightening to the uninitiated. Strong lungs send air over a bony sound box with phenomenal results. In a troop of these monkeys there is no particular leader. A typical group is composed of 3 males, 8 females, 4 juveniles, and 3 dependent infants. Howlers are not easily tamed.

Howlers are found from Vera Cruz, Mexico, through Central America to Brazil, Peru, and Bolivia.

Capuchin Monkey or Sapajou

Cebus capucinus · Cebidae

In the days of the hand organ most of us had a chance to see and to establish a reserved acquaintance with a capuchin monkey. The animal came to us at the end of a long cord and offered us a cup, seeking pennies, while its master ground out wheezing music for our "benefit." Macaques (next page) were also hand-organ monkeys.

Capuchin monkeys, a New World species, have a body length of 31 inches, including a 16-inch tail. They are 9 inches high at the shoulder. The head is rounded, the muzzle short, the body slender, and the hair on the crown short and bent forward. The face and ears are naked and show a purplish cast. The species include the weeper capuchin of Brazil, pictured above; the white-cheeked capuchin of Brazil; and others ranging over Central America and South America.

In the weeper, the hair down the back is reddish brown, the shoulders are gray to yellow, and the whiskers black. The white-cheeked capuchin has black fur and yellowish temples.

In the wild, capuchin monkeys live in troops of a dozen, led by a male. They go on early-morning foraging expeditions after their food of fruit, shoots, eggs, young birds, and insects. Captive animals share man's food tastes. They have been known to use stones to crush oysters and nuts. This approaches the ingenuity of man in using a tool to do his work. The tail of the capuchin is rarely used for swinging and probably never as an exploratory organ. Spider monkeys use their tails freely for swinging and investigating.

There are 1 or 2 young born from 5 to 6 months after a promiscuous mating period. It takes about 3 years to complete a generation from breeding to breeding.

When young, these monkeys are affectionate, safe, and interesting pets, but with maturity they become unreliable and hardly trustworthy. Their fur has some market value.

Rhesus Monkey or Macaque

Macacas mulata · Lasiopygidae

NEW World monkeys, such as the capuchins, howlers, and spider monkeys, may have prehensile tails, no cheek pouches, and a wide, flat interspace between the nostrils. Old World monkeys, like those described on this page and the next, never have prehensile tails, often have cheek pouches, and their nostrils are separated by a narrow space and are directed downward. They may have bare or calloused buttocks. Old World monkeys include the langur of India, sacred to the Hindus; the long-haired Colobus of Africa; and the proboscis monkeys of Borneo.

Monkeys of this group are of considerable importance in human affairs in religion and medicine. More than 300 million human beings are Hindus. According to their beliefs, monkeys of these types are sacred. About this, however, the farmers whose gardens the monkeys raid may have some reservations. Members of the medical profession recognize the debt we owe to rhesus monkeys, for as experimental animals these creatures have helped solve many health problems shared by the monkeys and by men. Rhesus monkeys are native to northern India, where they abound in the trees and on the ground, often living as parasites on native economy.

Rhesus monkeys have heavy bodies 15 inches long, tails of 6 inches, and a shoulder height of 15 inches. Weight: male, 24 pounds; female, 17 pounds. The snout is prominent, as are the brows. The ears are small, the eyes oval, the hair stiff, straight, and long. The hair is yellow to brown on the body, lighter beneath. The buttocks are flesh colored.

Adults are promiscuous. One young is born 5½ months (146–180 days) after the mating. At birth it weighs 1 pound. It nurses until a year old, when it weighs to 3½ pounds and is 1 foot high, seated. At 2 years it reaches 4 pounds and 14 inches; at 3, 6½ pounds and 16½ inches, at which size and age the female becomes sexually mature. The male matures at 4 years. Conception takes place 10 days after the menstrual flow. There may be twins. Pulse, 165–240. Temperature, 97°–104° F. Life span, 29 years.

Mandrill · *Papio mormon* · Cercopithecidae

MANDRILLS are baboons native to equatorial West Africa. They are 2 feet long, 1¾ feet high, have 2-inch tails, and weigh to 110 pounds. The canine teeth are long and conspicuous. Each of the prominent nose protuberances is blue and has 6 convolutions. The hair on their bodies is long, silky, and a greenish dark brown, with the under parts yellowish white and the hinder parts purple shading to light blue. The lips, nostrils, and nose are carmine. The prominent beards are white and head tufts black. The females are less husky than are the males and are more dully colored. While mandrills live for the most part on the ground, they favor forested areas. Large males may lead and rule troops of to 50 animals. When a troop moves, the young commonly ride on their mothers' backs. A troop of 50 animals, each weighing to 100 pounds and of an ugly disposition, and with an appetite for garden stuffs, is a rather formidable enemy for a farmer to meet. Life expectancy, 15 years.

Chacma Baboon

Baboon Skull

Mandrill

Rhesus Monkey

Chacma Baboon

Cynocephalus porcarius · Cercopithecidae

CHACMA baboons are native to southeastern Africa. Their bodies are about 2 feet long and they have 18-inch tails. They stand 1 foot 10 inches at the shoulder, on hind legs, to a height of 3½ feet. The tail curves conspicuously upward. The nostrils are large and the canine teeth prominent. The hair on the body is thick, shaggy, and greenish black. The ears are large and naked. The rump pads are dark. The purple face is also naked. The upper eyelids are white. These baboons live in rocky wastes in troops of to 40 animals. They feed on fruits, roots, vegetation, fish, and any animal they can overcome. They may also destroy many insects and insect larvae. Breed at 4 years; gestation, 210 days. When young, baboons may be friendly, but as they mature they become increasingly undependable. Life expectancy, about 10 years.

55

Gibbon · *Hylobates agilis* · Pongidae

THE family Pongidae is grouped with the family Hominidae in a superfamily which includes apes and man. The animals in this superfamily have no tails or cheek pouches. Gibbons are native to India, Burma, Malaya, and the Hainan Provinces. The related siamang, *Symphalangus,* is the largest of the gibbons and is found in Sumatra and Malaya.

White-handed gibbons, pictured on p. 57, are found in Hainan. They have a head and body length of 30 inches, legs 1 foot long, and arms twice that length. The head is small, the muzzle short, the ears round, and the body slender. The fur is coarse and has a reversed direction on the forearms. The thumbs are opposable. The animals are mostly black, with hands and feet yellowish and a white area around the face.

Gibbons walk rather erect on the ground, but when they are erect the knuckles can touch the ground. They cannot swim. In the treetops they are in their element. There they can leap from one handhold to another 40 feet away and catch flying birds on the way. In walking, the hips are rotated conspicuously. They may carry their hands locked behind their necks, after the manner of war prisoners.

Usually 1 young is born from 200–212 days after mating, which occurs in the treetops. The juvenile gibbon is carried on the mother's hips. It is paler than the adult. Young males may be grayish to black, while young females may be smoky gray. The young are carried in the mother's arms for the first 7 months. At 6 years, the young white-handed gibbon may turn to a silvery gray and become sexually mature. Breed at 8–10 years. Gestation, 210 days. Life expectancy, to 23 years. In zoos there have been successful crosses between gibbons of the different species.

In the wild, gibbons may live in noisy troops which, when in full cry, can be heard a mile away. They have the reputation among the natives of having a high degree of intelligence. In captivity, they feed on rice and fruit, but they do not thrive in cold, moist climates, and few live more than a year in European zoos. They do better in America.

Orangutan · *Simia* or *Pongo pygmaeus* · Pongidae

THE major zoos commonly have an orangutan, which is always popular with visitors who enjoy watching it swing from support to support. The animal is a native of Sumatra and Borneo.

Orangutans stand about 4 feet 3 inches high, but have a reach from fingertip to fingertip of more than 7 feet. When they stand erect, the fingers nearly reach the ground. The legs are short and weak, but the arms have phenomenal strength, and the hands are large and strong. The head is narrow, pear-shaped, with a high forehead; the snout bulging; the nostrils large. The mouth projects and the lips are thin. The ears are small and free

Skull

Skeleton

Gibbon   **Orangutan**

of hair. There is a beard of hair to 2 inches long, and no tail. The skin is a bluish gray to brown, and the long hair is shaggy and reddish.

Orangutans live in small families composed of a pair of parents and 2–4 young. Home is a sort of platform or nest in the trees, where the animals commonly sleep until midday, when they leave to feed. They may seek shellfish along the seashore. One young is born 8½ months after the mating takes place. The youngster is defended fiercely by the parents. First incisors at 147 days; 2nd at 229 days; canines at 343 days; molars at 169 and 303 days.

The favored food is the fruit called durian, from which they remove the spiny rind. They eat other fruits, of course. In captivity, they develop a liking for alcoholic liquors, which affect them as they do men.

Orangs are not so intelligent as some of their close relatives, but they submit to some training and are often popular when trained to imitate man. Temperature, 97°–100° F. Life span, to 26½ years.

Gorilla · *Gorilla gorilla* · Pongidae

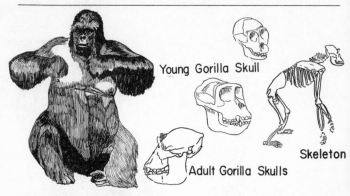

Young Gorilla Skull

Adult Gorilla Skulls

Skeleton

WHEN Stanley wrote *In Darkest Africa,* he probably wanted to give his readers the shivers and make them admire his bravery in facing the many dangers he described, including savage gorillas. Carl Akeley and other writers have given us what is probably a truer picture of gorillas, and have indicated that if left alone they behave with reasonable decency to most visitors. Friends of mine who have been in Africa with Akeley agree that while gorillas are powerful, dangerous animals, they generally mind their own business, if permitted to do so.

Gorillas are found in wooded parts of Africa and probably originally ranged across the continent. Two species are recognized, one of the mountains and one of the lowlands.

A male gorilla, standing erect, measures nearly 6 feet tall and may weigh to 600 pounds. The female is much smaller. Males commonly spend the night on the ground; females in nests in trees. Gorillas measure more than 9 feet from fingertip to fingertip when the arms are stretched out. They have no tail. The body is round and bulky and the muzzle short. The chest may be 20 inches across. The mouth is wide, and the canines are exceptionally large. The eyes are small, the nostrils large, and the ears small and set close to the head. The ears may also be hairless. There is usually dense hair on the chest and sometimes on the lower part of the belly. Face and chest are naked in old males. The skin of the body is black, as are the hands, feet, and face.

Nine months after the mating, 1 young is born. The youngster walks more erect than do its parents. It becomes a member of the troop, which is made up of a male, several females, and some young. At 4 years of age, a young gorilla may weigh 140 pounds; at 7 years it reaches sexual maturity. Life span, to 28 years. In zoos, there are records of gorillas having lived 8, 10, 12, 16, 21, and 24 years, males living the longer. Gorillas cannot swim.

58

Chimpanzee · *Pan troglodytes* · Pongidae

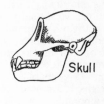

Skull

EQUATORIAL Africa is also the home of another species of apes, the chimpanzee. These are natives of the western and central parts. Chimpanzees stand to a height of about 5 feet, although the head and body length is but 2 feet 8 inches. When on all fours, the shoulder height is to 2 feet. They have no tail. Males may weigh to 170 pounds, although this is about the maximum. The thumb or big toe of the foot is exceptionally long and powerful. Although the arms reach to below the knees when the apes stand erect, the arms are probably proportionately shorter than in other apes. The body is broad. The head is also broad, domed, and covered with hair. The muzzle is wide. The thumbs of the forefeet are small but opposable. The fur is coarse. The body, sides, under parts, and cheeks are black, but the nose, ears, hands, and feet are flesh colored.

Eight months (216–265 days) after the mating, which occurs at any time of the year, 1 young is born, usually in a nest well guarded by the male. At 9 days the youngster weighs 2 pounds. At 5½ years the females become sexually mature. The males probably do not mature until from 8–9 years old. Incisors appear at 5½ years, canines at 7 years, premolars at 6 years, 1st molars at 3 years, 2nd at 6, and 3rd at 9–10 years. Temperature, 97°–100° F. Life span, about 40 years.

In the wild, chimpanzees live in troops built around a family group, usually dominated by a single male. Although they are at home in the trees, when pushed by circumstances they seek safety by running over the ground. In doing this, they plant the knuckles of the forelimbs on the ground instead of the palms of the hands.

The female is in heat for from 34–35 days, and a courting male shows his interest by beating the ground with his hands or feet at an increasing tempo.

Students have recognized 32 different sounds that have significance in a chimpanzee's vocabulary. Exhaustive studies have been made of these sounds in the hope that greater understanding of the intelligence of chimpanzees might result. The chimpanzee is probably the most intelligent of the apes.

59

Man · *Homo sapiens* · Hominidae

PROBABLY the most interesting animal to man is man himself. Recognition of the fact that man is an animal should in no way obscure the fact that man has characteristics which undoubtedly make him superior in many ways to all other animals. With equal justice, we should recognize that in many ways he is inferior to many other animals. We should pause here to recognize some of these differences, even if we must devote more space to the study of man than to other species of mammals.

An average 6-foot American man weighs 183 pounds if he is more than 45 years old. An average 15-year-old boy, 5½ feet high, weighs 128 pounds. A 45-year-old, 5½ foot man weighs about 156 pounds. A woman of the same age and height weighs about 12 pounds less.

In the average human body the muscles constitute 44.1% of the total weight; the bones, 17.6%; the liver, 2.3%; the brain, 1.9%; the lungs, 1.2%; the heart and kidneys, .4% each; the spleen, .2%, and the adrenals, .01%.

In a human body weighing 150 pounds, 97.5 pounds are oxygen, 27 pounds carbon, 15 pounds hydrogen, 4.5 pounds nitrogen, 2.4 pounds calcium, 1.5 pounds phosphorus, .45 pound sodium, .45 pound chlorine, .375 pound magnesium. Other items, minor in amount but not in significance, include iron, iodine, copper, cobalt, manganese, boron, and fluorine. An average man needs for consumption and other uses approximately 25 gallons of water a day, if we omit water used in transportation, for watering crops, raising livestock, and so on. If these are considered, the amount needed is much greater, and they must be considered if men are to live.

In 1900 the United States supported a population of about 25 humans per square mile. In 1950 it supported 50 per square mile and exported enormous surpluses of food to foreign populations. In 1950, 64% of the total population of 150 million were urban dwellers. Counting only individuals over 14 years of age, there were in 1950 in the United States 35,627,394 city residents, 11,284,735 rural non-farm residents, and 8,399,488 rural farmers. Of all these, there were about 10 times as many whites as colored folk. The total world population is estimated at about 2½ billion, with an expected annual increase of about 30 million. It is probable that the world population cannot continue to increase indefinitely.

Man's skeletal system is shown in the illustration on page 61. The most permanent bony structures in man are the teeth. As shown on page 61, the first set, the milk teeth, first appear normally at 6 months and may continue to appear for 2½ years. The first permanent teeth appear at from 5–9 years; by 22 years all should have developed. The order in which the milk teeth and the permanent teeth appear is shown in the diagram. It should be noted that the 2 sets do not appear in the same order. Since teeth add much to the joy the individual gets from

MAN

ARTERIES

Temporal
Facial
Carotid
Axillary
Subclavian
Brachial
Aorta
Femoral

BONES

Cranium
Cervical Vert.
Clavicle
Scapula
Humerus
Sternum
Ribs
Radius
Ulna
Carpus
Metacarpus
Phalanges
Femur
Patella
Fibula
Tibia
Tarsus
Metatarsus
Phalanges

Java Man

Neanderthal Man

Cro Magnon Man

Modern Man

Central Incisors		6-8 mos.
Lateral Incisors		8-12 mos.
Canines		16-20 mos.
1st Molars		12-16 mos.
2nd Molars	Milk Teeth and order of appearance	20-30 mos.

Central Incisors		6- 9 yrs.
Lateral Incisors		7-9 yrs.
Canines		9-14 yrs.
1st Bicuspids		9-13 yrs.
Bicuspids		11-14 yrs.
1st Molars		5-8 yrs.
2nd Molars	Permanent Teeth and order of appearance	10-14 yrs.
3rd Molars		16-22 yrs.

Man · *Homo sapiens* · Hominidae

eating, contribute to his health, and definitely affect his appearance, their care is most important. In some areas where there is an absence of certain chemicals in the water there is a great tendency to tooth decay. In other regions, deterioration may be caused primarily by diet. Of course, heredity may also affect the length of time a person's teeth are available for his use.

A glance at the skull sketches of mammals in this book will show that there is much less specialization in the teeth of man than there is, for example, in the teeth of rabbits, whales, elephants, horses, or sheep. The skulls pictured on earlier pages as a rule show less specialization than do those in the rest of the book. The same may be said of the bones, particularly of the hands and feet. For example, man has ordinarily 5 fingers on each hand and 5 toes on each foot. All of the fingers are more or less alike, as are all of the toes. The digits terminating the limbs of animals discussed so far in the book are for the most part more generalized, or alike, than in most of those near the end of the book. This is true, for example, when we compare our hands and feet with comparable structures in whales, elephants, horses, and cattle. See the illustration on page 257, which shows the supposed evolution and development of the highly specialized foot of a horse through the years.

The nature of the bony skeleton of man is definitely related to his behavior pattern. A man at best can sprint at only about 25 miles per hour, and only for a short distance. A whippet can speed at 35 miles an hour. A race horse can run at the rate of nearly a mile in ½ minute. The skeleton of each of these three mammals helps determine its speed. A sloth can go, at high speed, only 14 feet in one minute, but while the horse and whippet can go faster than a sloth on the ground, the sloth is more at home in a treetop than either. A glance at the skeleton of a porpoise and that of man will show how different they are, and may suggest the reason why a man requires about 20 minutes to swim his fastest mile, while porpoises have been reputed, although not proven, to be able to swim at something approaching 60 miles an hour.

Man's respiration rate is 4,000 at maximum work and 200 at rest. His pulse varies from 31–160 (average 60–80 a minute) or in embryo to 173 just before birth. Temperature 97°–104° F. (normal, 98.6° F.).

Of all the muscles in a man's body the most important is probably the heart. It beats about 100,000 times a day, pumping about 5,000 gallons of blood in 24 hours. It keeps this up during the life of the individual. The pulse can be taken as some indication of the health and current excitement of the individual. In the diagram, page 61, we have given a general idea of the location of the arteries in the human body. Among other things, this diagram indicates the location of the spots where, in case of accident, pressure can be safely applied to limit loss of blood in various parts of the body, if this is done properly. Diseases of the heart account for many deaths. Between the ages of 25 and 44, about 23% of deaths are due to heart trouble; between 45 and 64, 46%; between 65 and 74, 55%; and over 75, 60%. Advances in medicine may change these statistics at any time, just as they have with other diseases of man.

To turn to the 5 senses, man's hearing range is much less effective than that of bats, which use sounds to guide their flight—sounds that man cannot hear.

In man the sense of smell is much less acute than it is, for example, in dogs. Therefore, men train dogs to help them do things by means of this sense that they could not do by themselves.

The sense of touch in man is not developed to so high a degree as it is, for example, in moles. Raccoons also have this sense well developed and use it even in searching for food in crevices underwater.

Man's sense of sight is important to his survival, happiness, and economic success. It does not compare, however, with the vision enjoyed by some hawks. Vision varies greatly with different animals, as is shown in many accounts in this book.

Man has other senses than those of touch, taste, sight, smell, and hearing. He can judge time, has a sense of rhythm. He has a phenomenal memory, an ability to put the lessons of experiences together to help interpret the future, and the imagination to establish hypotheses which, by the use of ingenuity, may be proven to be valid or false. The employment of the nervous system by man to use past experience to dictate experiences to come is not matched by other animals, and gives man an unequaled ability to improve his future. With the use of machines devised by the use of his nervous system, he can see better than any hawk, can fly better than any bird, can detect chemical differences better than any animal can do through its sense of taste, can measure things infinitely finer than any organism can detect by touch, and can make himself heard over vastly greater distances than any other mammal.

One to rarely 5 young are born 9 months after human beings mate. Copulation may take place at any time. Fruitful mating may take place at any time of year or at any time during the years when a woman is capable of conceiving. With men, the capacity for fruitful mating may develop as early as 10 years, but more commonly not until about 16 years. It may continue until old age. With women, menstruation begins between 10 and 18 years of age, and conception may result from mating at any time until menstruation ceases, usually in the late forties. Apparently the happiest life centers around a family of the monogamous type, and when neither parent has a record of sexual behavior for which either can have regrets. Life span, to over 100 years.

Man · *Homo sapiens* · Hominidae

We have reasons to believe that some 60 million years ago, in Eocene times, there lived a little ratlike animal much like the modern feathertail of Far Eastern jungles. From this animal sprang a group of animals which developed into monkeys. Also from this source evolved a race that developed our present-day gibbons, orangutans, chimpanzees, gorillas, and men. About 25 million years ago, man declared his independence from the gorillas, and began making the world over to suit his needs and often his whims.

Some 6 to 7 million years ago, man was represented on the earth by the Java man, *Pithecanthropus erectus*. From this line developed the men of the Neanderthal and Heidelberg types, both of which disappeared from the face of the earth. For many years science believed that another type, the Piltdown man, evolved from the remaining stock, but modern physical science has provided tools which have exposed the bones on which this claim rested as a deliberate hoax. From the group did arise, however, men similar to modern Australian blackfellows, obviously the most primitive of existing human beings. Later, in approximately the Pleistocene era, there developed the Cro-Magnon type of man, among whose modified descendants is the modern white man.

We cannot safely assume that any race of modern man has all of the desirable elements to be found potentially in man. We have had too many wars, for which self-appointed "supermen" have been responsible, to believe that there is any such thing as a "super race." Some of us Americans like to feel that the combination of black, white, yellow, brown, and red races to be found here has been responsible for a mass record of inventiveness, generosity, understanding, and application of the Golden Rule that is not at present, at least, matched elsewhere in the world. Some of us feel that we cannot indefinitely go on exhausting our natural resources. We point with pride to the machines we have devised, which have progressively taken the yoke of hard labor from ourselves, from other men, and from domestic animals, and have, to a considerable extent, placed it on gas and electric engines. These engines, of course, are at present run only by exhausting non-renewable resources, though this system may be changed.

Man is justly proud of his mastery of space by machines, of his improved means of communication, of his use of electronics in making rapid calculations that permit accomplishments not possible otherwise. We feel pleased with what we have done in picturing what we see, mechanically or with a brush. We have found satisfaction in sounds conceived by great musicians and presented to us by great artists.

We like to think that we are pointing the way to a happy future for all deserving human beings.

ORDER PHOLIDOTA (NOMARTHRA)
(*Pangolins*)

Pangolin or Scaly Anteater

Smutsia temminckii · Manidae

MEMBERS of this order are not likely to be seen alive by most readers of this book. The animals look somewhat reptilian in their general shape and scaly covering, but they are true, warm-blooded animals, and give birth to living young that are suckled by the mother. Tree pangolins are classed in two genera. A West African species, and the ground pangolin of eastern, southern, and central Africa, belong to the genus *Smutsia*. A number of species of tree pangolins in the genus *Manis* live in southern Asia. The order is sometimes called the Nomarthra, and there is relatively little consistency among scientists in suggesting relationships, except that the group is considered to be near the Edentata, which includes the anteaters, sloths, and armadillos.

In the pangolins, there are 5–6 digits on each hand and foot, those of the forefeet being armed with strong claws of great use in tearing open insect nests. There are no teeth, and the tongue is long and sticky and suitable for picking up insects. The eyes are small and the ears do not protrude. When pangolins walk using the forefeet, they place the knuckles on the ground. They walk about, mostly at night, on their hind feet, using their tails to brace themselves. When disturbed, pangolins curl into balls and get protection from their sharp-edged scales. In *Smutsia,* the scales are small on the head, but are large and overlapping on the neck, back, legs, and tail. In the Asiatic *Manis,* the neck, cheeks, and under parts are not scaled.

Indian pangolins live in pairs, with one or 2 young, occupying a 2-foot den at the end of a burrow which slopes down to 12 feet below the ground surface. At birth, young pangolins have soft scales, but these normally become hard by the end of the second day. The mother may carry her young perched on the back of her tail. The great ground pangolin of Equatorial Africa, *S. gigantea,* is, including the tail, to 6 feet long, with scales to 3 inches long and 5 inches wide. The common pangolin of China is to 2½ feet long, including the tail, and weighs to 17 pounds. It is edible.

ORDER EDENTATA (*Toothless Mammals*)

Great Anteater

Myrmecophaga jubata · Myrmecophagidae

TROPICAL Central America and South America are the regions where the anteaters may be found. There they haunt wet forest lands and live in mud or in water to 6 inches deep. Of course they can swim in much deeper water. The great anteater has a body about 4 feet long and a 2½ foot tail. It stands to 2 feet high at the shoulder. The almost naked head is more than a foot long, slender, and looks like a continuation of the neck. The ears are short and close. The mouth is a tube through which the long, sticky tongue is thrust. The skin is thick and tough, and the hair stiff and bristly. While the hair on the head and neck is short and close, except for the erect mane which extends down the back, some of the hairs on the shoulders and tail may be to 16 inches long. The head is gray, as are the foreparts of the body; the mane black; the tail gray above and darker beneath; the forelegs white with brown patches. The belly, legs, and some other parts are brown. The claws are black.

Anteaters do not burrow, but use their strong claws to dig out insect nests. They normally feed almost wholly on insects, but in captivity may be fed on milk, eggs, and ground meat. The silky anteater and the three-toed anteater, however, do not survive long on this diet. The so-called three-toed anteater, *Tamandua tetradactyla,* actually has 4 toes on the front feet and 5 on the hind feet. It has a prehensile tail and lives in trees. It ranges from Mexico south. The silky anteater, *Cyclops* sp., is of squirrel size, has claws on only 2 toes, and lives in trees. It totals about 15 inches in length. It abhors sunlight. It ranges from Mexico to Bolivia.

Great anteaters breed only once a year and bear but 1 young. The young stays with the mother, riding on her back sometimes until 1 year old.

Anteaters are of tremendous value in areas where ants are so destructive to plant life. They are generally harmless, but when disturbed may lie back and fight with their powerful, hooked front feet.

66

Armadillo · *Dasypus novemcinctus* · Dasypodidae

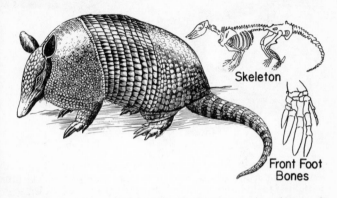

Skeleton

Front Foot
Bones

ONE of our most peaceful turtles is the box turtle, whose soft parts are almost completely protected by a hard surface; one of the most aggressive turtles is the snapping turtle, whose soft under parts are unprotected. In the armadillos, we have mammals protected on the outside with bony plates, which in some species extend even over the top of the head.

The nine-banded armadillo is about 28 inches long, with an additional foot-long tail. It weighs about 15 pounds. From 7 to 9 movable joints around the middle permit the animal to curl up and protect the soft under parts. There are 4 toes on the front feet and 5 on the hind feet. Teeth are: I 0/0; C 0/0; P 0/0; M 8/8. This species ranges from Kansas through Missouri to Florida and south into Mexico. They are found from sea level to 10,000 feet elevation. The home range is about 50 acres per individual, but there may be 1 animal per acre in suitable territory. They can walk safely underwater and remain 6 minutes without breathing. They swim well. They have a strong sense of smell and can locate insects 6 inches underground. Their hearing ability varies. They see poorly. Respiration rate, 201. Temperature, 86°–90° F.

Armadillos are great destroyers of insects and snakes, damage crops such as cantaloupes, and may eat poultry in rare cases. In captivity they eat horse meat and dog food. They do not hibernate. May be found in groups of over 60 animals.

Young number 4 or 8, of one sex, there being 4 per fertilized egg. Breeding season, July–September. Fertilization, 120 days after mating; birth, 120 days later. Young identical, open-eyed at birth. Breed at 1 year of age. From 2–15 may occupy a common burrow, although each individual may have 4–8 burrows. Usually there is but 1 sex in a burrow. The burrows may be from 2–12 feet under ground, and are rarely branched. The body temperature may drop safely 4°–8° in 4 hours.

Three-toed Sloth · *Bradypus griseus* · Bradypodidae

ALTHOUGH there is no especial reason to suppose that three-toed sloths are particularly happy, they seem to have an ideal life, with little to do but hang quietly by the toes in trees loaded with food which they can have for the taking.

As their name implies, there are 3 toes on each foot. Each toe bears a long, curved, hook-like claw. In the two-toed sloth, *Choloepus hoffmanni,* the forefeet have 2 toes each and the hind feet 3 toes. The Amazon River approximates the southern limit of both these sloths, and they are found north to Honduras. Huge fossil sloths have been found from Mexico to Patagonia. They were at least 20 feet long.

Three-toed sloths are about 20 inches long. They have a small round head and small ears and eyes. They can neither see nor hear well, depending on the sense of smell to get food and avoid danger. They are naturally of a uniform gray color, but may be green with algae. The males may also have a yellow spot in the middle of the back.

The body temperature may drop at night and rise considerably in the daytime; it ranges from 86°–100° F. The sloths may be torpid at the lower temperatures. They have been known to fall for 30 feet and land safely, and yet one was killed by a 5-foot fall. Respiration rate, 168.

Two-toed sloths are larger than three-toed sloths, and can move reasonably well over the ground. One individual studied traveled 4 miles in 48 days, swam 65 feet in 2½ minutes, and could move 14 feet per minute on the ground.

Usually 1 young is born 120–180 days after the mating takes place. It hangs tightly, and flat, on the mother's belly. It develops sufficiently to be able to feed itself by the time it is 5 weeks old.

Ordinarily sloths are probably short-lived, but there is a record of one having lived in captivity in a London zoo for 11 years. Sloths are not friendly animals and when a number are confined together, they may fight vigorously to the death. Of course they come together at the breeding season as a necessity. Respiration rate, 216. Temperature, 92°–97° F.

ORDER LAGOMORPHA (*Hares and Rabbits*)

Pika or Coney · *Ochotona princeps* · Ochotonidae

Skull

Front Foot   Hind Foot
Tracks

I⊤ is often supposed that hares and rabbits are rodents. However, in the hares and rabbits there are 4 incisor teeth on the upper jaw instead of the 2 to be found in the rodents. The second pair is usually not large and is hidden behind the first pair. As in the rodents, there are no canine teeth, and the incisors continue to grow as long as the animals live. If one becomes broken by disease or injury, the fact that its counterpart on the other jaw continues to grow may have distressing results. The animals are essentially plant eaters, commonly have large ears and short tails, and ordinarily hop and leap instead of running or walking.

The pikas, coneys, or little chief hares, differ from the other hares and rabbits, and from the rodents, in that they have no external tail. They should not be confused with the coneys known as hyrax (page 244). The pikas are found in Europe, Asia, and America, with 7 species in the United States. Teeth are: I 2/1; C 0/0; P 2/2; M 3/3. Notice the 4 upper incisors characteristic of the lagomorphs and distinctive from the rodents' 2 upper incisors.

Pikas range, in closely related species, from Alaska to northern California and to Colorado, and are common in Asia at elevations of from 3,000–12,000 feet.

Our pikas look like little guinea pigs. They hide in rock crevices and may store a peck of dried plant material for winter use. They whistle when excited and are therefore sometimes called "whistling hares." They are about 8 inches long and weigh 6½ ounces. The legs are short. The white-bordered ears are short and rounded, but broad. There are usually 3–4 young, with the first litter coming in May and the latest in September. Each little pika weighs about ⅓ ounce. Fur durability 20% that of otter. As plant eaters, they compete with sheep for fodder, but they provide basic nourishment for many fur bearers and their food caches may even help sheep in time of food shortage. Temperature, 102° F.

69

Varying Hare or Snowshoe Rabbit

Lepus americanus · Leporidae

THE members of the Leporidae differ from the pikas in the possession of a tail, even though it is small. In our varying hare, the tail makes up 2 inches of a total length of 18 inches. The hind feet are to 5½ inches long and the weight from 4¼–5¼ pounds. In summer, varying hares are reddish brown, peppered with black, on the back, light brown on the legs, and white beneath. In winter, they are pure white except for the black ear tips. A subspecies does not change color seasonally. The change to white can be prevented by exposure to artificial light for 18 hours a day, or if this treatment is given in January, white animals will become brown even at low temperatures. Teeth are: I 2/1; C 0/0; P 3/2; M 3/3. Tracks are: H, 6 x 3, 4; F, 1½ x 2, 4; Sp 8; L 66.

Varying hares range from Hudson Bay to Alaska and south to Oregon, Colorado, West Virginia, and Rhode Island. They vary greatly not only in color but also in their abundance, which varies cyclically. Like true hares, they do not dig burrows, although they will take refuge under cover. They feed almost exclusively on plant material, favoring aspen, evergreens, dandelions, and berry bushes. They defend a home territory of about 10 acres in breeding season, but there may be to 6 varying hares an acre at the height of the population cycle, which lasts for about 10 years. Their fluctuating abundance affects that of lynxes, foxes, and other animals that prey on them. Fur, known as "Baltic fox" or "white fox," is of little value. They are excellent game. May run at 30 miles an hour.

Courting males (March–August) fight with teeth. Both sexes are promiscuous. One–6 young, fur-covered and with eyes open, are born 30–40 days after mating. They weigh to 3 ounces; are sound-sensitive at 4 hours; can run first day, hop the third, raise ears the fifth, nibble hay the eleventh, and cease nursing the thirty-fifth day. Breed at 1 year. Temperature, 100°–103° F.

California Jack Rabbit · *Lepus californicus* · Leporidae

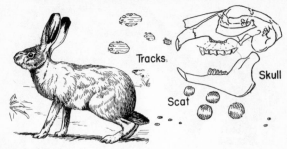

Tracks

Skull

Scat

SINCE we call a varying hare a hare and a jack rabbit a rabbit, we might reasonably assume that one was a rabbit and the other a hare. But we would be mistaken. Rabbits were originally small European burrowing animals which gave birth to naked young. By this rule none of our so-called American wild rabbits are rabbits; all are hares. To be sure, it will not do much good to call a jack rabbit a "jack hare," or a cottontail rabbit a "cotton-tail hare." Yet neither burrows, and both give birth to well-developed young, a characteristic of hares and not of rabbits.

The genus *Lepus* includes the varying hare just discussed. It also includes the Arctic hare, *L. arcticus*, which, like the varying hare, also changes its color. The Arctic hare, however, lives largely north of the tree belt. In the group also are white-sided jack rabbits, such as *L. alleni*, which has a white shoulder and rump and no black on the back of the ear tip, and the antelope jacks. There are also the white-tailed jack rabbits, such as *L. townsendi*, in which the tail is usually white, and the black-tailed jack rabbits or gray-sided jack rabbits, such as *L. californicus*, in which the tail is black.

California or black-tailed jack rabbits are found from Nebraska and Texas to California and Washington. They are to 2 feet long, including a 2-inch tail, and have 5½ inch hind feet. They weigh to 10 pounds. They are dark brown, with white patches on the forehead, around the eyes, and back of the ears. The ear tips and tail are black. The white-tailed jack rabbits turn white in winter.

Polygamous breeding takes place in warmer seasons. From 1–5 young are born 30 days after mating. At birth they are well developed and well furred, with open eyes and short ears. They are nursed a few days, and kept by the mother in separate spots.

These rabbits may run at 45 miles per hour. Tracks are: F, 1½ x 1½, 4; H, 2 x 6½, 5; Sp 7; L 150.* There may be 10–70 animals per square mile. They are pests to the farmer, but ordinarily are kept naturally in control by coyotes and hawks.

* See page 20.

European Hare · *Lepus europaeus* · Leporidae

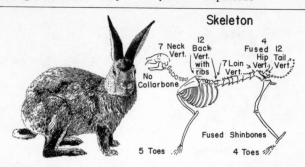

Skeleton

7 Neck Vert.

12 Back Vert. with ribs

No Collarbone

7 Loin Vert.

4 Fused Hip Vert.

12 Tail Vert.

Fused Shinbones

5 Toes

4 Toes

THIS page and the following ones will help to clear up this rabbit-hare question. The illustration shows a European hare, *Lepus europaeus,* sometimes called the brown hare, bettie, or mawkins. European hares average about 2 feet in length, including a 3¾ inch tail, and usually weigh about 8 pounds. They may weigh up to 13¼ pounds. The male (buck) has a slightly smaller head and body than the female (doe). They are yellowish red, lighter on the sides and white beneath. The tail is black above and white below. The ears are to 5 inches long and almost black at the tips. The hares moult twice a year—in summer and spring. In the mating season they fight desperately. The young (leverets), numbering 2–8, are born 30 days after the mating. They are covered with thin hair, have eyes open, and are soon able to run. They are independent at 1 month. There may be to 4 broods a year. The females breed at 1 year of age. Life expectancy, to 13 years.

The mother hare makes no nest for her young, but hides them in a "form," or hidden hollow, under a clump of grass or similar shelter. She visits her scattered young as she is needed.

Hares have acute senses of hearing and smell, and while they can see well to the rear without moving their heads they have relatively poor straight-ahead vision. When leaving or approaching a form, does may avoid pursuit by taking leaps of to 15 feet in length. They can leap to the top of a 5-foot wall. They swim well.

Hares are normally quiet, but in breeding season or in pain will grunt, hiss, scream, and make clicking noises, which may have meaning to other hares.

The food is wholly plant material, on which they gorge themselves. This may pass through the alimentary canal in a semi-digested form and be eaten a second or even a third time. Tracks are: H 5 x 3, 4; F 1½ x 1½, 4; Sp 9; L 20.

The European hare is locally established in America. The related blue hare, *L. timidus,* is also European, but of more limited range. It is smaller, rarely exceeding 20 inches in length and 8½ pounds in weight. It changes its color to white in winter.

Domestic Rabbit (Chinchilla and Himalayan Rabbits, Belgian Hare, etc.)

Oryctolagus cuniculus · Leporidae

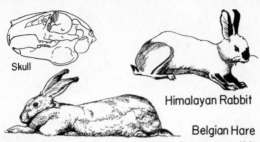

Skull

Himalayan Rabbit

Belgian Hare

DOMESTIC rabbits have been developed from the wild rabbit, which is also known as a bunny, coney, or cunning. Originally they were natives of Central Europe and the Carpathians, but they have become established in Australia and New Zealand, where they have been one of the worst pests. They have established themselves in some places in America in spite of laws forbidding their importation.

The sexes are superficially alike, but the males have shorter, rounder heads. Wild rabbits are about 18 inches long, with 3½ inch ears, and weigh to 3½ pounds. Tame rabbits, of course, exceed these measurements. The heads of the wild rabbits are relatively larger and the hind legs shorter than in the hares.

Rabbits breed through most of the year except possibly in the coldest months. Copulation lasts only for seconds. Unlike hares, they dig burrows which lead to grass-lined dens. Many burrows connected to one or more dens make up a "warren." From 30–32 days after the highly promiscuous mating, the 3–9 young are born. Unlike the young hares, they are at birth blind, naked, with closed eyes and ears. The eyes open the eleventh day after birth, the ears the twelfth. The young can run at 10 days and become independent at 1 month. Young breed at 3½ months, when the does usually start their own burrows, which typically go down 4–8 feet underground only to dip and then come up to the den. The does attend to the young but the bucks may assist in lining the nest. Chromosome number, 22. Respiration rate, 460–850. Pulse, 123–304.

Rabbits do not swim so well as do hares. They can make good speed overland for 80 yards, but then tire. They feed almost wholly on vegetation and may eat undigested food in their own droppings. Their chief enemies are man, foxes, badgers, stoats, cats, and birds of prey. They have formed the basis of an industry, producing hair for making felt. Their flesh is sold as food, but they are most inefficient users of forage and may be real pests. From the wild rabbits have been developed many domestic breeds, some of which are discussed on the next page.

73

Chinchilla Rabbit

Skull

THE biology of domestic rabbits has been briefly covered on page 73. In domesticity, the wild rabbit has been developed into breeds producing superior fur, breeds producing superior flesh quickly and cheaply, and breeds of value for show purposes. Some rabbits are raised by fanciers for exhibits because of their body form and size, others because of the color, length, and nature of their hair. They may be recognized as follows:

Rabbits of but 1 color are "self-colored." They may be black, gray, blue, lilac, "Havana" brown, or white.

Albinos are white rabbits with red eyes.

Polish Rabbits (under 3½ pounds) are albino rabbits with close fur.

Himalayan Rabbits are albino rabbits with some black on nose, ears, tail, and feet.

English Rabbits (to 9 pounds) are white rabbits with dark crescent markings and dark ears, nose, and tail.

Dutch Rabbits (to 6 pounds) are white rabbits with rear half mostly black, or of some other color, and head and ears black or of another color.

Siamese Rabbits are brown rabbits with black on ears, tail, feet, and back.

Martin Sable Rabbits are brown rabbits with yellow parts.

Belgian Hares (to 8 pounds) are orange rabbits with "ticked" or mixed longer black hairs, and white on belly.

Chinchillas are gray rabbits ticked with white.

Silver Fawns are orange rabbits ticked with white.

Silver Grays are blue-black rabbits ticked with white.

Silver Browns are brown rabbits ticked with white.

Flemish Giants are large, steel-gray rabbits with white bellies, to 40 inches long and to 22 pounds' weight.

Lop-Ears are large rabbits with ears that are enormous when spread, measuring to 28½ inches from tip to tip and to 7 inches wide. These rabbits are of different colors and patterns.

Rabbits with close, velvety fur are called *Rex Rabbits*.

Rabbits with wavy fur are often called *Astrachan Rabbits*.

Rabbits with long-haired fur, to 10 inches long, are often termed *Angora Rabbits* (to 8 pounds).

Cottontail · *Sylvilagus floridanus* · Leporidae

Skull

Trail

Scat

COTTONTAILS, in many forms and subspecies, are the common bunnies found wild in most parts of the United States. The species' range rarely extends north of the Canadian border. Cottontails are so abundant that they take the hunting pressure off more valuable and rare species. They probably inspire the sale of as many hunting licenses as any other mammal. Hunted in the snow in farming country with or without a dog, cottontails provide much sport. They are pests to crop-raising farmers.

Technically, cottontails are hares, although they are usually called rabbits. Hare-like, their young are well developed at birth. After promiscuous breeding, 4–7 young (fawns), each weighing ¾ ounce, are born 30 days after the mating. They are helpless, with eyes closed, and about 4 inches long. Furred and open-eyed in 1 week, by 2 weeks they can run from the nest, although they continue to get protection from the mother. Possibly 5 litters a year. Life span, to 8 years.

Cottontails are to 15 inches long, including the 2-inch, fluffy tail. They weigh 2½–3 pounds, have long ears, long and strong hind legs. They are dark brown above. The tail is brown above and white cottony beneath. The fur is shed twice a year—in May–June and in September–October. The fur has only 5% the durability of otter but appears in the trade as "electric seal." It is used in making felt for hats. The animal, like the other hares, may be infected with the organism causing tularemia, which can be fatal to man. Consequently, animals found dead should not be handled with the bare hands, and animals living where there is tularemia should not be used to stock areas where it is not present, no matter how cheap they may seem to be. Left hind foot valueless as a good-luck charm.

Tracks are: F 1 x 1; H 1½ x 3½; Sp 5; L 84.

Apparently cottontails cannot be raised efficiently in crowded quarters or under artificial conditions. It is more economical to trap animals where they are abundant and protected, and to free them where they may be harvested.

75

Marsh Rabbit · *Sylvilagus palustris* · Leporidae

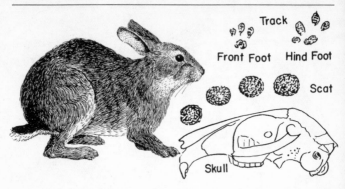

ALONG the coast from Virginia to Alabama lives the marsh rabbit. From Georgia to Oklahoma and eastern Texas and in southern Illinois, we find the swamp rabbit, *S. aquaticus.* In western Oregon and northwest California, we find the brush rabbit, *S. bachmani.* While the cottontail, brush rabbit, and swamp rabbit have tails that are white beneath, the tail of the marsh rabbit is gray, reddish brown, or white. A marsh rabbit's tail rarely exceeds 1⅗ inches in length, while in the other rabbits listed the tail is almost invariably longer than this.

Marsh rabbits have the peculiar habit, when walking or even running, of using the legs alternately, as would a dog or cat, although, of course, they can also hop like other rabbits. Even cottontails may do this when feeding in a limited area, but ordinarily they do not do so. Marsh rabbits are from 17–18 inches long, swamp rabbits are usually from 21–22 inches, and cottontails are from 15–18½ inches. The ears of marsh rabbits are rarely over 2 inches long, those of swamp rabbits usually more than 2½ inches long, and those of cottontails from 2–2½ inches.

The related pygmy rabbit, *S. idahoensis,* of the Idaho, Nevada, southeastern Oregon area, is smaller than any of those discussed, rarely being more than a foot in length, with tail not more than ⅕ inch long and ears under 1¾ inches.

Other rabbits of this general group include the Western cottontail, the Washington cottontail, and the New England cottontail, differing in minor ways, but all within the general range suggested for cottontails.

All of these rabbits have essentially the same life history as that of cottontails, given on page 75. The common names "march," "brush," and "swamp rabbit" have habitat suggestions that are appropriate but not always defining. Superficially, the differences are not important. All provide good sport for hunters, destroy farmers' crops, and are potential disease carriers.

ORDER RODENTIA *(Gnawing Mammals)*

Mountain Beaver · *Aplodontia rufa* · Aplodontiidae

THE cartoon character "Bugs Bunny" accentuates the most distinctive characteristic of the Rodentia, namely the presence of chisel-like incisors and the absence of canine teeth. While the Lagomorpha are represented by animals having 2 pairs of incisors on the upper jaw, in the Rodentia there is but a single pair, or 4 incisors in all, instead of 6. In North America, the largest rodent is the beaver; the smallest is one of the mice. There are probably more Rodentia living in America than there are members of any other order. Their economic importance is tremendous, as is their relation to human health and comfort.

While there are 9 recognized races of mountain beavers in America, all belong to 1 species. They are found in parts of California, Oregon, and Washington. They look like chunky, tailless, short-eared woodchucks or rabbits. The ½ inch tail is usually hidden. The total length is about 13½ inches and the weight about 4 pounds. The teeth are: I 1/1; C 0/0; P 2/1; M 3/3. The animals are grayish red, sprinkled with black, with a white spot at the base of the ears. The young are darker than the adults. Adult females have prominent dark spots around the nipples.

Breeding is from February through March and is probably promiscuous. From 2–4 young are born from 6–8 weeks after the mating. They are well furred but have their eyes closed. By the end of June they are half grown and able to leave the den in which they have spent the first part of their lives. The males do not assist in caring for the young.

The animals require an abundance of good drinking water and live almost exclusively on plant material. Plant food is often stored, after having been dried, and piled in storerooms off the burrow which are sealed off for more complete protection. The animals may be a pest to growers of small fruits such as raspberries. Their pelts have no commercial value. The burrows are to 6 inches in diameter, and winding. Tracks are: F ½ x 1, 5; H 1 x 1½, 5; Sp 3.

Hoary Marmot · *Marmota caligata* · Sciuridae

Tracks

Front Foot

Scat Hind Foot

WHAT woodchucks are to the grassy lands and wooded borders of the East and Southeast, hoary marmots are to mountainous western North America. In one race or another they range from the Arctic Circle in Alaska to the Cascades and Olympics, mostly south into Washington, Idaho, and Montana. Some forms are found on into California and New Mexico. They whistle, either in warning to their companions or in defiance of intruders, from the crest of some rather exposed rocky perch. They share their range with the pikas and packrats.

Larger males weigh to 15 pounds or more and exceed 30 inches in length, of which 10 inches is tail. These are our largest marmots. They are silvery gray, or whitish peppered with black, on the back and rump. The feet are black. The face is black with white on cheeks and forehead. Under parts are white. Teeth are: I 1/1; C 0/0; P 2/1; M 3/3. Tracks are: F 1 x 2, 4; H 1½ x 1½, 5; Sp 4.

Russian marmot fur is sold as Brazilian mink, but its wearing value is only 20% that of otter. Since marmots feed almost wholly on plants, they may be considered as competitors for grass with sheep and the few cattle to be found in such an environment. They serve, incidentally, as food for predators that might otherwise kill animals useful to man, and in this sense are buffer species. Their protection lies primarily in their ability to escape promptly into their rock-bound lairs. They may reach their feeding areas by rather long, well-marked, and worn trails.

Mating takes place in the spring and 35–42 days later 2–5 young marmots are born. Young born about June 1 may run with the mother from late June to late August. The mother and young may share the den the first winter; maturity is not reached until 2 years of age. With the advent of new young, the family breaks up. Life span, to 13½ years. There is a 7–8 month hibernation period. Pulse, 120–206. Temperature, 93°–103° F.

Woodchuck or Groundhog · *Marmota monax* · Sciuridae

Trail

Skull

Scat

Tracks

Hind Foot   Front Foot

PENNSYLVANIA once protected woodchucks by law, since the animals dug burrows in which rabbits found shelter in winter and thus survived to serve with the woodchucks as targets for hunters, young and old, who roamed the hills of the state. The more cottontails, the more satisfied hunters and the bigger the license take by the state, seemed to be the philosophy. In many parts of the United States February 2, or Candlemas Day, is known as Groundhog Day, the superstition being that if the woodchuck emerges from his burrow on that day and sees his shadow he will return to hibernation because the end of winter is still remote.

Woodchucks are not liked by farmers whose crops they destroy. Their burrows are a hazard to horses and cattle. They range from the Gulf of St. Lawrence to Hudson Bay and central Alaska south to Montana, Nebraska, Louisiana, North Carolina, and New England. Their diet is largely plants but may include insects, mice, and even birds. They may be serious competitors for forage.

Males measure to 27 inches, including a 6-inch tail, and females total to 22 inches. An acre may support 3 or 4 woodchucks. Sexes are colored alike but young are lighter. Teeth are: I 1/1; C 0/0; P 2/1; M 3/3. Tracks are: F 1½ x 1¼, 4; H 1¾ x 1¼, 5; Sp 5. Body temperature in hibernation, 40°–57° F.; normal, 94.8°–104° F. Hibernation respiration rate, 14; normal, 262. Mate immediately after hibernation (March–April); 2–8 blind, naked, helpless, 4-inch young with ½ inch tails are born 28–32 days later. Young crawl at 3 weeks, take solid food at 4 weeks, play at 5 weeks, and cease nursing then. Average weight of male adults in March, 5 pounds 10 ounces; in September, 10 pounds. Full growth in 2nd year. Active mostly in daytime. Life span, 9 years.

Prairie Dog · *Cynomys ludovicianus* · Sciuridae

PRAIRIE dogs are known for the "towns" they build. One authority estimated that at the beginning of the present century the state of Texas supported 800 million prairie dogs. With the building up of the countryside, they have been greatly reduced in numbers. They range from North Dakota to central Texas west to northern Mexico, Arizona, Utah, and western Montana. They favor dry, open clay soils, while a close relative, the white-tailed prairie dog, favors mountains and elevations to 6,000 feet.

It is estimated that 32 prairie dogs require as much grass as 1 sheep and 256 as much as 1 cow, and prairie-dog flesh is of course valueless. Under natural conditions prairie dogs were kept in control by coyotes, burrowing owls, snakes, and hawks, most of which thoughtless farmers have considered to be pests.

Prairie dogs reach a length of 14½ inches, including a 3-inch tail. Males weigh 3 pounds; females, to 2⅛ pounds. They are reddish brown, flesh colored, or gray, with pale muzzles and eyespots. In this species the last third of the tail is black. Teeth are: I 1/1; C 0/0; P 2/1; M 3/3. Tracks are: F ¾ x ½, 4; H 1 x ⅝, 5.

Burrow, which may go to 16 feet with lateral listening post near the entrance, is protected from flooding by bowl-like crater. Upward-swinging end traps air helpful in floodtime. White-tailed prairie dog does not build entrance mound.

After 28–32 day gestation, 2–10 young, blind, naked, helpless, each weighing about ½ ounce and 2¾ inches long, are born in April–June. Increase 40% in weight in 1 week; on thirteenth day, weight 2½ times birth weight; stand and have hair at twentieth day; crawl at twenty-seventh day; eyes open thirty-third to thirty-seventh day; weaned at 7 weeks; weigh more than 2 pounds at 9 months, and mature at 2 years. One annual litter. Life span, to 8 years.

Rock Squirrel or Rock Ground Squirrel

Citellus variegatus · Sciuridae

Track

Scat

IF one should make a composite map showing the distribution of the 20 commonest species of the genus Citellus, it would show that in one form or another these squirrels can be found over most of western North America, extending west of a line running from west of Hudson Bay through western Ohio, northern Indiana, Illinois, Missouri, and Texas into northern Mexico. Four of the commoner of these species, which are to be seen generally in the western U.S. and Canada, are illustrated. The area richest in number of species is the Southwest, and the 2 species probably most likely to be seen are the golden-mantled ground squirrel and the thirteen-lined spermophile, described with the Franklin's ground squirrel on the next 3 pages. The rock squirrel, pictured on this page, is to be found in eastern California, Nevada, through most of Utah and much of Colorado, through southwest Texas and almost all of Arizona and New Mexico.

In effect these ground squirrels turn vegetation into flesh acceptable as food for predatory birds and mammals and often represent for these animals the difference between survival and extinction. They compete for forage directly with sheep and cattle, and because of this are not popular with farmers.

Rock squirrels are among the largest of the group, measuring to 21 inches long, including a bushy 10½ inch tail. They are brown to blackish, being darkest forward, the under parts grayish. They favor rocky slopes and canyons where they are commonly seen on some rocky perch. They also climb trees and may be seen in winter as well as in summer. There may be 2 litters a year, ranging from 5–7, and appearing in May or June and August or September. They have been known to live as long as 10 years.

81

Thirteen-lined Spermophile or Thirteen-lined Ground Squirrel · *Citellus tridecemlineatus* · Sciuridae

Skull

Scat

THIS animated tent pin is often abundant on lawns and prairies from central Ohio to southeastern Alberta south to Texas and Arizona. Its range is probably expanding.

Males measure to 11 inches, with 4½ inch tail. Females slightly smaller. Tail is not conspicuously bushy. The squirrels sit erect with noses pointed straight up, and show the alternating dark brown and dirty white stripes which give them their name. Teeth are: I 1/1; C 0/0; P 2/1; M 3/3. Tracks are: F ¾ x ½, 4; H 1 x ¾, 5; Sp 3. Body temperature may vary from 35.6° F. in winter to 105.8° F. in summer, and the pulse from 96–378 per minute. During hibernation the weight may drop to one third the maximum. Soil temperature does not control hibernation too closely.

These spermophiles feed largely on animal matter when most active, much of the plant material collected being stored. Their diet includes insects, mice, small birds, frogs, and the like. Spermophiles are hunted mercilessly by hawks, owls, cats, weasels, some snakes, and parasitic insects. They probably do more harm than good to man's crops.

Mating takes place in April, with the breeding season over by June. After a 28-day gestation period, 3–14 young are born in an underground nest. Males desert family before young are born. At birth, young are blind, naked, toothless, helpless, to 2¼ inches long, including a ⅜ inch tail. By the thirtieth day their eyes are open, by the thirty-fifth they come above ground, and by 90 days they are full grown. There is but 1 litter a year. Temperature, 92°–106° F.

Boys commonly snare spermophiles by placing a noose around the burrow opening and pulling it as the animal emerges. Their pelts have no value. Their period of activity is such that they do no harm to stored crops, feeding only when food is abundant.

Franklin's Ground Squirrel · *Citellus franklinii* · Sciuridae

Skull

THE prairie states of Indiana, Illinois, Wisconsin, Minnesota, Iowa, Missouri, the Dakotas, Nebraska, and Kansas, and a narrow strip northwest into Canada, support the Franklin's ground squirrel. These ground squirrels are 14 inches long, including a 4½ inch tail. They share much of the territory held by the thirteen-lined spermophile and superficially resemble that animal, but are uniformly grayish white to dusky above, with only the slightest suggestion of dots and stripes. The tail is black and white and bushier than in the striped relative.

A third of the food of the Franklin's ground squirrels may be animal matter, including mice, insects, birds, toads, frogs, and even rabbits. Not infrequently the animals become highly destructive to garden crops. They favor the edges of woodlands and fields, and in their whole lifetime may spend only 10% of their time aboveground. An individual may never range more than 100 yards from its den burrow. Tooth and track formulas are the same or essentially the same as for the striped relative. They compete directly with livestock for forage and may migrate in a body from one area to another. They appear aboveground in April, usually later than their relatives. Their abundance is definitely cyclic over the years.

Mating takes place when the females make their spring appearance, but males desert families shortly after. From 4–8 blind, nearly naked, and helpless young, each 3¾ inches long, including a ¾ inch tail, are born a month after the mating. They are suckled for 6 weeks, are one third grown by August, and by first autumn nearly equal adults in size. There is 1 litter a year. Temperature, 93°–103° F.

One may be surprised to find these animals in wasteland in the heart of cities, but they are often there.

83

Golden-mantled Ground Squirrel

Citellus lateralis · Sciuridae

EASTERNERS casually familiar with the chipmunks of their homelands may easily assume that the golden-mantled ground squirrels they see in some Western national park are just chipmunks. The thumbs of the Eastern and the Western chipmunks have well-developed nails, while those of the ground squirrels of the genus *Citellus* bear only rudimentary nails which normally do not show in their tracks or in their track formulas. The antelope chipmunk and the golden-mantled ground squirrel have broad, contrasting stripes down the back, and the golden-mantled has golden color on the head and neck. It looks like a large chipmunk whose face is *not* striped. These animals measure just over a foot in length, and have tails to 4½ inches. They weigh to 10 ounces. They are larger than the Western chipmunks and have more conspicuously striped upper parts.

Golden-mantled ground squirrels are found along the mountainous eastern borders of British Columbia south to near the Mexican border, except close to the coast, and range east through central Montana, Colorado, and Wyoming, and on into Arizona and New Mexico. In the cooler parts of this range they hibernate, beginning with the early frosts.

Golden-mantled ground squirrels dig short, simple burrows under brush, to 1 foot deep and to 1½ feet long. They have been known to take to water when pursued by weasels. Normally they are at their best in brush and among fallen timbers or in rocky rubble. Many haunt public camp sites in search of free meals. The annual litter is 2–8, whose development is usually similar to that of the close relatives already discussed.

Eastern Chipmunk · *Tamias striatus* · Sciuridae
Least Chipmunk · *Eutamias minimus* · Sciuridae

Chewed Hickory Nut

Scat

Skull

Least Chipmunk

Eastern Chipmunk

Trail

ROUGHLY the states from Texas to the Dakotas form the dividing line between the ranges of the Eastern chipmunks, genus *Tamias,* and the Western chipmunks, *Eutamias,* of which the least chipmunk is a representative. In Canada, the dividing line is roughly from the Dakotas to the northern limit of the Gulf of St. Lawrence, with the Eastern chipmunk to the south and the Western chipmunk to the north of Lake Michigan. The least chipmunk is found west of a line reaching from Lake Michigan to southern Alaska. The Western chipmunks have 2 premolars in the upper jaws; the Eastern have but one. Teeth of *Eutamias* are: I 1/1; C 0/0; P 2/1; M 3/3; of *Tamias*: I 1/1; C 0/0; P 1/1; M 3/3. The track formula for each is F ½ x ⅜, 5; H ¾ x 1¼, 5; Sp 2. The Eastern chipmunks are 9½ inches long, including a 3¼ inch tail. They have well-developed cheek pouches and usually 5 conspicuous black stripes alternating with gray or brown. In general the color is grayish and the stripes may run to the tail base. They are fawn colored beneath.

Breeding may take place in fall or spring, and there may be 2 litters a year. Young numbering 4–5 are blind, naked, and helpless at birth and stay with mother until 3½ months old. They weigh ¹⁄₁₀ ounce at birth, increasing this by 4 times in 8 days, nearly 6 times in 2 weeks, 11 times in 4 weeks, to 1⅔ ounces in 5 weeks, to 2¼ in 6 weeks, and to 2½ ounces in 7 weeks. Young can breed at 2½ to 3 months. Pulse, 660–702. Temperature, 97°–105° F. Life span, to 7 years.

Individual range of a chipmunk may be to 2 acres. There is a well-developed storage instinct. Hibernation is variable.

Least chipmunks measure to 9 inches, including a 3½ inch tail. They may be found at elevations up to 11,000 feet. Some Western chipmunks reach a length of to 11½ inches.

Gray Squirrel · *Sciurus carolinensis* · Sciuridae

Skull

Trail

Scat

F

H

Track

Gnawed Nut

POSSIBLY some credit for American independence is due to the gray squirrels, which served so effectively as targets for early pioneers. They deserve even greater credit as planters of trees, since they bury nuts and acorns that are thus saved from destruction by freezing. These nuts germinate. These are the common squirrels of most Eastern parks and bird-feeding stations, where they are ¹liked or disliked, depending on one's point of view. Undoubtedly they may rob birds' nests, but they also provide thrills for hunters young and old and for those who find their flesh a delicacy. Why they should be killed, unless they are destructive, is hard to understand.

Gray squirrels measure 18 inches in length, of which half is tail. They weigh about 1 pound, are pepper-and-salt gray in color, over slaty underfur. Hairs are white tipped over black, buff, and lead bases. There are albinos, and black varieties have been common. They have cheek pouches on each side. Teeth are: I 1/1; C 0/0; P 2/1; M 3/3. Tracks are: F 1 x 1⅛, 5; H 1¼ x 2½, 5; Sp 3¾; L 60.

Gray squirrels are found from Maine to the Dakotas and south to central Texas and the Gulf. Periodically mass migrations of these squirrels have taken place, and the animals may be absent from an area for long periods only to return in considerable abundance.

Mating takes place December to August, and some observers consider it to be a life pairing. Young, 1–6, are born 44 days after the mating, are blind for 37 days, when they have reached a weight of ¼ pound. They can leave the den at 6 weeks, are well furred at 9 weeks, and stay with mother until full grown. There may be 2 litters a year. Three den trees per family are favored; one for male, one for mother and young, the other for immatures. Life span, to 15 years.

Kaibab Squirrel · *Sciurus aberti* · Sciuridae

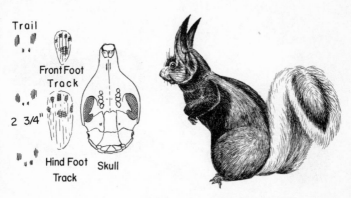

Trail

Front Foot Track

2 3/4"

Hind Foot Track   Skull

MOST of us get our introductions to kaibab squirrels through postcards sent us from the Grand Canyon by some vacationing friend. The conspicuous white tail and the ears with tassels on them are the characters most likely to persist in our memory until someday on a trip to the area we ourselves see the animals. Then our interest is greater than ever, because no picture can in this case match the reality, and possibly, since the squirrels vary greatly, because the squirrels we see differ in some respects from the animals represented by the picture.

The ear tufts may not be present the last 6 months of the year. There are 2 color phases, differing primarily, but not wholly, in the color of the tail, the under parts, and the ear tufts. In the Kaibab phase, found in an area extending 20 by 40 miles from the north rim of the Grand Canyon, the ear tufts are brownish black, the under parts black, and the tail all white. In the Abert phase, common in Colorado, the ear tufts are blackish, the under parts white, and the tail white below or black, gray, or mixed.

These squirrels live chiefly in areas supporting yellow pines or other conebearers. One or 2 litters a year of 3 or 4 young each may vary in frequency with the food supply. In winter, activities may not be noticeable, but there is probably no true hibernation. Shelter is found in bulky nests of vegetable material, including twigs, barks, grass, and leaves placed rather conspicuously on some tree branch.

In part because of their greatly limited range, but also because of their conspicuous appearance and unsuspecting nature and friendliness, these animals add much to the attractiveness of their home region to tourists. They are considered legal game.

Fox Squirrel · *Sciurus niger* · Sciuridae

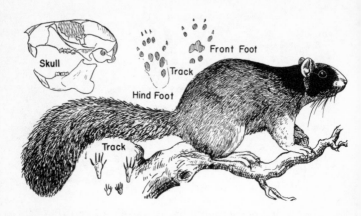

Skull

Front Foot

Track

Hind Foot

Track

To one reared in gray-squirrel country the first sight of fox squirrels is startling. Fox squirrels appear to be so large that to miss hitting them seems an impossibility, and yet they have a remarkable ability to make themselves scarce in no time flat. They can lie out on a limb and be completely invisible from below, or they can vanish like ghosts into leafy cover. They need to do all of these things, because they are hunted mercilessly for sport and for their flesh as food.

Fox squirrels range normally from Rhode Island through southern New York to Minnesota and South Dakota, south through central Texas to the Gulf, and east and south to the Atlantic, with related forms in the West. In general, their range coincides with that of oaks, for a reason—they feed on the acorns.

The larger males may weigh to 3 pounds, have a length of nearly 2 feet, half of which is tail. They have 4 cheek pouches on each side. Teeth are: I 1/1; C 0/0; P 1/1; M 3/3. Tracks are: F ¾ x 1 ¾, 5; H 1 x 2, 5; Sp 6; L 60.

Fundamentally, fox squirrels are of great use in planting nut trees as an incidental to burying their food. Food is buried piecemeal, not in a huge cache. They have a superior sense of smell and their diet includes not only nuts and other fruits but buds, bark, and, unfortunately, sometimes birds and their eggs and young. Their stored food constitutes approximately 10% of the total eaten.

Maturity is reached at the end of the first year. They have been known to live for more than 6 years. They probably pair, breeding in midwinter. Six weeks later 2–5 pink, blind, naked, helpless young are born. They nurse for 5 weeks, leave nest at 6–12 weeks, leave parents at 3 months. Possibly 2 litters a year.

88

Red Squirrel or Chickaree

Tamiasciurus hudsonicus · Sciuridae

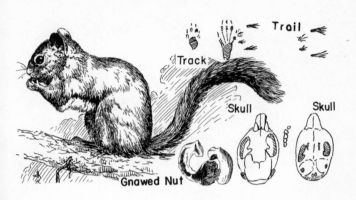

THE one word that best describes red squirrels is "sassy." They rollick noisily through life, defying their enemies from some safe perch. Disturbed by something strange, they are the personification of vituperation. They gallop through attics, slither down tree trunks headfirst, dangle at the end of slender branches, or leap recklessly but usually safely from one high perch to another. In winter, they burrow endlessly under snowdrifts, making little caches of food here and there.

They are essentially New World animals, with the *hudsonicus* group in the East, the *fremontii* group in the Rockies, and the *douglasii* group to the west of the Rockies.

Red squirrels are just over a foot in length, including a 4½ inch tail that appears flattened and bushy. There are 2 color phases and more than 20 related species. Teeth are: I 1/1; C 0/0; P 2/1; M 3/3. Tracks are: F ½ x ⅜, 5; H 1 x ¾, 5; Sp 3; L 36. Over level ground they can cover 75 feet in 8 seconds when necessary.

Mating takes place in February and March. Then, 40 days later, 3–6 1-ounce young are born. They are blind, naked, helpless, to 4½ inches long, and have 1½ inch tails; are weaned at 5 weeks. They open their eyes on the twenty-seventh day. The mother trains the young to gain their independence. There may be 2 litters a year. Temperature, 99°–106° F. Life span may be to 12 years.

Food, such as pine cones, may be cut green and stored for use later. Often this results in the ground beneath the tree being strewn with unused twig tips. In July and August the squirrels may cut, dry, and store fungi for food. One red squirrel may kill to 200 birds a year; thus they rival domestic cats as predators. Fur has little value, but has brought up to 15¢ a pelt.

Flying Squirrel · *Glaucomys volans* · Sciuridae

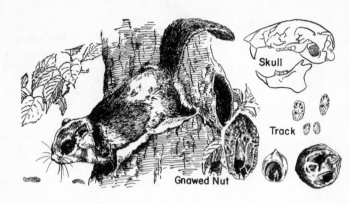

Skull

Track

Gnawed Nut

In defining elves, the dictionary uses such descriptive terms as "small," "lively," "elusive," "frail," "mischievous," "of dazzling beauty." "Dark elves" are supposed to dwell in woods, caves, or the sea. Flying squirrels fit about all of the above terms except that they do not dwell in the sea, and so it would not be too difficult to consider them as material counterparts of "mystical beings," the elves.

The larger northern flying squirrels, *G. sabrinus,* are to 1 foot long, half being tail, and are dirty white beneath and drab above. They range from the tree limit in North America from central Alaska to Labrador south to southern California, Minnesota, and Maryland, and in the Appalachian Highlands to Georgia. They are not found in the Great Plains area or much of the Southwest. They are active all winter. The southern group, *G. volans,* is found east of a line from Minnesota to central Texas and south of a line from Minnesota to southern Maine. These squirrels measure 9½ inches, including a 4½ inch tail. Teeth are: I 1/1; C 0/0; P 2/1; M 3/3. Tracks are: F ½ x ½, 5; H ¾ x 1¼, 5; Sp. 2.

Flying squirrels do not fly, but glide with the help of extensible folds on their sides. They can glide more than 160 feet from a 60-foot perch or cover 75 feet in 12 seconds over the ground. They hide in dens in hollow trees or in buildings, and feed on nuts, fruits, and other foods. They are America's most nocturnal mammal. Mating occurs in winter. Forty days later 2–6 young are born, in March–April. Young are blind 4 weeks, squeak at 5½ weeks, begin storing at 11 weeks, become light-sensitive at 15 weeks, begin shedding at 17 weeks, and get new fur at 18 weeks. Respiration rate, 2,000. Temperature, 95°–101° F. Flying squirrels are too small to be considered as game, and make fine pets.

Pocket Gopher · *Geomys bursarius* · Geomyidae

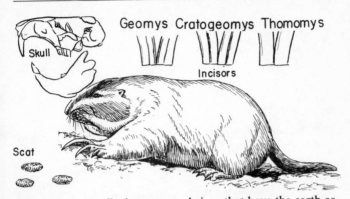

Geomys Cratogeomys Thomomys

Skull

Incisors

Scat

PARACELSUS described gnomes as beings that have the earth as their element, with the ability to move through it as easily as fish move through water. Pocket gophers cannot quite do this, but if we can liken flying squirrels to elves, pocket gophers might be considered the gnomes of the mammal world. They are sometimes called "earth mice."

Pocket gophers have forefeet strongly modified and suited for digging, much as do moles. They also, however, have the upper incisors of the rodents. In the 3 genera whose incisors are pictured, the Plains and the Southeastern pocket gophers of the genus *Geomys,* have 2 grooves down the front of the incisors, one close to the inner margin. In the Mexican pocket gopher of the genus *Cratogeomys,* each incisor has a single frontal groove; and in the genus *Thomomys,* the incisors lack frontal grooves, as shown in the sketches above. All of these pocket gophers have external, reversible, fur-lined cheek pockets. The yellowish incisors are always visible. The tail is naked, or almost so, and shorter than the head and body. The Mexican *Cratogeomys* is limited in the United States to western Texas and New Mexico. The Eastern gophers of the genus *Geomys* are found in the Plains, mostly west of the Mississippi, and also in Georgia, Alabama, and Florida. *Thomomys* is represented in a number of Western species. Pocket gopher meat is edible.

Males of *Geomys bursarius* are to 1 foot long and have 3½ inch tails. They are reddish with sprinklings of black. Teeth are: I 1/1; C 0/0; P 1/1; M 3/3. Unlike moles, which feed on animals, pocket gophers feed on plants. These are commonly cut into 2-inch lengths. They do not drink. Two to 8 naked young are born in April, each weighing ⅕ ounce. They are without cheek pouches at birth, and are blind until 5 weeks old. Their ears are also sealed until then. Young nursed for 10 days. The family stays together until the young are 2 months old. There is 1 litter a year. Temperature, 93°–97° F.

Spiny Pocket Mouse   *Perognathus spinatus* · Heteromyidae

Skull

WHILE the smallest American mammal is a shrew, the smallest American rodent is a pocket mouse, found in the San Diego region, close to the Mexican border and the Pacific. This is the Pacific pocket mouse, which measures only 4½ inches long and weighs ⅓ ounce. The largest pocket mouse, *P. californicus,* measures 7¾ inches and weighs about 1 ounce. All of these pocket mice have long hind legs and poorly developed forefeet, tail as long or longer than the head and body, and external fur-lined cheek pouches. There are more than 2 dozen species.

The spiny pocket mouse is to 3½ inches long, and has a tail to 4½ additional inches. The tail is crested and there are spine-like hairs on the rump.

Spiny pocket mice are essentially desert creatures. They do not drink, and while they live in sun-bleached deserts they spend little time in the sun. They take to their burrows in the daytime and come out at dusk to stuff their cheek pouches so full of seeds and other vegetation that it would seem that they should burst. When their pouches are full, they return underground, empty them quickly, pack the food under soil, and go back for another load.

Each little pocket mouse has its own burrow. This is usually relatively straight, unbranched, and ends in a grass-lined den, or it may be winding, with many storerooms for food as well as the home den. The burrows are to 7 feet long. When not in use, they are blocked with earth, and if the mouse is pursued by an enemy it builds additional earth blocks where they may be effective.

Breeding may take place at almost any time. The females usually bear 2 litters a year. The 2–8 young are born 3–4 weeks after the mating. While the desert is the home of most spiny pocket mice, some may live in woodlands or in cultivated fields. At times some of these may do harm to farm crops.

Kangaroo Rat · *Dipodomys deserti* · Heteromyidae

Trail 2 3/4"

Track

Skull

Scat

KANGAROO rats make excellent pets if you do not have too many of them. If you put 3 in a cage, the next day you will probably have 2, and the following day 1 battle-scarred veteran. Some writers characterize these animals as "desert ghosts," and others have called them "pygmy kangaroos." Both names are suggestive of their habits.

Kangaroo rats of the genus *Perodipus* have 5 toes on the hind feet. Those of the genus *Dipodomys,* like the kangaroo mice of the genus *Microdipodops,* have 4. In all, the hind legs are well developed and the forelegs are not. They all have large heads, large eyes, external, fur-lined cheek pouches, and long, soft fur. They are nocturnal and hop about on their hind feet, which have furred soles. Their front feet do not touch the ground. Including a 7½ inch tail, the length is to 13 inches. They are bluish fawn-colored above and glistening white beneath. Teeth are: I 1/1; C 0/0; P 1/1; M 3/3. Tracks are: F ¼ x ¼; H ½ x 1½, 5; Sp 3; L 30. Respiration rate, 950.

Kangaroo rats range from Washington to Manitoba and south to Panama, in many species. A square mile of suitable terrain may well support 1,000 animals, few of which will ever be seen by man because of their nocturnal habits. The sexes are colored alike and there is little seasonal variation.

These rats' food is wholly plant material gathered at night. They may leap 8 feet at a jump. They do not hibernate or migrate. While usually friendly, they sometimes fight, using their hind feet. Families commonly live in separate tunnels in lined underground dens which may measure 8 x 10 x 5 inches and be to 3 feet underground. The nests are cool and clean and separate from the dung heaps. In April, 2–4 young are born. Ordinarily of little economic importance.

Beaver · *Castor canadensis* · Castoridae

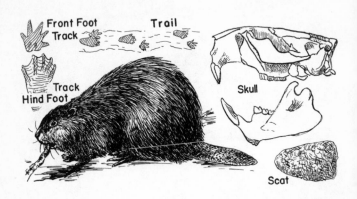

Front Foot Track

Trail

Track Hind Foot

Skull

Scat

FEW mammals have been more effective in changing the economy of man and the nature of the land he lives on than the beaver. Its hide was at one time a unit of currency and symbol of wealth. Its dams, marvels of engineering skill, controlled flooding and built rich lowlands. Its behavior and industry have become legendary. Its flesh has served as emergency food. In many areas it is a valuable drawing card for tourists, and in other areas, a serious threat to timberlands.

Beavers measure to 43 inches, including a 16-inch tail, which may be 4½ inches wide and is naked, thick, broad, and paddle-like. The tail is not used as a trowel. Weight may be to over 60 pounds, but average is 30 pounds. Teeth are: I 1/1; C 0/0; P 1/1; M 3/3. Tracks are: F 2½ x 3½ 5; H webbed, 5½ x 7, 5.

Beavers may dig a den in a high bank bordering a stream or lake if an underwater entrance is possible. This entrance permits the animals to swim out under the ice in winter to get food —tree bark stored there earlier in the year. If no bank is available, a house of coarse sticks paved with mud is built, and this has the underwater entrance. The house has a high, dry platform above high-water level, and while ventilation is possible through the top, enemies cannot tear open the frozen roof. A group of beavers is known as a colony, and the basis of a colony is usually a family. Apparently beavers pair for life. They breed January–February, and 65–128 days later 2–8 young are born. At 1 month, young seek and eat solid food. They cease nursing at 6 weeks, weigh to 8 pounds by midsummer, and mature at 2–3 years. At this time a new home is set up and 2-year-olds are driven from the group. Pulse, 140. Life span, to 19 years. Beavers apparently are on the increase in many areas.

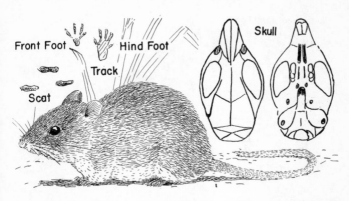

WHILE there are more than 150 species and subspecies of rice rats in the genus *Oryzomys* to be found over the world, we can deal here with but 1 species, *O. palustris*. We devote 13 pages to the family Cricetidae, to which these rates belong. While this family includes the New World rats and mice, it does not include the common rats and mice of our homes and barns. These belong in the family Muridae, and are not native to the New World. The crowns of the lower molars of members of the Muridae have tubercles in 3 longitudinal series, while similar teeth in the Cricetidae have only 2 such structures, or less. This is possibly the basic difference by which arguments may be settled.

Rice rats are much like Norway rats, but have 2 rows of molar tubercles instead of 3. They are found from New Jersey to Kansas and in one form or another south into Texas and Florida and even on into Central America. They are highly destructive to rice fields, and because of this are hated and killed by rice farmers. They are eaten freely by weasels, skunks, minks, foxes, cottonmouth moccasins, alligators, and birds of prey, yet they persist.

Rice rats measure to a total of 11 inches, about half of which is tail. Weight, 3 ounces. They are gray or brown above, with lighter under parts. The under parts are never pure white. The tail is dark brown to black above and paler beneath, slender, scaly, and poorly haired. Rice rats are found mostly in marshy areas along the coast but may also live in brush in the mountains. They dive readily to escape their many enemies.

A study showed that near the Mississippi delta, breeding extends from February to November. Twenty-five days after the mating, 1–7 young are born. They are blind at birth, see at 6 days, and at 11 days are weaned and independent.

Harvest Mouse · *Reithrodontomys humulis* · Cricetidae

Front Foot Hind Foot

Track

Skull

Scat

Trail

ONE might confuse harvest mice with house mice but for the fact that their feet are always white. One might also confuse them with deer mice but for the fact that they are smaller and their bellies are dusky or buff, and there is a buff to orange line along the sides of their bodies.

Harvest mice are not found northeast of Illinois to Maryland, but in one form or another occur throughout most of the rest of the United States. *R. albescens* and *R. humulis* are in the Middle West and Southeast; *R. megalotis, R. montanus,* and *R. catalinae* in the West. *R. montanus* is found west of the Mississippi except for a few spots in Wisconsin.

Harvest mice are to 5 inches long, of which nearly half is tail. Ears are nearly ½ inch long. They are inconspicuously colored, as are house mice. In the Southeast, breeding begins in March and runs through to December. After a 21-day gestation period, 5–9 young are born. They are blind at birth. At 5 days the first hair appears, at 6 days sex can be identified, at 10 days eyes open and teeth can be detected. At 11 days they climb about the cage, at which time ears are haired and eyes wide open. In the wild, young do not leave mother until 10 days old. There are several litters a year. Nearly always the young are born in ball-like nests of vegetable matter, sometimes placed in shrubs well above the ground.

These mice are active day and night through the year and show little if any sign of hibernation. They usually favor wet spots, where they may establish definite runways to the nest. This has but 1 entrance. They are rarely if ever a menace to crops and are eaten freely by valuable fur bearers wherever the two are to be found together. In this way they take the pressure from larger game, birds, and poultry, which might otherwise be sought.

Deer Mouse or White-footed Mouse

Peromyscus leucopus · Cricetidae

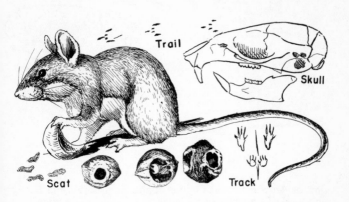

Trail

Skull

Scat

Track

IF one could just watch deer mice for a while and forget the messes they make of stored food and clothing, and the sleepless hours caused by their rummaging in the walls, one could really like them. They appear so innocent, harmless, clean, and helpless that it seems a shame to have to trap them in self-defense.

There are at least 17 species from this genus in America. The common *P. leucopus* has the tail less sharply contrasted in color above and below than does *P. maniculatus*. *P. leucopus*, in one form or another, ranges through most of North America east of the Rockies, while the *P. maniculatus* species of deer mouse covers most of the continent except the Southeast.

Deer mice are to 7½ inches long, including a 3½ inch tail. The ears and eyes are large. The ears are white inside and blackish outside in the young, but dusky in the adults. The mice are dark brown above and have white feet and under parts. The young are slate gray above. Tail is white beneath and brown above, with a pencil of hairs at the tip.

Of one group of 675 young deer mice studied, 70% of the males and 80% of the females settled within 500 feet of their birthplace. Of 186 litters, 4%–10% were offspring of mated brothers and sisters or mated parents and offspring. They may hibernate. Males assist in making nests and transporting young but the females protect home territory. Young are born 3 weeks after the mating. At birth they are 1½ inches long. They open their eyes on the eighteenth day and are weaned by 3 weeks, when they are half grown. Females mature at 29 days and may conceive at 39 days. Males mature at 39 days. May breed until 33 months old. Pulse, 324–858. Temperature, 93°–106° F. Life span, to 5½ years, but few even approach that age.

Grasshopper Mouse · *Onychomys leucogaster* · Cricetidae

Trail

Skull

Scat

ONE of America's most famous mammalogists, Vernon Bailey, who worked on grasshopper mice, used to tell of keeping them in cages where he fed and observed them and where he made some clever wheels on which they could exercise themselves. After he had learned what he needed from the mice, he turned them loose in the pup tent that had been his home. For many nights afterward he was surprised to be awakened by the sound of the wheels being run by the mice, who had returned voluntarily to their cages for exercise in spite of the freedom offered by the great outdoors.

This story is mentioned in part to indicate that much of the knowledge we have of mammals has been obtained by dedicated naturalists who were willing to reserve judgment until they had adequate data on which to work. Vernon Bailey was one of these.

Grasshopper mice are found west of a line running from the southern tip of Texas to the western Minnesota border, with some extensions north into Canada and south into Mexico. The northern grasshopper mouse, *O. leucogaster,* which is to 5 inches long, including a 2½ inch tail, ranges west of this line to a line from central Washington to south-central Arizona. The southern grasshopper mouse, *O. torridus,* is limited to our Southwest and has a length of to 4 inches, including a 2-inch tail. Both are gray or pinkish cinnamon, with white-tipped tails. Both live in either prairies or deserts.

Since the food of these mice is almost wholly small animals, such as insects, scorpions, mice, and lizards, and almost no plant material, they are essentially useful to man. They do not hibernate; are great roamers. Young number 2–6; are born 32 days after the mating. They are furred by 12 days, eyes open by 19. Females breed at 3 months of age. More than 1 litter a year.

Cotton Rat · *Sigmodon hispidus* · Cricetidae

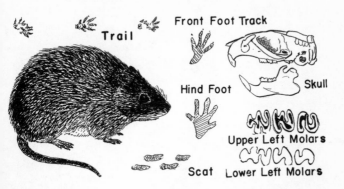

Trail

Front Foot Track

Hind Foot

Skull

Upper Left Molars

Scat

Lower Left Molars

SOME 11 subspecies of these rather nondescript cotton rats range from Virginia to Florida and west to Tennessee and Arizona. Closely related species extend the range south to Peru. As the species name implies, cotton rats are harsh-haired, and as the genus name implies, the tubercles on the molars are S-shaped. In other words, here is a rat with an "s" on its teeth, and with harsh hair.

To the above simple description one should add that while the rats resemble rice rats, in general they are larger. Cotton rats are to 13 inches long, including a 5¼ inch tail, and weigh to ½ pound. Rice rats are to 2 inches or more shorter and rarely if ever weigh ¼ pound. Tracks are: F ⅔ x ½, 4; H ⅔ x 1, 5.

The fur of cotton rats, besides being coarse, is blackish above, with brown tips to the hairs. The tail is scaly or finely haired, dark above and shorter than the head and body. The ears are black and the feet gray to dark brown.

Cotton rats are probably the most destructive of all animals in the agricultural South, sometimes destroying half of a sugar-cane crop, wrecking the market value of sweet potatoes, and eating seeds as fast as they are planted in the ground. They are the chief food of many snakes, fur bearers, and birds of prey, who are thus friends of agriculture. They themselves destroy the nests of quail and other game birds and eat the young. They also eat fish, crabs, and insects.

Cotton rats begin breeding when 1 month old and breed at any time of the year. The 8–12 young are born 27 days after the mating, and 2 hours later the female may again be fertile. The young develop rapidly and leave the nest as independent animals when 5 or 6 days old. There is, of course, more than 1 litter a year. Populations vary greatly but are usually high in numbers.

99

Eastern Woodrat or Packrat

Neotoma floridana · Cricetida(

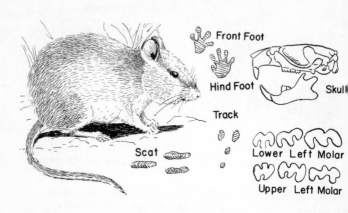

Front Foot

Hind Foot

Skull

Track

Scat

Lower Left Molar

Upper Left Molar

WOODRATS or packrats are known by many names to the zoologist—and have been called many names by those who suffer from their activities! Their habit of picking up almost anything—trinkets, socks, nuts, paper wads, jewels, and other objects—and hiding them, provides tremendous possibilities in snafuing domestic relations. It is always easy to accuse someone of having taken a thing that has vanished! Since these animals may cause so much excitement and misunderstanding, it seems reasonable to give them a little extra space here.

Of 9 listed species of the genus *Neotoma,* the bushy-tailed woodrat or packrat, *N. cinerea,* is the largest, or appears to be the largest. As a matter of careful measurement, dusky-footed woodrats, *N. fuscipes,* may measure a total of 18 inches, including an 8-inch tail, but the bushy character of the tail of *N. cinerea,* which has a total length of 17½ inches, makes it seem the larger. *N. fuscipes* is confined to a narrow strip along our Pacific Coast. Bushy-tailed packrats are found north of central California and from the western part of northwest Texas to the Dakotas and through British Columbia. *N. floridana,* the Eastern or Florida woodrat, ranges from southwestern South Dakota south to eastern Texas and south of a line running from South Dakota through southern Illinois to Connecticut. There are other species found in rather restricted and usually rather desert areas in the West and Southwest.

The tooth formula for all of these rats is: I 1/1; C 0/0; P 0/0; M 3/3. Track formula for the bushy-tailed packrat is: F ½ x ¾, 4; H ¾ x 1, 5; Sp 4; L 9.

Bushy-tailed woodrats have rather long, loose fur that may be light tan to dark chestnut brown, with the under parts of both the body and the tail white. While a total length of 17½ inches has been recorded, the normal length is slightly less. The tail is about 7⅓ inches long. The bushy-tailed woodrats build their nests in rocks, hollow stumps, or hollow trees, or in dwellings or other buildings.

Bushy-tailed Woodrat

In the Eastern woodrats, the total length is 17 inches, the tail to 8 inches, and the weight to ¾ pound. In these rats the tail cannot be called bushy. Whereas the hairs on the tail of the bushy-tailed woodrats are to ⅕ inch long, in the others they are much shorter. This is an important character, because in so many other ways the animals are alike. The Eastern woodrats are found in swamps or in piles of rocks. They may build good-sized nests of plant material on the ground, among the rocks, or even in the branches of trees. They feed mostly on plant materials, such as nuts, berries, and soft plant parts.

Dusky-footed woodrats, *N. fuscipes,* are famous for the enormous nests of sticks and rubbish which they build.

Woodrats are adaptable to general laboratory use and may become important for this purpose. They store foods that do not perish easily and eat the perishable stuffs they collect. In the South, woodrats breed through the year. The gestation period in *N. floridana* is 43 days; in *N. magister,* 30–36 days; in *N. albigula,* 37 days. Males court by drumming on the ground with their feet; may effect repeated matings in a few minutes. Probably monogamous. The 1–4 young weigh ⅓ ounce at birth, and have uncoordinated movements. At 4 days they have sparse wooly hair; at 2 weeks are well furred; at 3 weeks may leave parents. Females become mature at 200 days.

Hamster · *Cricetus cricetus* · Cricetidae

To a nutrition-conscious nation hamsters have been a blessing, through their use in nutrition research. They have assisted greatly also as laboratory animals in the study of disease and genetics. Because of their great reproductive capacity, strong measures are observed to prevent their establishing colonies of their own in the world, where they might become serious pests.

Hamsters are natives of temperate Europe and Asia, and are especially abundant in Syria. In native haunts they live in burrows at the end of tunnels to 6 feet deep. They burrow quickly in favorable terrain. They are favored as laboratory animals because of their cleanliness, freedom from odor, and rapid growth. Hamsters are gentle and normally can be handled safely by human beings.

Hamsters have 6-inch bodies and ½ inch tails that are not apparent. Front feet have 4 toes; the hind, 5, and all are clawed. Fur is fine, long, reddish gray above and white below, or all black. Food, largely small animals and grain. In captivity may thrive on dog biscuit, lettuce, and corn. Live comfortably at 70° F. but hibernate at 45° F. Have strong storage instinct. May store 5 or 6 pecks of grain in underground rooms. These are regularly robbed by other animals, including man. Introduced into United States in 1938 as laboratory animals.

Males fight each other for females. About 15 days and 21 hours after mating, from 7–15 young are born. At birth, young are naked, blind, and weigh 1/10 ounce. Backs become black at 3 days, at 12 days are golden brown. At 2 weeks, young are weaned and eyes are open. Females are receptive to males at 43 days, at 8–10 P.M., and may bear young at 59 days. May have monthly litters through the year. Respiration rate, awake, 2,900; hibernating, 70. Pulse, 300–600. Die at 2 years of age.

Hamsters can swim. Before entering water they usually inflate their cheeks, thereby increasing their buoyancy.

Brown Lemming · *Lemmus trimucronatus* · Cricetidae

Skull

Upper Left Molars

Lower Left Molars

To most of us the name "lemming" will mean little in our field experiences. However, lemmings appear frequently in popular literature, in the news, and sometimes in the movies because of their phenomenal migrations, when hordes of them may swim out to sea to their death. Somehow these migrations remind us of the story of the Pied Piper of Hamelin, although it is a long way from Hamelin to the range of the lemmings.

Brown lemmings range from Alaska east to Hudson Bay and south into British Columbia. They are 6½ inches long, including a ¾ inch tail. They weigh ¼ pound. They are generally brown through the year, thus differing from the collared lemmings or varying lemmings, *Dicrostonyx,* which are brown in summer but white in winter. These animals range farther to the east. Lemming mice or bog lemmings of the genus *Synaptomys* range through most of Alaska and Canada south approximately to the Mason and Dixon line and east to the Dakotas and Colorado. They are occasionally to 5 inches long and have ¼ inch tails. Temperature, 96°–106° F.

Brown lemmings are active through the year, day and night. Populations preceding migrations build up every 3 to 4 years. Breeding begins when animals are not yet full grown. There are 3 to possibly 9 young born about 3 weeks after the mating takes place, and there are several litters a year in spite of the unique conditions in the North.

Trappers depend indirectly on the abundance of lemmings of one sort or another, because of the fact that with few lemmings there are few of the fur bearers that feed upon them. In the game situation the story is different, since lemmings compete for food with caribou, and with many lemmings there are fewer caribou to supply dwellers of the North with food, leather, bones, and other useful materials, and to serve as draft, pack, and riding animals.

Red-backed Mouse · *Clethrionomys gapperi* · Cricetidae

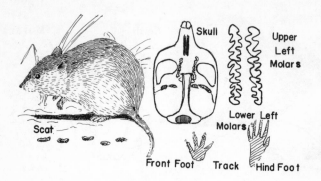

Skull

Upper Left Molars

Lower Left Molars

Scat

Front Foot   Track   Hind Foot

THROUGHOUT Canada and most of the wooded portion of the northern United States, among the litter of the forest floor, live little, brightly colored mice that usually have a reddish-brown area on their backs. These appropriately named red-backed mice are to the woodlands perhaps what the meadow mice are to the grasslands, and muskrats, rice rats, and beavers are to the marshes. There are about 20 species of red-backed mice in North America, but few go farther south than the Appalachian Highlands.

Our species has a length of 6 inches, including a 1½ inch tail. These mice weigh about 1½ ounces. The crowns of the molars are corrugated, as shown in the sketch. The fur is generally long and loose, but may vary greatly in different areas.

Red-backed mice can be serious pests in new forest plantations, where they may destroy great numbers of young and old trees by girdling them. They may even destroy trees a foot in diameter. They are preyed on persistently by the ordinary flesh eaters, such as foxes, weasels, bears, and the birds of prey, but at times this seems to have little effect on their numbers. They are active day and night, summer and winter, and may store food against difficult times. Temperature, 98°–104° F.

Red-backed mice begin breeding in late winter or early spring and continue on into the late fall. From 2–8 young make up the litter, which are born from 17–19 days after the mating takes place. Young may bear their own young before the end of their first year. The young are born in rather elaborate grass-lined nests hidden under logs, rocks, or other protective materials close to the ground.

The food of red-backed mice consists largely of plant material, but may include insects, some of which may be serious pests.

Meadow Mouse or Field Mouse

Microtus pennsylvanicus · Cricetidae

Upper Left Molars

Lower Jaw

Trail

Tracks

Lower Left Molars

THERE are few grass-covered spots in North America north of our southern states where meadow mice may not be found in abundance. The word "ubiquitous" has been repeatedly, aptly, and well applied to them, and yet with all their abundance, until relatively recently their life histories and habits have been little understood. They probably affect the economy of farmers more than do foxes, raccoons, weasels, hawks, or owls, and yet farmers have a well-established and often unwarranted enmity toward these archenemies of the mice, which are the archenemies of agriculture.

Meadow mice are properly considered as voles. Members of the genus range in length from 4–10 inches, including tails from ¾–3½ inches long. The pictured species is 5¼ inches long, has a 2-inch tail, and weighs ¼ pound. These mice are approximately, if not actually, identical with their Old World relatives. Teeth are: I 1/1; C 0/0; P 0/0; M 3/3. Tracks are: F ½ x ½, 5; H ½ x ¾, 5; Sp 1 ½; L 6. In reversing, the tracks of hind feet and front feet may be superimposed.

At least 3 million tons of hay are destroyed each year in the United States by meadow mice. While the average population is probably about 300 mice to the acre, populations of to 12,000 per acre have been recorded in the Southwest.

Female meadow mice may produce 13 litters a year. Breeding is promiscuous, and 4–8 young are born 21 days after the mating, followed immediately by a new mating. Young are weaned when 10–15 days old. Females may breed when 25 days old; males, at 45 days. One female is believed to be able to produce 100 mice a year. Each mouse requires water and eats its own weight in plants each day, but destroys much more than it eats. For survival each mouse requires about 23 pounds of green food per year. The life expectancy is thought to be about 1½ years. Temperature, 94°–110° F.

105

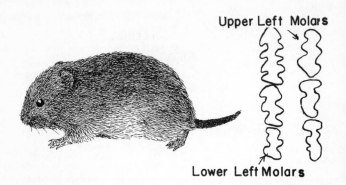

Upper Left Molars

Lower Left Molars

RUN a line from central Texas to central Wisconsin and east to southern Maine, and another line from southern Texas to the Atlantic coast of northern Florida, and you mark the rough boundaries of the range of some short-tailed, sleek-looking mice that favor wooded country. These pine mice may reach almost 6 inches in length, but the tail rarely if ever exceeds 1 inch or the weight 2 ounces. They burrow, apparently aimlessly, through the leafmold of the forest floor, leaving raised ridges over their runways. As surface burrowers, they are somewhat like moles. In this world halfway between open air and solid earth, shrews, moles, and some mice work out their problems. The moles are the most aggressive diggers. The shrews may run in the mole burrows, or dig burrows themselves where this is not too difficult. The pine mice, of course, can burrow for themselves, but not through such firm earth as the moles can.

The fur of pine mice, like that of moles, may be rubbed smooth either way, as one would expect in an animal living in burrows as do these mice. The eyes and ears are greatly reduced in size, with the ears almost hidden in the fur. The feet are a pale gray; the tail is brown above and paler beneath. The feet are strong enough to do some digging, and where the soil is soft, a burrow may go to more than a foot beneath the surface. Normally, however, 4 inches is about the maximum burrow depth. The nests are hidden a few inches below the surface, in some protected area, and are lined with dry grass and leaves. Breeding takes place from March through November, or even through the winter. Rarely are more than 2–4 young born. Pine mice have 4 teats instead of the 8 teats found on field mice. Young pine mice open their eyes when 9 days old and shortly afterward are weaned and on their own.

Muskrat or Musquash · *Ondatra zibethicus* · Cricetidae

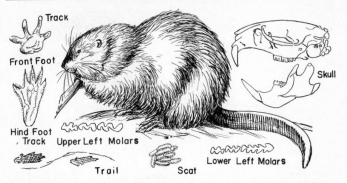

Track

Front Foot

Hind Foot Track

Upper Left Molars

Trail

Scat

Skull

Lower Left Molars

THE fecundity of muskrats has been responsible for many a successful person's college education or start in business. Whether the production of synthetic furs, the popularity of some substitute endorsed by the style dictators, the recognition of their value as a source of edible flesh, the elimination of their breeding grounds by the spread of cities, or some other factor will affect the muskrats' future, remains to be seen. Their ability to turn apparently useless vegetation that grows on wasteland into valuable fur and flesh is commendable. They produce fur with a durability 40% that of otter, which sells in the trade as "Hudson seal," "Russian otter," "red seal," or "river mink." Because of the damage to the hide they may not be legally shot in some areas, and to insure a harvest of superior-quality furs certain seasons are closed to muskrat trapping. Unfortunately muskrats may be trapped at times when the new generation is still dependent on the mother, and it is not practical to trap only males or nonbreeding females. Practical, humane traps permitting the freeing of nursing mothers do not seem to have been developed, but frequent visiting of marked traps is required by law in some states. Best practice is to set the trap so as to insure prompt drowning. Probably the increase in popularity of synthetic furs will do more to prevent inhumane trapping than anything else.

Muskrats are found through most of North America north of Mexico. They are to 25 inches long, with a 10-inch tail that is scaly and barely haired. They weigh to 3 pounds. They are a uniform dark brown above, with the long hairs the darker. Teeth are: I 1/1; C 0/0; P 0/0; M 3/3. Tracks are: F 1½ x 1¼; 4; H 3½ x 1½, 5; Sp 3. There is no seasonal and little age change. Muskrats are polygamous. They mate in water, may remain submerged to 12 minutes. Have not been raised economically in confinement. To 3 litters a year of 4–11 young are born 19–42 days after the mating. Mothers alone protect young. Temperature, 99°–102° F.

107

Black Rat · *Rattus rattus* · Muridae

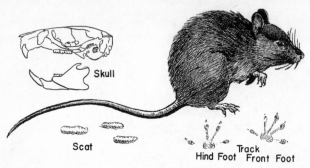

Skull

Scat

Track
Hind Foot Front Foot

WE include the black rat, the Norway rat (page 109), and the house mouse (page 110) as representatives of the European rats and mice, the Muridae. Zoologists recognize that in the Muridae the upper molars have 3 longitudinal series of tubercles, while those of the Cricetidae, considered on pages 95–107, have 2 or less of these series. The Cricetidae are the American rats and mice. There are some 130 species of Old World rats and mice, and in the United States about 50 species of the New World group. The New World animals seldom carry the diseases common to the Old World group, and lack their characteristic odor.

Until about 1727, the black rat was the common rat of houses in Europe and eastern Russia. Then it began to be replaced by the more aggressive Norway rat. In pre-Revolutionary War times in the American colonies, it was the common house rat, but after the Revolution the Norway rat took over. The body length of the two rats is about the same, but the black rat is glossy black and has an 8–9-inch tail, while the Norway rat is brown above and gray beneath, with a 6- to 7-inch tail.

Black rats may take to trees, and in some parts of their range are recognized as serious enemies of tree-nesting birds. Zoologists know them also as enemies of tree snails, whose shells are so highly prized by collectors. The white-bellied rats are the more common tree-dwellers. All these rats may be found in houses and barns, on croplands, and in marshes or dumps, through most of North America where man lives. Black rats give a twittering call, as contrasted with the squeak or squeal of the Norway rats. Black rats may weigh to 10 ounces, while Norway rats may weigh up to 24 ounces. All of these rats are highly destructive to things important to man. The teeth of black rats and Norway rats are: I 1/1; C 0/0; P 0/0; M 3/3. The tracks, which also show the tail track, commonly are: F ½ x ½, 5; H 1½ x ½, 5; Sp 4. Black rats can breed at 11 weeks, are in heat 9–20 hours beginning 4–10 P.M. Gestation, 22 days. Life span, to 4 years.

Norway Rat · *Rattus norvegicus* · Muridae

Front Foot | Hind Foot | Track | Skull | Scat

IN the vernacular, a "rat" is a despicable character, and the verb "to rat" means to betray. And yet we use the term "rats" when we wish to pass off a situation as being wholly nonsensical. Even when we consider the Norway rat objectively, we find confusion, because on the one hand it may be man's best friend in time of need, and on the other his worst animal pest. Laboratory albino rats are Norway rats, and have proven to be among the most valuable animals for studying the diets, genetics, and diseases of man, ranking in this respect with guinea pigs, hamsters, and monkeys. As pests, wild Norway rats destroy in the United States from 300 million to 2 billion dollars' worth of farm products a year, and in Canada about 20 million dollars' worth. One part of barium carbonate to 4 of soft food gives effective poison control, but is dangerous. Rats are found in houses and buildings wherever man lives. The home range may have a radius of 40 feet. Of 362 marked rats, 84% of recaptured females and 73% of males were taken within 40 feet of original capture. Only 10% changed buildings.

Rats can swim well and may remain submerged more than 3 minutes. Critical low temperatures are −40° F. and critical high 104° F. Rats may work in unison in capturing food. They will attack humans, and have killed pigs, calves, and chickens. They carry bubonic plague, typhus, tuberculosis of poultry, and trichinosis of swine, and are subject to many diseases of man. Respiration rate, 2,000. Pulse, 261–600. Temperature, 90°–101° F.

Norway rats live 30 times faster than man, in wild may produce 6 litters of young a year, and are old at 3 years of age. Females are in heat 5 days, with the climax lasting 13 hours. Breeding is promiscuous and at any time of year. About 4–20 blind, naked, deaf, helpless young are born 21–30 days after mating. Ears open at 3 days; eyes at 14–17 days. Double weight first 6 days. They become sexually mature at 2 months, and cease breeding at 18 months. Norway rats came to Europe in the eighteenth century, to England about 1729; Prussia, 1750; Paris, 1792; United States, 1775. They did not originate in Norway.

109

House Mouse · *Mus musculus* · Muridae

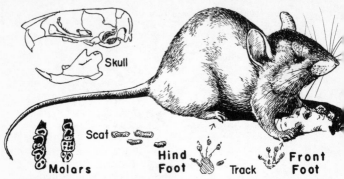

Skull

Scat

Molars

Hind Foot

Track

Front Foot

WE speak of things as being "meek as a mouse," and yet we read that the meek shall inherit the earth. Maybe the two statements have significance when we think of house mice, which probably originated in Asia and yet have spread through Europe, America, and other parts of the world, where they not only share man's house and barns but his fields, his beds, and his meals, and even use stored clothing for protection. If man can inherit the earth, the chances are that house mice will be right along with him in doing so.

Length, to 7 inches, including a 3½ inch, sparsely haired tail. Sexes are alike in color, a uniform brownish gray with light under parts, and are generally sleek in appearance. Body is rather conspicuously slender and the feet small and inconspicuous. Teeth are: I 1/1; C 0/0; P 0/0; M 3/3. Tracks are: F ¼ x ¼, 5; H ½ x ¾, 5; Sp 1½.

Populations in fields may often be high, a square yard sometimes supporting 17. An acre in California was estimated to support 82,000. Can see for 45 feet.

House mice are highly destructive to stored food and household articles, fouling books and clothing and carrying diseases such as spotted fever. They do not hibernate, practice little sanitation, and show only slight storage instinct. Individuals may "waltz and sing," but these are probably diseased animals. They will eat anything man will eat, will gnaw disfiguring holes in walls, and hardly have the admirable qualities of Walt Disney's Mickey Mouse, or of Minnie Mouse either. While children are admonished to be "quiet as mice," there are few things noisier than a mouse in the walls in the middle of the night.

Mice breed promiscuously, bearing young at any time of the year, in litters of 1–12, some 19–31 days after the mating. Young are weaned at 3 weeks and the females breed at 2 months. In heat, 9–20 hours. Theoretically, a pair could produce 1,000 descendants a year. Respiration rate, 1,530–3,500. Pulse, 328–780. Temperature, 95°–100° F. Life span, 5 years.

Meadow Jumping Mouse · *Zapus hudsonius* · Zapodidae

Track

Front Foot

Hind Foot

Skull

Scat

SOMETIME you may turn over a board or old log in a grassy field and be surprised to see some little mice go leaping wildly away, taking jumps of up to 10 feet and balancing with their long tails while in the air. The meadow jumping mice differ from the woodland jumping mice in that the meadow jumpers lack the white tail tip found in the woodland species and the meadow jumping mice have 4 upper cheek teeth (molars and premolars), instead of 3 as in the woodland jumping mice.

A meadow jumping mouse may have a total length of over 8 inches, of which more than 5 may be a slender, poorly haired tail, ending in a tuft of hair which, in this species, is brown. The hind legs are excessively long. The upper incisors have prominent longitudinal grooves. Teeth are: I 1/1; C 0/0; P 1/0; M 3/3. Tracks are: F ⅜ x ¼, 4; H ½ x 1¼, 5; Sp 1½; L 2½–120 inches. In summer meadow jumping mice are yellow, fawn-colored, and black; in winter, duller and yellower.

While they may eat insects, major food is plant stuff, including seed-bearing tops of grasses brought to earth by successive cuttings of the stem, which gradually bring tops down to eating position. Do not store plant food, but do build up a reserve of fat which helps them through a deep hibernating period that may extend from September through April. Even on cold summer nights they may approach hibernation.

After a mating in May, 3–6 young are born in June, 18 days later, and a second litter in late summer. Young protected in grass-lined nest. At birth, young are blind and hairless except for whiskers, are about 1¼ inches long, and weigh 30 to the ounce. In 17 days they are furred; a black stripe down back appears in 15–19 days. Eyes open in 3 weeks, and in 4 weeks they leave nest as independent mice. By fall there may be a dozen mice per acre. They swim well and may burrow to below frost line, but make no fixed runways and have no mound at the burrow entrance. May give a high-pitched squeak. Temperature, 96°–103° F.

111

Woodland Jumping Mouse

Nepaeozapus insignis · Zapodidae

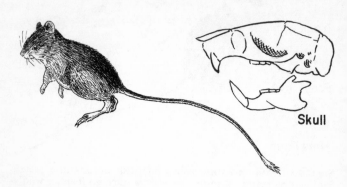

Skull

SLEEP in mixed woodlands some quiet night, and you may hear what sounds like the gentlest of footsteps, or something hitting the ground periodically but moving from place to place. Flash on a light in the direction of the noise, and you may be surprised to see a little mouse go leaping off into the darkness in wild jumps. If you catch one of these in a peanut-baited mouse-trap, it may be 10 inches in length, of which at least 6 inches is tail, the tip of which is white. The weight of these mice when mature is about 1 ounce. There are 3 upper check teeth (molars only), instead of the 4 found in the meadow jumping mice, and the incisors are grooved as they are in the meadow mouse relatives.

Three subspecies of woodland jumping mice are found in North America, mostly in eastern Canada near the border, and in the United States in the area bounded by Maine, Wisconsin, and North Carolina.

Undoubtedly woodland jumping mice serve as food for some of our fur bearers. Their own food is mostly plant material, none of which is stored. They hibernate intensely for half of the year and may sleep in pairs. Their numbers vary greatly in different areas and at different times in the same area.

From 3–6 naked young are born about 3 weeks after the mating, the first litter appearing in June or July, and a second in early September. At birth, the young lack even the whiskers so common with some of their relatives. The home range of females may be to just over 6 acres; that of males to over 9. They have a grass-lined nest deep underground at the end of a burrow, the entrance of which may be plugged during the day-time. They are lovely little animals, difficult to keep in captivity, but intensely interesting to study in the wild. They do little if any harm to man's interests.

Chinchilla · *Chinchilla laenigera* · Chinchillidae

Skull

Lower Jaw

HERE in a little mammal 9 inches long, including a 5-inch tail, we have the makings of many dramatic stories. The chinchilla is threatened with possible extermination, and the exportation of living animals is forbidden. It is the source of the most expensive and perhaps the most beautiful of all furs, and around it revolves a breeding industry started with a few animals smuggled into the United States from South America. The cause of fortunes made and lost by breeders, the victim of style whims and of competition in recent years with synthetic furs—all in all the chinchilla has indeed an interesting story.

Chinchillas are natives of the higher Andes from Chile to north of Bolivia. They have practically vanished in the wild state and have become successful domestic cage animals. There are 2 species. The short-tailed chinchilla is larger than the common chinchilla. Nocturnal in habits, the animals are clean and affectionate. The United States stock started from 18 animals smuggled into the country in 1923. One hundred twenty–140 pelts are needed to make a coat, but the animals are more valuable for sale as breeders than for their pelts.

Chinchillas are monogamous, mating for life. From 1–4 young are born 111 days after the mating. Their eyes are open and they can run within an hour. They are nursed for 45 days, but stay under care of parents for more than 10 weeks. Young may mate at 5–8 months and may bear 1–3 litters a year. Life expectancy, 10 (?) years.

In captivity the accepted diet includes yeast, molasses, wheat germ, oat middlings, peanut oil, soybean oil, alfalfa meal, and bone meal, with carrots three times weekly and orange juice twice weekly. The daily ration is about 2 ounces.

Chinchilla coats have brought as much as $100,000 each, making pelts worth under $1,000 apiece, but breeding pairs have sold at over $3,200—$1,600 apiece. This is not the only case in which living mammals are worth more than dead ones.

Porcupine · *Erethizon dorsatum* · Erithezontidae

MANY who learned their natural history from Longfellow's *Hiawatha* think that porcupines can hurl their quills at a target. Instead, the animals usually strike with their tails, freeing quills into the flesh. Once in flesh, ¾ inch quills may penetrate 2 inches in 30 hours and ¼ inch quills 1¾ inches in 48 hours. Quills are best removed by quick, direct jerk. Quills, which may cause death of dogs and many wild animals, have been used effectively by Indians in decorative work. Porcupine's worst enemy is the fisher.

Porcupines are found in wooded areas from West Virginia to the Gulf of St. Lawrence to the Arctic Circle in Alaska and south to central California and New Mexico. Related animals live in other continents. They eat plants almost exclusively, favoring evergreens and salty substances. Will eat water plants, feeding mostly at dusk or dawn or in moonlight. Do not hibernate, but may hole up in bad weather. Build crude nests in trees or in cavities or dens.

Length to 3 feet, including 6-inch tail. Weight to 40 pounds, with males the larger. Brownish black in color, speckled with black-tipped, white-based quill. Teeth are: I 1/1; C 0/0; P 1/1; M 3/3. Tracks are F 2½ x 3⅓, 5; H 3½ x 2, 5. Tail drags, making trail a trough. In mud, footpad tracks are pebbled.

Courting males may urinate on females but do not fight each other for mates. Females may make advances in November. Single young usually born, but twins may occur. Some authorities say gestation lasts 112 days, others 217. Well-developed young weigh to 20 ounces and are 10 inches long at birth, although mother may weigh only 13 pounds. Young have eyes open at birth, waddle in 6 hours, can climb trees at 2 days, nurse for 10 days. They weigh to 3½ pounds and measure to 18 inches in first summer; 8 pounds, 21 inches, second summer; 12 pounds, 25 inches (mature measurements), third summer. Males may breed at 16 months. Pulse, 280–320. Temperature, 96°–101° F. Life expectancy, to 20 years.

Guinea Pig · *Cavia porcellus* · Caviidae

IT is said that "if one picks a guinea pig up by its tail its eyes will drop out," the gimmick being the assumption that a guinea pig has no tail. Guinea pigs do, however, have short tails. Guinea pigs are about 11 inches long, weigh about 1 pound, have stocky, heavy bodies. Hind legs are relatively short and have 3-toed feet with large, angular nails. The front feet are 4-toed. The fur of wild animals is coarse and long, but in domestic breeds may vary greatly. There are some 20 known wild species native to South America, where the primitive Incas raised them for food. Commonest variety is English, with smooth, short hair to 1½ inches long, in many colors. The Abyssinian has hair radiating in rosettes, rough and also short. The Peruvian has hair to 6 inches long, which extends over head and the rear. The Angora has smooth, long hair, never in rosettes.

Guinea pigs reach full size at 15 months of age. The heads are rabbit-like but for short ears. Skin is thin and strong. Domestic guinea pigs are born 58–75 days after the mating, have eyes open and hair fully developed; run in a few hours. Females are in heat 6–11 hours. Litters number 4–12, although in the wild there are only 1–2. Nursing lasts 21 days, when young are ready to breed. Mother ordinarily has but 2 mammae. Milk produced is proportionately equal to that of a good dairy cow. Life span, to 8 (?) years. Pulse, 260–400. Temperature, 96.8°–104.5° F. Respiration rate 1,250 at 100–150 breaths per minute. Teeth are: I 1/1; C 0/0; P 1/1; M 3/3.

Guinea pigs make excellent pets in spite of unpleasant odor. They feed best in dull light, cannot survive low temperatures. Greatest value to man is as laboratory animals in study of disease, in nutrition studies, in production of serums for disease control, and in studies of heredity. Best diet includes bone meal, skimmed-milk powder, soybean meal, meat tankage, wheat shorts, and cottonseed meal, fed frequently but in small amounts. Known also as cavies.

115

Capybara, Water Pig, or Cavy
Hydrochoerus capybara · Hydrochoeridae

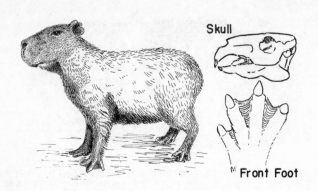

Skull

Front Foot

In the waterways of South America east of the foothills of the Andes, in lakes, marshes, wooded swamps, rivers, and streams, live the capybaras. On land they may run much like horses, but when excited take to water, where they may swim long distances underwater. These are the largest of the living rodents, measuring to 4 feet long and having no tails, or almost none. They may weigh more than 100 pounds. The hind legs are longer than the front legs; the toes have short webs and short nails, and there are 3 on the hind feet and 4 on the front feet. The hair is long and coarse, reddish brown above and yellowish brown beneath.

The 2–8 young are born 119–126 days after the mating, weigh 2–3 pounds at birth, and are well developed. While they gain independence relatively quickly, the families may stick together longer than seems necessary. Capybaras have been known to live 10 years, but this is unusual, since they have so many enemies, so little defense, and by some are considered to be good food. Jaguars hunt them on land, alligators in the water, and man on both land and water. Men commonly hunt them in canoes, and the wild animals must be alert to survive. Only rarely do they fight among themselves or in defense against their enemies. In captivity they soon become tame and gentle, but apparently they do not thrive well in domestication.

When we remember that these animals may stand 21 inches high at the shoulder and weigh more than 100 pounds, we realize that they are substantial creatures. They feed almost wholly on plants, which they eat in large amounts. They are rather social in nature, and family groups are probably more commonly found than are lone individuals. Their rather large teeth are sometimes used as ornaments by natives.

Golden Agouti · *Dasyprocta aguti* · Dasyproctidae

WHILE there is some question about the food value of the flesh of capybaras, there seems to be little doubt about the popularity of agoutis, which are found in the forests and wooded areas of southern Mexico, Central America, and on south into South America. There are a dozen closely related species living in the same general area.

The golden agouti is slightly larger than an average rabbit and is covered with a coat of sleek golden or reddish-brown hair. The tail is negligible in size, eyes large and appealing, and ears small. The forefeet have 5 toes and the hind feet 3 toes. Tracks are: F 1¼ x ¾, 3; H 1½ x 2, 3; Sp 5. While the front feet normally have 5 toes, only the 3 central ones show in the tracks. When the animal is running, the tracks of the forefeet may be obliterated by those of the hind feet.

Agoutis are chiefly nocturnal and spend much of the day in cavities in trees or in holes in the ground. They come out when they think it safe and feed on available fruits and other vegetable material. Agouti hunters sometimes toss stones into the air. These fall to the ground, possibly suggesting that fruit has freshly fallen. The agoutis that come out for the fruit are then killed. Agoutis are the prey of most of the common flesh eaters. Their flesh is tender, white, and delicious, and one of the best of wildlife foods. Since the animals themselves feed on plants, it is only to be expected that at times they become pests when they feed in gardens and on agricultural crops.

From 5–6 young are born 64 days after the mating. Within 1 hour after the young are born, they may begin nibbling plant food. Naturally, under these circumstances, they soon become independent of their parents. Families remain together for a considerable time. Young captured early may be made into good pets. Life span, to 10 years.

117

Nutria or Coypu Rat · *Nutria myocaster* · Capromyidae

It is reasonable to assume that the nutrias or coypu rats will play an important role in our future. If the production of fur-bearing mammals continues to be economically important, nutrias will surely be in the picture, possibly replacing the muskrat as a basic source of supply. If synthetic furs supplant natural furs, then nutrias may well become major pests in those waterways that yield economic crops such as rice.

Nutrias are natives of South America south of Peru, on both sides of the Andes. They live in waterways, burrowing freely in stream banks. About 1930 a few were introduced into the United States as controlled fur bearers. About 1940 several hundred were washed from their enclosures by floods. In 1948, 50,000 were taken by trappers of the lower Mississippi delta.

Length, about 3 feet, but usually smaller, with tails two thirds the length of the bodies. Tail scaly or sparsely haired. Weight, about 20 pounds. Have dense, soft, yellowish underfur with long, dusky or brownish guard hairs Many thousands are killed each year for the guard hairs alone, which are used in making felt. The fur of the under parts is the more valuable, since females bear nipples above rather than below. This arrangement permits the young to nurse while the mother and young float in the water.

Many people may be confused by nutrias, thinking they are beavers. Both have webbed hind feet, but the nutria's tail, unlike the beaver's, is not broad and flat, but slender, and the front teeth are orange red.

From 100–132 days after mating, nutrias bear 3–12 rat-sized young. Litters may be borne every 4 months. Young swim a few hours after birth. They may reproduce in their first year. Commercial pelts may be produced the first year, but growth continues through 2 years. Females may breed at 6 months and rarely live more than 3 years, or males over 6. Nutrias are also known as "river mice" or "mouse beavers," and have legal protection in some areas. Used in marsh management to create open water. Temperature, 99°–102° F.

ORDER CETACEA (*Dolphins and Whales*)

Sperm Whale · *Physeter catodon* · Physeteridae

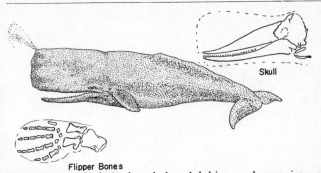

Skull

Flipper Bones

THE cetaceans include the whales, dolphins, and porpoises, all
lacking necks in the ordinary sense, and some having dorsal
fins. The forelimbs are broad, paddlelike flippers without nails.
The hind limbs are lacking. The tail ends in 2 broad flukes.
There are no skin glands except the mammary glands, and there
is a thermal layer of blubber or fat which is not a reserve food
supply.

Sperm whales are most abundant between 50° N. and 50° S.
Old males may appear far north in the Arctic and far south in
the Antarctic. Male sperm whales may measure to 80 feet and
females half as long. Their greatest circumference is between
the eyes and the flippers. Tail flukes may spread to 14 feet.
Upper jaws are toothless, or practically so; lower jaws bear to
24 teeth, to 8 inches long, on each side. Blubber is to 14 inches
thick. The animals are black above and white beneath. There
is but one blowhole, forward to the left, and the "spout" is inclined forward from left side of snout. It is fetid, lasts about 6
seconds, and may be repeated 60–70 times in 10 minutes before
the diving or sounding. May remain submerged 75 minutes. In
diving, the flukes as well as the dorsal hump are shown. There
is no dorsal fin. When diving, can renew 90% of air in lungs
prior to sounding. Man can exhaust only 20%.

Favored food of sperm whales is squid and cuttlefish. One
swallowed a 10-foot shark whole. Irritated intestine may produce ambergris, an opaque white wax which melts at 60° C.
and is useful in medicine, the arts, and in making candles.
Spermaceti in head may serve as cushion to counteract pressure in deep diving.

Probably polygamous. Young, 1–2, to 14 feet long, born 10–
12 months after the mating; may reach 20 feet before nursing
ceases. Mature at 8 years. May double length first year. Young
nurse as mother lies on side. Mother alone protects young. Female breeds every other year. Life expectancy, to 20 years.

"Moby Dick" was a sperm whale. (The movie *Moby Dick*
could not have been directed by one who knew sperm whales
and how they spout.)

119

Narwhal · *Monodon monoceros* · Monodontidae

Male

Female

THERE is little doubt but that early zoologists once reconstructed a whole animal—the unicorn—from one part of a narwhal. About the only thing they got right was that it was a mammal. The legendary unicorn had the body of a horse and a single twisted horn. Actually the body of the animal that bore the horn was more like that of a whale than that of a horse.

Narwhals are to 16 feet long. They have 1 tusk, or, rarely, 2. The single tusk (usually the left) is hollow, white, spirally twisted clockwise. Tusks are seldom present in the female. The eyes are small, the head blunt, mouth narrow; no external ears or dorsal fin. The body is to 2 feet through at the shoulder, and the color black, gray, dark mottled, or white.

There is but 1 species in the genus. The family includes another genus, *Delphinapterus,* the white whale, with 2 species. *M. monoceros* is found in Arctic seas north of Cape Halkett in Alaska, at 71° N., and from Labrador's Atlantic coast to northern Hudson Bay. Relatively common in Lancaster and Eclipse Sounds, off Bylot Island.

Narwhals may submerge to 1,200 feet. They are usually found in small groups, ordinarily of 1 sex. Mothers may roar in calling young, or may give low-pitched bleats. Narwhals' worst enemies are killer whales and man.

Narwhals feed on shrimp, cuttlefish, water scorpions, and fish, all swallowed whole. Tusk probably not used in capturing food, but may be used in fighting other males for mates. One or 2 calves are born; they are to 5 feet long at birth. Blue gray, and darker than adults, they remain a long period with the mother.

Horn, once believed to have mystical power to counteract poison in drink, is of value for ivory. Mentioned in Psalms 92:10 as "horn of unicorn." Eskimos eat narwhal flesh, burn their oil, and make lines and clothing of intestines.

Bottle-nosed Dolphin · *Tursiops truncatus* · Delphinidae
Common Dolphin · *Delphinus delphis* · Delphinidae

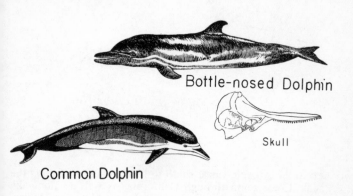

Bottle-nosed Dolphin

Skull

Common Dolphin

THE common name "dolphin" is applied both to a fish and to a group of mammals. The mammal family includes dolphins and porpoises, both of which are small, whale-like animals, usually with numerous teeth on both jaws. We consider here the dolphins, killer whales, pilot whales, and porpoises.

Bottle-nosed dolphins are to 12 feet long. They have a well-defined snout. There is a prominent dorsal fin. They have 20–22 teeth on either side of each jaw, each to ⅜ inch in diameter. The lower jaw is the longer. Dolphins are conspicuously white beneath, and black to gray or purplish above. They have a heart-beat of 110–150 per minute when resting at surface, and to 50 per minute when submerged. They can see well for a distance of 50 feet through the air, but can hear fish hit water farther away. They can swim at 20 knots and leap twice their length from the water. Schools may be kept together by whistling. They are almost worldwide in distribution. Their food is fish, and one was reported to have eaten a 4-foot shark whole.

They court by swimming upside down. Early-season schools of 1 sex; late season, mixed. Young born 10 months after the mating. Newly born young nurse about 15 minutes at 30-minute intervals, but can submerge only 30 seconds. Beginning the eleventh week, they eat to 11 pounds of fish daily.

The common dolphins are found on both the Atlantic and Pacific coasts of North America. They are about 7–8 feet long, black to dark gray above and on tail and fins, white to greenish white beneath. Variously marked. They weigh to 160 pounds. Each jaw has a row of 80–120 conical teeth. The slender, narrow jaws form a beak. Food is primarily fish. Body temperature, 96° F.

Risso's Dolphin or Grampus

Gramphidelphis griseus · Delphinidae

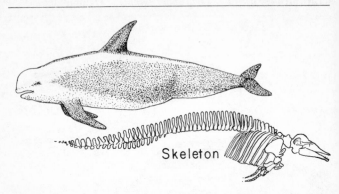

Skeleton

ALONG the Atlantic Coast south to New Jersey, and along the Pacific Coast south through California, as well as along the coasts of eastern Asia, India, New Zealand, and western Africa, sport the Risso's dolphins or grampuses. These animals may reach a length of 20 feet, but are more commonly less than 13. Mature males are bluish white, marked with dark-brown patches, while the females are uniform brown. The head bulges but there is no beak. The flippers are narrow and about one fifth the total length The dorsal fin is high and recurved, and the mouth is horizontal but turns up at the rear as though the animals were laughing.

For 32 years Pelorus Jack, a famous grampus, escorted vessels into Pelorus Sound in New Zealand, and was so popular it gained protection from the New Zealand legislature. It disappeared in 1912.

Usually dolphins are solitary or found only in small schools. It is believed that they feed mostly on fish and cuttlefish. There may be 2–7 teeth on each side of the lower jaw, and there are none on the upper jaw of an old animal. The teeth on the lower jaws are usually more than ½ inch in diameter, exposed for ¾ inch, and borne forward for about one fifth the length of the jaws. The behavior of the animals is much like that of killer whales, but apparently they feed on smaller animals, as suggested above.

Little is known about the breeding habits of grampuses, although they probably mate about the end of the year, with the young born about 1 year later. A female has been found bearing young that was 5 feet long, or half the total length of the mother. The young may have rows of whitish bristles on the upper lips, 8 on each side.

Grampuses seem to be decidedly friendly, unlike their close relatives the killer whales. Formerly they were both placed in the genus *Grampus*.

Killer Whale · *Grampus orca* · Delphinidae

KILLER whales have the reputation of being the scourges of the sea. Feared by other animals large and small, they attack huge whales many times their size in schools that tear wildly at their victims. A large whale may be killed by 3 or 4 killer whales working in unison. Sometimes killer whales work in packs of 40 or more.

Killer whales are found in almost all oceans over the world, from Bering Sea in the north to Ross's Sea in the south. They may even pursue migrating fish up rivers and frequently become grounded in so doing. In attacking large whales, walruses, and seals, killer whales frequently first attack the lips, tongues, and mouth. They can outswim the fastest dolphins. One killer whale had the remains of 14 seals and 13 porpoises in its stomach. In attacking seals, killer whales are believed to jolt them from the ice floes on which they may be resting.

Male killer whales may be to 30 feet long, with erect 6-foot dorsal fins. Females may be to 20 feet long, with 2-foot dorsals. The bodies are stout and rounded, the flippers, short and narrow. The eyes are large and oval, with a white patch to the rear. The mouths of killer whales are to 18 inches wide, with 11–14 long, narrow, strong, slightly recurved teeth which interlock with corresponding teeth on opposing jaw. The animals are black above, white beneath, with a yellowish-purple patch under the back fin on each side. They have a glossy appearance.

Killer whales mate at the end of the year—about the same period when the young are born, as gestation takes about 12 months. The young may be to 7 feet long at birth. Little is known about the life expectancy or the growth habits, but they are obviously successful animals in their own environment.

Pliny claimed that killer whales could fill a boat with the water they spouted. Fabricius, in 1780, first explained whales' spouting.

Pilot Whale or Blackfish

Globicephala melaena · Delphinidae

PANIC is a ruling force with many mammals. Buffalo and cattle stampede; from this comes the expression "thundering herd." Similarly, pilot whales or blackfish may be stampeded, and from their behavior comes another common name— "caa'ing whales." They are called *grindhval* by Scandinavians. Obviously any creature with so many common names must be reasonably well known over a wide portion of the earth. As a matter of fact, the genus is worldwide in its distribution. In the North Pacific we find *G. scammonii*. *G. macrorhynchia* is found in the South Seas. *G. melaena* is found with these species off the American coasts. In the Indian Ocean we find *G. brachyptera*. Of these *G. scammonii* and *G. brachyptera* are all black.

The pilot whale is from 16–20 feet long. The head is swollen forward so that it bulges toward the eyes. The back fin has a long base, rounded tips, and apparently inclines toward the rear. The flippers are one fifth the total length, and narrow. There are 11 joints in the second finger in the flipper. The body is cylindrical.

Each whale may yield about 40 gallons of blubber oil and 2½ gallons of head and jaw oil. The whales may appear in schools of 5–40 near the shore, and spouts may rise to a height of 5 feet. When a school approaches a village in their range, it is common for many small boats to put out, circle the animals, and drive them by noise and splashing to their death in the shoals and on beaches. They follow a leader to death.

In the North, these mammals apparently pair in warm waters and bear the young on their return the next year. One English record reports a female in April with 3 unborn young. In September many females have full-term or newly born young. A young pilot whale may be to 6 feet long, half the length of the mother, and may nurse several months.

Harbor Porpoise · *Phocaena phocaena* · Delphinidae

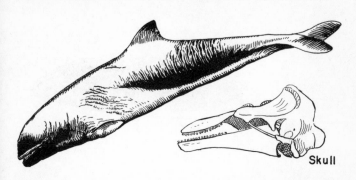

Skull

In *Alice in Wonderland* we read: " 'Will you walk a little faster?' said a whiting to a snail. 'There's a porpoise close behind us, and he's treading on my tail.' " Even if compared to more rapid creatures than snails and whitings, porpoises are indeed speedy. So active are they that when they dive they may first jump clear of the water. When they break water, the top of the head appears first. Their "spouts" are short and inclined rather than straight up. Even if they submerge in a leisurely fashion, they usually show their dorsal fins. They may be found in schools of to 100 swimming in graceful leaps, and are frequently most active before squalls.

Porpoises reach a length of 8 feet, a width of 2½ feet, and a weight of 120 pounds. They are widest between the flippers and the base of the dorsal fin, and lack ridges on their flukes. The eyes are small and have a yellow iris. The ear openings are pinpoint size. They are plain dusky above and paler beneath. The skin is smooth, the back fin low and triangular, and the flippers oval, blunt, and small.

Porpoises are found in many parts of the world, frequently in harbors. They have round mouths with 23–27 teeth on each side of each jaw, and feed on fish.

Porpoises pair in late summer, and 11 months later young to 34 inches long are born. The mother swims on her side as she nurses her young. Porpoises do not survive captivity so well as do some of the dolphins. Respiration rate, 360. Pulse, 150. There is a reported life span of 30 years.

The flesh of porpoises is sold as meat for human consumption. The oil has been used in lamps. The flesh looks like pork but to most persons has a disagreeable flavor. In the Middle Ages it was considered a delicacy and found favor at Lent, probably because the porpoise was considered to be a fish instead of a mammal.

Gray Whale · *Eschrichtius glaucus* · Eschrichtiidae

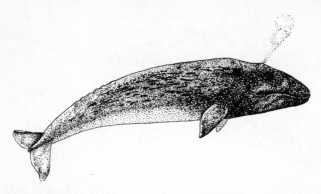

To Californians, this whale is one of the most interesting of mammals, but, like many famous natural-history subjects, it has its ups and downs. In the middle of the nineteenth century, as many as 1,000 gray whales were said to swim by San Diego each day during the southern migration. Then for some years they disappeared completely. They were rediscovered off the coast of Korea and in recent years have made a comeback on our Pacific Coast. Today it is estimated that some 3,000 swim by San Diego each year on their way south. Given the protection they deserve, they may regain their former numbers.

Gray whales are animals of the shallows. Unlike most whales, they can survive being grounded by an outgoing tide. They swim at the rate of 7 miles an hour, surfacing every 7–8 minutes, and spouting to a height of 20 feet. Entire herds may submerge simultaneously, giving credence to the idea that they can communicate with each other through the water.

Gray whales are to 50 feet long, and weigh about 20 tons. They are black but heavily blotched with gray scars, so that the black may be obscure. There is no dorsal fin, only a series of dorsal lumps. The snout is high, and there are 2–4 throat grooves about 15 inches apart and to 6 feet long. Unlike the cetaceans so far considered, this and the remaining species are whalebone whales, which strain out fine food through the whalebone in the mouth. In this species the whalebone is heavy, thick, yellow, to 14 or more inches long, but under 20 inches.

Late in January, young whales to 16 feet or more are born, usually in some quiet cove. The youngster is nursed for 6 months, when it has reached a length of 25 feet and can be independent. The mother defends its calf, even by attacking boats if necessary. Whales get, and deserve, protection from the law. Temperature, 95°–100.4° F.

Finback Whale · *Balaenoptera physalus* · Balaenopteridae

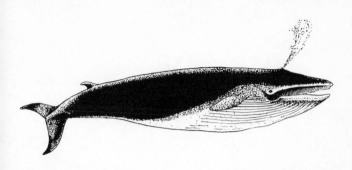

ORIGINALLY all large oceans supported finback whales. They are more abundant in the Atlantic than is the blue whale. They reach a length of 84 feet. A 70-foot animal weighs over 65 tons, with the skeleton weighing 9½ tons; the whalebone 1,000 pounds; the lungs, 2,700 pounds; the heart, 840 pounds. The triangular head, as seen from above, is under one fourth the total length of the animal. Females are longer than the males. The undersides of the flippers and flukes are white. The throat is fluted and the body is ridged toward the tail. The dorsal fin is low. The color is black to dark gray above, lead-colored near the mouth, and white or pale brown beneath.

Finbacks are the fastest of all whales, moving at 26 knots. They may dive 4 times in 15 seconds and submerge for 30 minutes. They can dive to 1,150 feet. They may spout to 20 feet high, 7–12 times in rapid succession. They feed mostly on fish and adult crustaceans (krill). The whalebone is slate-colored, marked with brown, and to 3 feet long, with some 4-foot units that are yellow and slate-colored. The bone is in 370 plates.

Finback whales are pursued relentlessly for their oil and whalebone.

Mating takes place in the warm seas in winter, and a year later 1–2 young, each to 22 feet long, are born. They nurse for 6 months. Males mature in 3 years at 64 feet; females in 3 years at 66 feet. They are full grown by 8 years, in their prime by 10 years, and old at 20 years. They may mate over a 7–8 month period, reaching greatest activity in the Antarctic from May through August. In the south, they may summer in the Antarctic and winter off Africa. One marked animal was taken 2½ years later, 1,900 miles away.

These animals do not show the flukes in diving. A reddish slick may appear where they dive. Their spout is sonorous and to 20 feet high. Body temperature, 94°–101° F.

Blue Whale, Sulphur-bottom Whale, or Rorqual
Balaenoptera musculus · Balaenopteridae

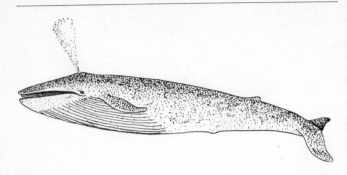

THIS is the largest animal that ever lived. It may reach a length of 109 feet. One 90-foot blue whale had a 45-foot circumference, weighed 150 tons, and had a tongue weighing 3 tons. Females are the larger. Flippers are one seventh the total length. The throat has 80–100 longitudinal grooves and often has a yellowish tinge. The dorsal fin is low and small. General color is bluish, with back and sides the color of corrugated iron. The flippers are white below. The whalebone is black, not slate-colored, as in the finback, and is in about 400 plates. The "sulphur bottom" is caused by diatoms on the underside. The animals have beards of 20–40 hairs.

One blue whale that was marked traveled 500 miles in 88 days, another 300 miles in 42 days. The spout lasts 304 seconds, is single, reaches a height of 49 feet, and produces a loud sound. Blue whales may remain submerged 49 minutes and on emergence can quickly renew 90% of the air in the lungs.

Blue whales winter near the Equator. They formerly migrated to the north and south annually, now mostly to the Antarctic. The food is almost wholly young krill (crustaceans) strained through the whalebone in the mouth. The stomach holds about 1 ton of food.

The speed of these whales is from 12–14 knots. One towed a small vessel, which had its engines reversed, for 7 hours at 8 knots.

Blue whales are of great economic importance, 1 animal yielding 133 barrels of oil and 6 metric tons of red meat, to say nothing of the whalebone and other materials.

Blue whales are probably monogamous, mating underwater in May to August. A year later a 25-foot calf is born that weighs 4 tons, nurses for 7 months, when it has reached a length of 50 feet. At 1 year the female is 56 feet long. At 3 years they are about 77 feet long and sexually mature; at 10–14 years, fully grown. Young born every other year. Temperature, 96.4°–96.6° F. Life span, 50 years.

Humpbacked Whale

Megaptera novaeangliae · Balaenopteridae

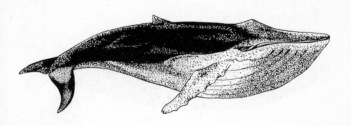

HUMPBACKED whales have short, thick bodies sometimes reaching a length of 75 feet, but averaging 45 feet. There is a short beak and the dorsal fin is represented as a long, low hump. The flippers are long and narrow and are scalloped along the margins at the ends. These whales have what appears to be a large head, which is disfigured with rows of swellings. When the whales dive or "broach," they may leap freely into the air, often falling on their sides. The spout issues from 2 blowholes, forming 1 broad jet if seen from the side. The spout is vertical, nauseating, and to 20 feet high. The whales may remain underwater for 20 minutes and may be found singly or in small schools or "pods." A 45-foot animal may weigh 9,000 pounds and yield 425 pounds of black, 2-foot whalebone. The oil produced is not of the best quality, and it would take 2½ average humpbacked whales to produce the amount of oil an average blue whale would yield. Temperature, 95.2°–100° F.

Humpbacked whales are found in the Pacific from the Bering Sea south to Panama, and in the Atlantic from north of Iceland to Bermuda and Trinidad. They are surprisingly regular in their migrations. They feed on krill strained through the whalebone, and also eat small fish. They have been known to swallow cormorants whole.

Calves are born in the winter months, most in the Northern Hemisphere being born in March, less than 1 year after the mating takes place. The rule is 1 young, measuring 15–16½ feet and weighing between 3,000 and 4,000 pounds. At the end of a year, the calf is 25 feet long, and at the end of the second year 41 feet long. The under parts of the young are black in contrast with the white under parts of the adults. The mother is highly protective of the young and will attack those that interfere with it. The former habit of killing the calf first is now outlawed by international law. The known life span is to 20 years.

Right Whale · *Eubalaena glacialis* · Balaenidae

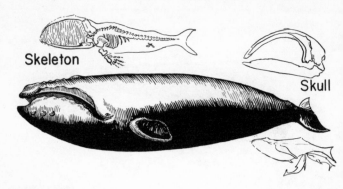

Skeleton

Skull

ECCLESIASTES tells us that the race is not to the swift. Right whales tell us through their record that the race toward survival is not to the slow either. At any rate, these slow, ponderous creatures, which are easy to capture, are now among the rarer whales, whereas formerly they were among the commonest. Through international agreement, these whales are now gradually recovering their abundance, but the greatest boon to their recovery would be the discovery by scientists of substitutes for the products derived from them.

E. glacialis lives in the North Atlantic, *E. sieboldii* in the North Pacific, *E. australis* in the Antarctic. The related bowhead, or Greenland right whale, which lives near the ice, has a lower jaw that bows upward, white chin, and black whalebone. Its head is more than one third the total length. *E. glacialis* is to 70 feet long, has no back fin, no throat grooves, pinpoint-sized external ear, upward-arched lower jaw, and head about one fourth its total length. Its color is black, but 20% of the belly is white. The whalebone is blackish, to 14 feet long, and in 250 plates. In the bowhead there are 360 plates of whalebone.

Right whales spout vertically in a double spout, 1 branch of which is shorter than the other. They show their flukes in diving, and as they submerge expose a large part of the back behind the dorsal fin. They rarely dive to depths beyond 80 feet, but can remain submerged for 80 minutes. They may float on their backs, and when dead sink to the bottom. In the Arctic these whales probably mate in July. In February, a 15-foot calf is born, which is nursed and cared for by a most affectionate mother for 6–12 months—longer than most other whales, although the right whale nurses for a shorter period over all than the related bowhead. Rarely are twins born. Newly-born bowhead calves are blue-gray; young bowheads, blue-black.

ORDER CARNIVORA
(*Dogs, Bears, Weasels, and Cats*)

ANIMALS with usually 5 but sometimes 4 toes on each foot, all toes clawed, and usually having 3 incisors and 1 canine tooth on each side of each jaw, in addition to the molars. Food, primarily animal matter.

Skull

Scat   Tracks
Hind Foot Front Foot

Coyote · *Canis latrans* · Canidae

SINCE a Westerner's success may depend on the growth of grass that feeds both useful cattle and harmful mice, it is difficult to understand why coyotes should be so unpopular. The stomachs of more than 8,000, examined with care, showed that 33% contained rabbits, 25% carrion, 18% rodents, and only 13% sheep and goat meat. The stomachs of 161 "pegleg" or injured coyotes showed 21% rabbits, 21% sheep or goat meat, 35% carrion, and 12% rodents. If these statistics mean anything, an injured coyote is more destructive to man's interests than a healthy one. The winter diet, as shown by examination of more than 2,500 stomachs, indicated 36% carrion, 34% rabbits, 15% rodents, 8% sheep, and 3% deer. A coyote's full meal equals 2 ground squirrels totaling 1¾ pounds.

Coyotes are to 4 feet long from snout to tail tip, one third being the tail. An average male weighs 26 pounds, a female 22 pounds. The ears are conspicuously long and erect, and coyotes, in running, carry their tails low, not high as do the wolves. The nose pads of coyotes are usually under 1 inch wide, being narrower than the wolves'. Coyotes are brown, sprinkled with black and gray. Teeth are: I 1/3; C 1/1; P 4/4; M 2/3. Tracks are: F 3 x 3½, 4; H 3 x 3½, 4. Coyotes can run at 40 miles per hour, often chasing prey in relays but not ordinarily in wolf-like packs. They are about the only animals that can catch and kill destructive jack rabbits. Coyotes may kill deserted newborn horses, cattle, sheep, and goats.

Coyotes have an individual range of 6 square miles, are found in open country from Alaska to Central America and east even to New York and Florida. They probably pair for life, and breed in January. After 60–65 days' gestation, 5–10 blind but furred pups are born. They nurse for 2 weeks, may venture on own at 6 weeks. They run with parents until fall. Breed first winter. Life span, 14 years.

131

Gray Wolf or Timber Wolf · *Canis lupus griseus* · Canidae

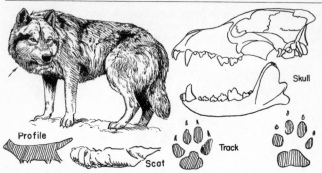

Profile

Skull

Scat

Track

THE word "wolf" has many connotations. We "wolf" our food, are "lone wolves." Wolves "have eyes that glare in total darkness." There are werewolves that cannot be killed, yet wait indefinitely to destroy their victims. There are "wolves in sheep's clothing" and "wolves" that haunt the streets and parks of our cities. And then there's the Big Bad Wolf. In spite of these maligning influences, wolves somehow have managed to survive in many parts of the world where man has lived the longest and has hunted them ruthlessly.

Gray wolves may measure 64 inches, including a 16-inch tail, the bitches measuring 56 inches with a 12-inch tail. They stand to 27 inches at the shoulder. Males may weigh 150 pounds and females 80 pounds. They have slanting eyes, curved canine teeth, and dense underfur. Fur is gray, sprinkled with black. Legs and under parts are yellowish white. They have hair between the toes. Teeth are: I 3/3; C 1/1; P 4/4; M 2/3. Tracks are: F 4 x 5½, 4; H 4 x 5½, 4. Unlike foxes and coyotes, wolves may run in packs of great size. Temperature, 105° F.

Wolves rarely eat vegetable matter. One large wolf can alone bring down a large steer and kill it. Wolves can survive on 1 meal a week. Packs kill deer, cattle, sheep, horses, and other animals .and eat them on the spot. Occasionally food may be stored by burying it. A pack may range over several hundred square miles of territory. Originally wolves ranged over most of North America, but the gray wolf is now found in the United States probably only in Michigan and Wisconsin. The fur durability of wolf pelts is 50% that of otter. In spite of their potential destructiveness, wolves are superb representatives of the carnivore group and should not be exterminated.

Wolves probably mate for life, breed in January–March. After 63 days' gestation, 3–13 blind young are born in den prepared by female. Eyes open at 9 days. Nurse 6–8 weeks. They run with family a year and in mixed packs at different seasons. Life expectancy, 15 years. Serve as check to some grazing animals.

External Parts of a Dog
(See p. 134 for index to dog section.)

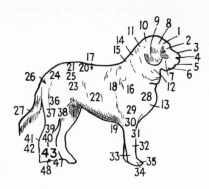

To judge a dog and to understand descriptions it is necessary to know the names of the external parts. These are shown above, as follows:

Head: forehead	1	Croup or rump	24
Eye and eyelash	2	Hip	25
Crest of nose	3	Tail root	26
Nose	4	Tail	27
Mouth and upper lip	5	Shoulder	28
Flews	6	Upper arm	29
Cheeks	7	Elbow	30
Ear	8	Forearm	31
Ear flap	9	Wrist or carpus	32
Back of head	10	Metacarpus	33
Nape or poll	11	Toes	34
Throat	12	Claws	35
Dewlap	13	Hip joint	36
Crest	14	Upper thigh	37
Withers	15	Stifle of knee	38
Upper chest	16	Lower thigh	39
Back	17	Tarsal joint	40
Chest	18	Heel	41
Under chest	19	Hock	42
Loins	20	Metatarsus	43
Cross	21	Toes	44
Abdomen	22	Claws	45
Hindquarters	23		

Height is measured to the shoulder.
Where weight does not vary greatly in the sexes, but 1 weight is given.

Domestic Dog · *Canis familiaris* · Canidae

WITHOUT apology we devote 50 pages of this book to domestic dogs. The average man probably learns more about the feeding, breeding, and behavior habits of mammals by observing dogs and men than from observing any other mammals. Here, then, is specific information about the major breeds of dogs and general information about all dogs.

This directory will help:

Pointer · *Canis familiaris intermedius* · Canidae

POINTER and Dalmatian were developed from Italian spaniel, a descendant of Samoyed. First breed created primarily for stand-

134

ing at game. Older breed than setters. Have great speed; work for strangers. Males weigh 55–70 pounds; females, 45–60 pounds. Little fat. Males stand 23–25 inches at shoulder; females, 21–23 inches. Head clean cut. Skull broad and well arched. Muzzle long, neat. Eyes usually dark brown, good-natured, and alert. Ears broad, set high on head and always fall flat to the head. Neck long, downward sloping, with distinctly muscular nape. Body strong, with wide hips falling to tail, and slightly arched loins. Tail held high; slender, pointed; two fifths total length of animal. Legs strongly boned; front legs conspicuously straight. Skin close, tight, and firm. Hair short, rather stiff, lies flat. Color usually white with solid areas of black, liver, or lemon.

In competition, must have good lungs and strong legs, good nose and sight, and always be energetic. May point at age of 2 months. German short-haired pointer is cross of Spanish pointer and bloodhound with English foxhound.

Retriever (Labrador)

Canis familiaris inostranzewi · Canidae

DEVELOPED in Newfoundland, not Labrador. Formerly popular in England. Valuable in retrieving birds, particularly from water and ice. Should be strong, active, alert, and always willing to act promptly. Males weigh 60–75 pounds; females, usually 55–70 pounds. Males, 22½–24½ inches high; females, 21½–23½ inches. Head wide, with pronounced brow, strong jaws, and wide nose. Eyes medium sized, brown, black, or yellow. Good-tempered. Ears set low and hang rather close to head; not commonly large. Neck of medium length, joined to long, sloping shoulders. Have wide, deep chest and long, unusually strong loins. Tail round, well haired, thick at base, unfeathered, tapering to tip. Hind legs are powerful; feet well padded, compact, and strong. Coat dense, thick, firm, unfeathered, of short, straight hairs. Usually black, with no white favored. Related breeds include golden retriever (golden brown), Chesapeake (brown to tan), curly-coated (oldest of breeds and flat-coated, of American origin).

Males should have great stamina. Retrievers are usually friendly with acquaintances of the family, and ordinarily obedient to masters.

Setter (English) · *Canis familiaris intermedius* · Canidae

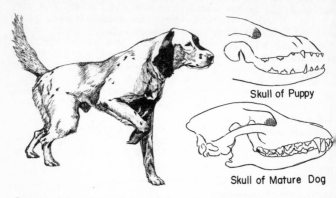

Skull of Puppy

Skull of Mature Dog

ORIGIN from Spanish spaniel, Italian spaniel, and Samoyed stock. In U. S. before 1875. Used as field-trial, shooting, and show dogs. Setters are possibly 400 years old as a breed or group. Weight of good English setter male is normally 55–75 pounds. Height, male, 23–25 inches; female, to 24 inches. Head long, narrow, with angled brows and square-tipped muzzle. Eyes usually brown, bright, friendly, and always intelligent. Ears set low, close to head, silky and soft, always drooping. Neck arched, long and lean, but solid, and leading into deep chest. Broad shoulders, strong back, and widely spread hips. Tail straight, well feathered, silky, not curled above back line. Thighs of hind legs muscular; forelegs also muscular and strong. Coat flat, not curly or wooly, with legs lightly feathered. Color white and black, liver, lemon, or tan, but largely white. Need excellent stamina, good nose, and intelligence.

Friendly and excellent pet, but needs space for adequate exercise. Related breeds include Irish setter, basically golden; and Gordon setter, which is black, black and tan, chestnut, or mahogany.

Cocker Spaniel · *Canis familiaris intermedius* · Canidae

LIKE springer, developed from Norfolk field and Italian spaniels and Samoyed. Superior pet, bench, obedience, field dog. Smallest sporting breed. Used mostly for birds like woodcock, hence name. Able hunter. Between 22 and 28 inches high. Apparently height is not considered as character in judging. Head broad, deep, and well rounded; smooth, square muzzle. Eyes usually dark, brown to black or hazel, appealing, round, full. Hanging ears may be extended to nostril tip, have long, silky hairs. Neck long enough to allow nose to reach ground easily in the

field. Height at withers equals length from withers to tail. Short body. Tail extends on line with back, not curled, commonly wagging. Legs well boned; front legs straight and hind legs strong. Coat flat or waved, dense. Feathered ears, chest, legs. Color black or tan, but not white, at least for bench dogs.

An alert, friendly, persistent hunter and pet, obedient and willing. English cocker is larger, weighing 26–34 pounds, and springer (page 138) is still larger. Cockers have long rated tops in America among registered breeds.

Classes of Dogs
The Sporting Dog Class

FOR centuries dogs were bred for particular purposes. For convenience in judging the relative merit of individual dogs, classes have been established by the various organizations interested in maintaining standards and in developing the breeds that make up these classes. In these pages we have emphasized points used in judging breeds of dogs.

Possibly the Sporting-Dog Class is a misnomer, since dogs in the hound classes and in the terrier classes are also used in sport and in taking game. However, this name has been agreed upon to cover the first 7 groups of breeds to which we choose to give special attention:

These represent the more common sporting-dog breeds.

Irish Water Spaniel

Canis familiaris intermedius · Canidae

DERIVED from poodle, Spanish spaniel, Italian spaniel, and Samoyed. An excellent pet and superior hunter of ducks and similar game and a good watchdog when given responsibility intelligently by master. Males weigh from 45–65 pounds; females usually the lighter. Height varies from 21–24 inches; females slightly the smaller. Head high domed; showy topknot of short, closely matted curls. Eyes small, dark brown to chestnut, and appearing to be intelligent. Ears set low and hang down closely to the cheeks; very rarely raised. Neck long, arching, held erect, and strong-looking. Body barrel-shaped; powerful shoulders, deep chest, broad back. Tail long, slender, and curving upward. Front legs spreading; broad feet. Hind legs powerful and strong. Coat of tight ringlets, heavier on front of legs. Color usually solid, rather dark liver, alike above and below. Eager, persistent, hard-working, bold, and obviously intelligent.

The Irish water spaniel has been a most popular dog with sportsmen as a duck retriever, but is being replaced by larger, more powerful, and more attractive dogs such as the retrievers.

Springer Spaniel · *Canis familiaris intermedius* · Canidae

DEVELOPED, like the cocker, from Norfolk, field, and Italian spaniels. Ancestry ultimately goes back to Samoyed. Used as hunter, pet, and watchdog. Uses nose ably in hunting upland game birds. Males weigh 42–50 pounds; females, up to 47 pounds. Height, from 18–18½ inches in both sexes. Dignified head with deep muzzle, strong jaws. Eyes hazel to darker, medium in size, alert, and almost always kindly. Ears long and wide, but not longer than to nose tip when held forward. Neck moderately long and muscular and often slightly arched. Shoulders wide and heavy, sloping from a deep chest. Front legs straight. Feet broad, well padded, with toes well feathered. Coat of medium texture and length, and either flat or slightly wavy. Color liver, white, black, or roan, or with these mixed in 2 colors.

A hard-working, persistent field dog, strong enough to work in thick brush for a long time without tiring unduly, friendly, aggressive. Appreciative of praise, but often of the 1-man type. There are 2 varieties, the English and the Welsh.

The Life History of Dogs

DOGS are obviously promiscuous. From 53–71 days after the male, or *dog,* breeds with the female, or *bitch,* 1–22 blind and deaf *puppies* are born. At 9 days, eyes open; hear at 10–12 days; nurse, 4–8 weeks, and are able to breed within year.

Dogs can inseminate bitches at any time after maturity, but bitches often are in heat but once a year, the period in heat lasting 1–3 weeks. Puberty is supposed to begin at 7–10 months. Copulation may last 1–2 hours.

Usually the appearance of the teeth is as follows: *milk teeth:* 1st and 2nd incisors, 4–5 weeks; 3rd incisors, 4 weeks; canines, 3–4 weeks; 1st and 2nd premolars, 4–5 weeks; 3rd and 4th premolars, 3–4 weeks. *Permanent teeth;* incisors and canines, 4–5 months; premolars, 5–6 months; 1st molars, 4 months; upper 2nd molars, 5–6 months, lower 2nd molars, 4½–5 months; 3rd molars, 6–7 months.

The mother alone usually cares for the young. Body temperature, 98°–105° F. Respiration rate, 580. Pulse rate from 70–130; newborn, 160–180. May go feral and lose bark. Bitches do not necessarily breed first year. Life span, to 34 years.

Weimeraner · *Canis familiaris intermedius* · Canidae

BRED from German pointer, pointer, Spanish and Italian spaniels. Developed in Germany for use on estates. Fearless, alert, active, obedient, and most hardy. Is a good hunter. In spite of size and determined nature, is good with children and loyal to master. Weight, 55–85 pounds, depending on age, sex, and inheritance. Males, 25–27 inches high; females, 23–25 inches. Head medium long. Foreface straight, clean-cut, with tight skin. Eyes light amber, gray, or blue-gray, often black in excitement. Ears medium sized, set high, slightly folded but drooping. Neck well moulded, round, and set firmly on compact shoulders. Body moderately long, solid, straight, with deep chest, clean-cut loins. Tail straight and usually docked to be about 6 inches at maturity. Legs strong, straight, and muscular, with webbed feet and firm pads. Coat smooth, sleek, close all over, and uniform in density and texture. Color usually gray throughout, appearing remarkably uniform. Awkward gait. Needs good range for exercise. May work hard on land and in water to 15 years of age.

The Hound Class
(Canidae)

HOUNDS have been bred primarily for running down game or, in the case of the dachshund, for going into holes after it. They have good endurance, a superior sense of smell, a good fighting spirit. Many have pleasing voices when on the trail, their baying permitting hunters to follow where they might otherwise become lost. Some may merely tree the intended game or hold it at bay until the hunter or stronger fighters of the pack catch up.

Afghan Hound · *Canis familiaris leineri* · Canidae

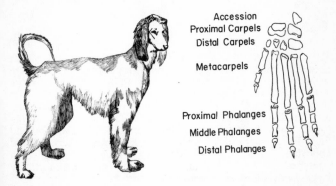

DEVELOPED primarily from Saluki for hunting by sight, the Afghan hound dates from before 4000 B.C. It is the progenitor of most hounds and terriers. Alert, powerful. Good hillside hunter, at its best in brushlands. Standard weight: males, about 60 pounds; females, about 50 pounds. Average height, males, 27 inches; females, 25 inches. Head long, carried high and well, crowned with long, silky topknot. Uses eyes instead of nose in hunting, always watching for movements. Ears long and silky haired; reach nearly to nose when stretched. Neck strong, long, and arched to the long, sloping shoulders. Body strong; usually has powerful loins and pronounced hipbones. Tail curved and carried high, but preferably not recurved to the back. Forelegs straight and long; feet heavily haired. Powerful rear. Coat of long, uneven, silky hair that ordinarily looks ragged. May be found in many colors, but white is considered undesirable. Runs with head and tail high, indicating game presence by wagging tail. Highly companionable. When running, usually does so at a gallop. Became popular in England and Europe after World War I, and returning soldiers brought Afghan hounds to America from Old World as pets and as hunters.

Basset · *Canis familiaris leineri* · Canidae

DEVELOPED, like the beagle, from St. Hubert hound, sleuth hound, Afghan, Saluki, and Egyptian greyhound, for use where scent is important. Brought to England from France before 1866. Bassets are used either in packs or as individuals. Best of companions. Weight, 25–40 pounds, depending on age, sex, and condition. Height, 11–15 inches; females usually being lower. Large head, narrow skull, wrinkled forehead, and sad face. Eyes usually deep, sunken, dark brown, mournful, and appealing. Ears long, reaching beyond end of nose when stretched forward. Neck powerful and seemingly abnormally large. Body short, very stout, solid, with heavy, sloping shoulders. Hindquarters are unusually powerful, and legs are short. Front legs may be crooked or half crooked. Feet are massive. Coat close, rather uniform, with medium-fine hair on loose skin. Color not ordinarily important in judging; usually much white present.

Stamina is expected and is remarkably well developed in packs. Affectionate, intelligent, and as a rule 1-man dogs. Apparently lack alertness of beagle, but may at times have a better nose for game.

Beagle · *Canis familiaris leineri* · Canidae

ANCESTRY like that of basset, with St. Hubert's hound immediate source. Beagles hunt well in packs or singly, having fine voice, excellent nose, and good spirit. Exceptionally good house dogs, clean and affectionate. Might be considered miniature foxhounds so far as weight is concerned. Height in 2 groups: 1, under 13 inches; other, 13–15 inches. Head fairly long, domed, with broad cranium. Loud, excited voice. Eyes hazel to brown, set apart, gentle, and unusually appealing. Ears set low, moderately long, close to head, never erectable. Throat full, free from skin folds. Neck stout and strong. Slop-

ing shoulders, deep, broad chest, and strong loins. Tail, held moderately high but not over back, is short for a hound. Legs straight. Hips and thighs strong. Feet always compact and firm. Coat close, hard, and uniform throughout; easily kept clean. Any color common to hounds is acceptable to the usual judge.

Have exceptional stamina and make beautiful sight working in pack. Intelligent dogs, used mostly in hunting game that seeks safety in flight, such as rabbits, foxes, raccoons, but not game that stands, as do pheasants and quail.

Uses of Dogs as Hunters of Game

MAN evaluates most things in terms of their usefulness to him. The uses of dogs to men are so varied, so real, and so extensive that we can only touch on them here.

Aside from the companionship man gets from dogs, we must mention the role dogs have played in helping man capture wild animals of many sorts, and in some cases in protecting man from wild animals. In hunting, men use dogs, such as hounds of many types, to follow the scent of escaping game; to locate hiding game by scent, as with the dogs classed as sporting dogs, or by digging out game and other animals; and to hold, worry, or fight game until man can enter the fray, as with the terriers. Another group has been most useful in retrieving game, such as ducks, from the water. This experience of dogs and men working in harmony in the taking of game has built some of the closest relationships imaginable, and the field trials in which dogs compete against each other for excellence in this, and obedience classes, are always challenging and stimulating for all involved. So specialized has this work become that we have not only "bird dogs," but dogs trained to find particular kinds of birds, and this goes for mammals, such as fox, deer, and elk.

143

Bloodhound · *Canis familiaris leineri* · Canidae

LIKE foxhound, developed from sleuth hound, Afghan, and Saluki. Bloodhounds are nose trailers of exceptional ability. One known to have followed successfully a trail 100 hours old, another a trail for 150 miles. Weight, 80–110 pounds; males, to 110; females, to 100 pounds. Height, 23–27 inches; males average 26, females, 24 inches. Forehead deeply wrinkled. Muzzle to 1 foot long. Foreface long. Eyes hazel, deeply sunken, kindly and usually sad in expression. Ears thin, soft, long, drooping, and flexible. Neck long, reaching to heavy, highly muscular shoulders. Chest extends down between legs. Back and loins strong. Tail rather typical of hounds—long, straight, slender, little curved. Hind legs strong. Forelegs straight, stout, and solid. Feet strong. Rear is heavy. Coat close, soft, short-haired, rather coarse but not harsh. Color usually black and tan, ordinarily with black predominating.

Stamina remarkable. Persistent, docile, shy, affectionate dogs. Gait elastic. Baying deep and far-reaching. Bloodhounds have found many lost persons and escaped criminals, and probably have done more in this field than any other breed of dogs.

Dachshund · *Canis familiaris leineri* · Canidae

EXISTED in fifteenth century. Descended from Afghan and Saluki hounds. Dachshunds are good field dogs, and among the best for badgers and other burrow game. Good, persistent trailers, with excellent noses and voices. Heavy variety, 14.3–15.4 pounds; dwarf, from 7.7–8.8 pounds. Height apparently does not figure too strongly in judging. Head tapers uniformly to nose; jaws and teeth strong, powerful. Eyes of an appealing, heart-warming nature at all times. Ears near top of head, rounded, wide; forward edges on cheeks. Neck long, muscular, and clean cut. Body long, low, sturdy, muscular, straight, and round. Tail tapers to point, not curled or heavily haired any-

where. Legs short, stout, but active, and apparently tireless in field. Coat: short-haired, wire-haired, and long-haired varieties occur. Color red, black, red and yellow, black and tan, or chocolate.

Confident, courageous little dogs. Always clean, odorless, gay, playful, and dependable. Have been used to go into burrows after game or to serve as field dogs in brush, which because of their small size they can readily enter.

How Dogs Help Men See and Fight

DOGS sense many things so much more keenly than do men that it is not surprising that men have used dogs to help them know what is occurring in their environment. In war, dogs serve as sentinels and scouts. In peace, they serve as alarm clocks and as burglar and fire alarms. In the past, before such modern devices as radar were available, dogs were used to detect approaching airplanes, which they could do long before man could himself. When men have lost the sense of sight, the Seeing Eye dogs have helped them regain confidence in their future and have saved them from what seemed hopeless despair.

Countless dogs have fought to the death in the interests of the men with whom they were associated. The lives of innumerable men have been saved by dogs that have fought off threatening bulls, boars, bears, and other beasts. Dogs have also been trained to fight each other in pits to win wagers for their masters, but this, fortunately, is becoming a thing of the past.

Dogs have done remarkable work for men by helping them manage other animals, as in herding sheep and cattle, and in finding lost persons and criminals. Often these services call for great intelligence.

145

American Foxhound · *Canis familiaris leineri* · Canidae

DEVELOPED from Afghan hound, Saluki, and Egyptian greyhound. Brought to America for sport as early as 1650. Used
mostly in packs to pursue game that seeks safety in running,
particularly foxes, but also bears. Weight not considered a factor in show judging. Height: males, 22–25 inches; females, 21–
24 inches. Should have straight, square muzzle, broad cranium,
and strong jaws. Eyes brown or often hazel; large, well separated, gentle, pleading. Ears soft, low, long, nearly reaching
nose tip; rounded at the tips. Throat should be strong, of medium length, without loose flesh. Sloping shoulders; body clean
and muscular, with strong loin muscles. Tail set moderately
high, curved slightly upward, but not over back. Legs strong
and muscular, clean cut. Feet close and firm; good pads. Coat
close, hard, compact, of medium length, with rather coarse
hair. Color may be anything acceptable for the hounds in general, and is not considered in judging. Real foxhound merit
lies in behavior rather than in bench points.

Foxhounds must be fast runners, with great endurance; fearless fighters but friendly under other circumstances. Most popular, of course, with those who "ride to the hounds."

Greyhound · *Canis familiaris leineri* · Canidae

BREED established by 4000 B.C. from borzoi, Afghan, Saluki,
and Egyptian greyhound. Greyhounds use sight, not scent, to
follow prey, and can easily outrun most game. Standard weight:
males, 67–70 pounds; females, 60–65 pounds. Height, 25–26
inches, is apparently not a factor considered in show judging.
Muzzle of good length. Head long, slender. Jaws exceptionally
strong. Eyes dark, bright, intelligent, and sparkling; fiery when
in action. Ears small, of firm texture, usually folded, but may
be partly pricked. Shoulders oblique, muscular, and supple.
Chest deep but slender. Body long, slender to rear. Back square.
Forelegs straight and well muscled in upper parts; hind legs

long. Coat short, smooth, close, uniform; of relatively fine sleek hair. Color is not important as compared with behavior. Have remarkable stamina for relatively short time; may run to 525 yards in about 29 seconds in competition. Now chiefly used in racing after a mechanical rabbit on a course, before a wagering crowd. Formerly used in packs to overtake and delay game for sturdier dogs that caught up and took on the work of holding or fighting.

What a Dog's Nose Knows

WHILE men can undoubtedly hear and see some things that dogs cannot, few, if any, would question the ability of the average dog to make better use of his nose than man can make of his. True, some dogs have poorer noses than others, but the poorest dog probably has a keener sense of smell than any man.

The ability of dogs to use their noses effectively is probably best represented in the hounds. One bloodhound helped locate more than 2,500 wanted persons. By frequent urination, dogs leave trails of their own which other dogs may follow by scent. So keen is this sense in some dogs that it has been demonstrated that a dog may be able to detect the difference between pure water and that in which there is 1 teaspoonful of salt to 13 gallons of pure water, 1 part of acetic acid to 1 million parts of water, or 1 teaspoonful of sulphuric acid to 10,000,000 teaspoonfuls of water. Apparently odors of plant origin are much less significant to dogs than are those of animal origin.

147

Norwegian Elkhound
Canis familiaris intermedius · Canidae

BREED is some 5,000 years old, and was derived probably from Samoyed stock. Elkhounds are popular as companion dogs, but bred for hunting by scent. Hunt elk, deer, bear, otter, birds; reputed to be able to scent elk 3 miles. Weight not considered as an element in show judging. Average height: male, to 20½ inches; female, to 18 inches. Face intelligent, fearless, with no loose skin. Eyes dark brown, not protruding, always alert, usually kindly. Ears medium-sized, set high on head, may be erected and directed. Neck should be medium, strong, compact, with no excessive loose skin. Body solid, straight, powerful, compact. Stomach not drawn up. Tail set high, rather tightly curled to one side, thickly haired. Forelegs straight and strong; hind legs strong and tireless. Coat thick, hard, of medium length, with body hairs usually longest. Color gray and black, with lighter chest, stomach, and legs; face dark gray. Tops in stamina when hunting. Bold, courageous fighters, able to hold powerful game until arrival of hunter, and to obey commands. One of the best breeds for use in obedience classes, and an ideal family dog of the 1-man type, that can discourage strangers.

Saluki · *Canis familiaris leineri* · Canidae

POSSIBLY the oldest of all breeds, derived from Egyptian greyhound. Progenitor of borzoi, Afghan, and greyhound. Great family dogs and protectors of children. Salukis hunt mainly by sight and marvelous speed. Weight not usually important in judging the individual's merit. Height: males, 23–28 inches; females somewhat smaller. Head long, narrow, not domed or fleshy, strong jawed. Eyes dark hazel, large and oval, but not prominent; kindly, alert. Ears long, silky, hanging close to cheek, somewhat movable. Neck long, narrow, supple, reason-

ably straight, and not fleshy. Deep, narrow chest; back long and rather broad. Forelegs straight and strong; hind legs bent. Gait commonly a gallop. Coat "smooth" or "rough," but soft and silky, or woolly on the forward part of the back. Color may be white, fawn, gray, brownish red, golden, or mixed. Have great stamina. Trained to join in pursuit of small mammals being hunted by falcons, and to hold quarry until arrival of master. Have good nose as well as good eyes. Make good watchdogs, as they will give warning of the approach or presence of a stranger, but do not make independent, aggressive attacks on people or animals.

The Hearing and Vision of Dogs

THE excellent hearing and vision of dogs are highly useful not only to them but also to their masters. The sound of ordinary human speech is generally considered to be about 2,000 cycles per second (c.p.s.). Man normally can hear sounds ranging from 20 to 20,000 c.p.s. Middle C on the piano is 256 c.p.s.

It is doubtful whether dogs can hear sounds pitched lower than those audible to man, but while man can hear sounds up to 20,000 c.p.s., it is certain that dogs can hear up to 30,000 c.p.s., and it has been stated that they can hear up to 100,000 c.p.s. While man's hearing is most acute at 2,000 c.p.s., that of dogs is most acute up to 4,000 c.p.s. Also dogs can locate the direction of sounds better than man can.

The eyes of such breeds as greyhounds and borzoi are highly sensitive to motion. Some dogs that can see stationary objects at 600 yards can detect the same objects in motion at 900 yards. Whereas man's vision extends only 180 degrees, that of dogs extends 250 degrees. Man's stereoscopic vision, however, is better than the dog's. While dogs are probably color blind, they have good ability to recognize variations in brightness.

A LITTLE greyhound descended, like the great Dane, from the Italian greyhound and Saluki. Developed in England in middle of nineteenth century as poor man's racing dog. Whippets are good family dogs, particularly because of small size and short hair. Also good ratters and experts in track racing. Weight is not considered as important in show judging. Height: males, 19–22 inches; females, 18–21 inches. Head long, lean, but relatively wide between ears. Nose black. Eyes large, dark hazel, keen, alert, intelligent, and kind. Ears small, slightly pricked, thrown back and slightly folded. Neck should be long, slender, muscular, widening gradually to shoulders. Strong back, slender to rear; shoulders long and flat. Tail long and tapering, carried no higher than top of back when dog is in motion. Legs straight, long, and slender; hind legs have long, flat muscles. Coat close, smooth, firm, uniform, with little or no loose flesh. Color varies greatly with individual preferences—red, black, white, brindle, fawn, blue, or mixed. Animals judged on performance. Can cover 200 yards in less than 12 seconds—about 35 miles per hour. May bring as high as $4,000 as racers.

Borzoi or Russian Wolfhound

Canis familiaris leineri · Canidae

DEVELOPED.with greyhound from Saluki and ultimately from the Egyptian greyhound. Originally considered the pet of Russian royalty, and because of speed and power was used in chasing hares, wolves, and game. Standard weight: males, 75–105 pounds; females, up to 80 pounds. Height, males, 28–31 inches; females, 26–29 inches. Head long, narrow, slightly domed. Jaws long, deep, powerful. Eyes, set obliquely and with dark lids, are intelligent, quiet, soft. Ears small, firm; normally lie back on neck slightly, but are raised at attention. Neck slightly arched, clean, powerful, shorter than in greyhound. Body narrow, deep; sloping shoulders; back rises at loins. Forelegs

straight and slender; hind legs long, muscular, and powerful. Tail long and carried normally in a low-rising, easy curve. Coat long and silky, flat or curly, and feathered on rump region. Color white with yellow, tan, gray, brown, lemon, or brindled.

Temperament is quiet and behavior dignified and graceful. Borzois have great courage and sense, making good companions and hunters, particularly of the larger forms of game that seek safely in flight.

Dogs as Sources of Power

ON many a farm one may still find remnants of the treadmills that used to be operated by horses, cattle, or even by huge dogs to provide power for churning butter and doing other work now accomplished much more efficiently by electricity.

Powerful dogs have given and are giving more direct service, however, as beasts of burden, as draft animals, and in other ways. In war, dogs have frequently served as carriers of ammunition to outposts difficult to reach. Similarly they have carried medicines to the wounded, food and water to the lost, and duffel on expeditions over difficult terrain. In many a home the dog has served as a "horse" to youngsters whose weight was considerable so far as the dog was concerned.

As draft animals, dogs have of course been especially useful in drawing sledges in Arctic areas (Jack London dramatized this most effectively in his *Call of the Wild*) and in pulling light carts in Old World countries.

In a great many cases, too, dogs have actually rescued human beings from danger in fire, flood, and other calamities. For these examples of directly applied power, man is duly appreciative.

151

The Working-Dog Class

THE working-dog class includes dogs that work their muscles, their heads, and their jaws. They may or may not have superior ability to follow a trail. Some are suited for working in water, others in snow, and others in a variety of places. Voice not important in judging.

Boxer · *Canis familiaris inostranzewi* · Canidae

LIKE schnauzer, developed from mastiff, alaunt, and Tibetan mastiff. Boxers are used as work dogs and have proven highly useful in war situations. Also valuable as intelligent pets and pit fighters. Weight: males, 60–70 pounds; females, slightly less. Height: males, 22–24 inches; females, 21–23 inches. Clean, dark face with blunt muzzle and no deep wrinkles. Eyes dark, directed forward, round, alert, intelligent, bright. Ears relatively small, erect; frequently trimmed to conform. Neck round, strong, erect from shoulders, distinctly muscular. Body square, compact, solid; sloping shoulders and deep chest. Tail docked almost invariably to a relatively short stub. Legs trunklike, straight, strong; hind legs inclined forward. Coat smooth, tight, shiny, of short, rather rough, stiff hairs. Color fawn, yellow, dark red and yellow, or almost black. Great stamina and much speed for dogs of their build.

Boxers are highly courageous. While they have a forbidding appearance, they are usually kindly with humans whom they know, particularly with children. They begin fighting with front feet; hence their name.

Collie · *Canis familiaris metris-optimae* · Canidae

ORIGINATED before 1800 from Persian shepherd, like German shepherd and Old English sheep dog. Progenitor of border collie and Shetland sheep dog. Most dependable herder. Weight, from 50–60 pounds, but behavior is most important in judging. Height: males, 22–24 inches; females, about the same. Head is slender and light, wedge-shaped, lean, never massive. Eyes clear, bright, almond-shaped, with plainly arched brows. Ears mobile, pricked to break forward at about the middle. Neck broad, strong, and heavily haired, particularly below. Body straight, muscular, with massive shoulders, sloping hips. Tail heavily haired, carried low but with a turned-up tip. Legs straight, with forelegs heavily feathered to rear; feet small. Coat abundant except on head and legs, with long hair on surface. Color yellow, tan, white, or blue. Coat double: inner coat soft and woolly, outer coat has harsh, lighter hairs. Collies occur in both smooth and rough forms, which are similar except in coat.

Shetland sheep dog ("sheltie" or "keltie") stands 12–15 inches high.

All collies rank high in obedience competition. They are hardy in severe weather, as required for herding.

German Police Dog or German Shepherd
Canis familiaris metris-optimae · Canidae

LIKE collie and Old English sheep dog, derived from Persian shepherd. Bred as work dogs, watchdogs, herders of large domestic animals, police dogs, and, more recently, for use as Seeing Eye dogs. Weight: males, 75–85 pounds; females, 60–70 pounds. Height: males, 25 inches; females, 23 inches. Head clean cut, strong, pointed, with long muzzle; jaws strong. Eyes medium-sized, almond-shaped, dark, keen, composed. Ears moderate in size, pointed. Pups raise ears at 4–6 months. Neck strong, compact, muscular, rather erect, well covered with hair. Animal should be longer than tall. Body is solid, but heaviest forward. Tail is bushy; has a slight saber curve at rest, but is raised in action. Legs strong, muscular; forelegs straight; hind legs inclined forward. Coat is double, providing protection against weather and insects. Color: black, brindle, and gray, with black emphasized above and on head. Almost tireless dogs of tremendous vigor. Fearless, intelligent, self-confident. Not ordinarily hostile, unless necessary for protection of associates. Gait is largely a trot. German shepherds make superior actors, war dogs, police dogs, and Seeing Eye dogs.

Doberman Pinscher
Canis familiaris inostranzewi · Canidae

DERIVED from Manchester and schnauzer, bulldog, mastiff, and Tibetan mastiff. Dobermans were formerly used as work dogs in Europe. Capable of much work for size, because of strength. Medium-weight dogs for size. Weight not factor in show judging. Height: males, 26–28 inches; females, 24–26 inches. Head a long, blunt wedge. Jaws powerful. Cheeks flat. Lips close. Eyes almond-shaped, brown, alert, intelligent, not always friendly. Ears erect, usually cropped to form forward-pointing triangles. Neck upright, muscular, and somewhat arched; heaviest at base. Body square, muscular, compact; relatively short

back. Tail straight but usually docked very short. Seen from front, legs are straight; hind legs inclined forward. Coat short-haired, smooth, thick, sleek, and unusually clean. Color: black, brown, or blue, but usually in dark shades.

Doberman Pinschers have great endurance and speed. They appear proud and elegant, and are very popular as alert watch-dogs of the 1-man or 1-family type. They do not ordinarily make friends with strangers quickly, and sometimes never.

Dogs in War

WITH the advent of war a new usefulness for dogs quickly becomes apparent. Fortunately they can be trained to differentiate between a friend and a foe. Their greatest usefulness, however, lies in their ability to detect the approach of strangers when this would be impossible to man alone. They can also be trained to carry messages, medicine, and water over difficult terrain. The importance of dogs' role as companions to men in misery should not be overlooked or underestimated. They have proven exceptionally useful to medical teams seeking to find men who have been wounded and may have crawled to protective cover.

Germany was the first country in modern times to make great use of dogs in war. In World War I she used about 30,000 war dogs. In World War II she used some 200,000. Entering the war late, the United States used only about 20,000. Ever since the war, dogs have been useful to military men, particularly those who have lost their sight and become dependent on Seeing Eye dogs to help them lead a somewhat normal life.

155

Great Dane · *Canis familiaris intermedius* · Canidae

PROBABLY developed from greyhound, Saluki, and Egyptian greyhound. Crossed with mastiff, the great Dane was involved in developing bulldog, boxer, and schnauzer. Ancestry believed to have been traced to about 3,000 B.C. Strangely enough, not of Danish, but of German origin. Great Danes have been important work dogs. Weight not usually factor in show judging. Height: males, 30–37 inches; females, over 28 inches. Head majestic, with full, square jaws and generally dignified pose. Eyes medium-sized, dark, intelligent, with well-developed eyebrows. Ears pricked forward, erect, rather large, movable, pointed. Neck medium, strong, erect, in vertical line from throat to toes. Body and shoulders heavy, compact, but not bulky. Tail long, slender, pointed, and drooping, but upcurving at end. Legs strong and muscular. Haunches strong but not heavy. Color: brindle, black, blue, fawn, harlequin, or golden yellow. Coat close and short. Have remarkable strength and stamina. Formerly vicious, but now a kindly breed with great affection for home and masters. Used at one time in boar hunting, in which courage, strength, and intelligence were needed.

Great Pyrenees · *Canis familiaris inostranzewi* · Canidae

DEVELOPED, like alaunt, from Tibetan mastiff, Great Pyrenees are among forebears of St. Bernard, Newfoundland, and the retrievers. First brought to America by Lafayette in 1824, but not recognized as a breed by dog fanciers in America until 1933. Developed as 1-family dogs, as shepherds, and as protectors of home and of stock. Used as work dogs sometimes. Males weigh 100–125 pounds; females, 90–115 pounds. Height: males, 27–32 inches; females, 25–29 inches. Head large, some 11 inches from dome to tip of nose. Cheeks flat. Lips black-edged. Eyes dark brown, medium-sized, oblique, usually kind. Ears U-shaped, medium-sized, close to head, but can be raised in attention. Neck short, stout, muscular, usually not so erect as in great Dane. Shoulders oblique to body. Deep chest. Sloping rump. Tail, well plumed, hangs to below hocks; carried low or curved over back. Legs somewhat plumed, strong and powerful. Can withstand any weather. Coat double: outer coat, thick, wavy, but not curled; undercoat, fine, heavy, white. Great stamina when going is tough. Kindly, intelligent, gentle, majestic, and always courageous. Formerly used in guarding flocks of sheep in Pyrenees Mountains.

Dogs in Medicine

Dogs may live to about 20 years; human beings live to over 100. We have shown that dogs can reproduce at 1 year of age, while humans can begin to reproduce only in the second decade of their lives. If we can be satisfied that there are similarities between men and dogs, possibly we can learn about men through dogs more rapidly than we can by studying men directly, particularly as regards changes that come with age. We have learned some things about men by using rats, hamsters, and guinea pigs as laboratory animals, but these animals lack the intelligence of dogs or of monkeys. Consequently, research doctors have found that the use of dogs as laboratory animals in the study of senescence, of cancer, of nutrition, has frequently led to the discovery of general facts which have proven to be significant in men.

Of course there are those who feel that we have no right to use dogs as experimental animals. Neither do we have the right to deny to children, to old people, and to others anything that may give them health and save their lives. What would you choose?

157

Mastiff · *Canis familiaris inostranzewi* · Canidae

DEVELOPED from alaunt and Tibetan mastiff and involved in ancestry of bulldog, boxer, schnauzer, and bull terrier groups. The mastiff and bulldog strains are combined in the bull mastiff, which is a quieter dog than the mastiff. Mastiffs are valuable work dogs. Weight, 140–200 pounds. Average height: males, 30 inches; females, 27½ inches. Head massive, wide, rounded between ears; temples well developed. Eyes dark brown, set widely apart, medium-sized, alert, kindly. Ears small, dark, V-shaped, moderately thin; hang close to cheeks. Neck thick, powerful, muscular, slightly arched; little loose skin. Back straight. Chest heavy; low between legs. Shoulders sloping. Tail moderately high, tapering to end; hangs down in repose, erect in action. Forelegs straight, wide apart; hind legs broad, powerful. Coat double: outer coat, coarse and harsh; undercoat, dense, soft, and close. Color: dark fawn to brindle, darker around ears, eyes, and mouth.

Noted for loyalty to masters and, in spite of size, considered ideal home pets. Roman emperors used mastiffs to fight wolves in the circus arena. They have been popular draft animals, drawing small carts in town and running treadmills on farms.

Newfoundland · *Canis familiaris inostranzewi* · Canidae

DEVELOPED, like St. Bernard, from Great Pyrenees, and the chief ancestor of the retriever group. Newfoundlands are famous as work dogs, and unexcelled as lifesavers around water. Males weigh 140–150 pounds; females, 110–120 pounds. Height: males, 28 inches; females, 26 inches. Head broad, massive, short, with clean-cut, blunt muzzle. Face hair is short and close. Eyes dark brown, small, set wide apart, and always

158

kindly. Ears small, set back close to the skull, with short hair but no fringe. Neck strong and set well into shoulders, not erect. Broad back. Deep chest. Broad, hairy, muscular loins. Tail well

haired and moderately long, reaches little below hocks and has slight upward curve when in action. Feet large, webbed. Coat oily, flat, dense, and coarse; brushes but one way. Color: black, white, or bronze. May have white on toe tips, tail tip, and breast.

A kindly breed, ideal as children's pets. Can swim comfortably in icy water and are strong enough to help pull nets set by fishermen.

Ancestry of Dogs

(See back end papers.)

SOME 20,000,000 years ago, in early Oligocene times, lived a long-tailed carnivorous animal with some of the characteristics of cats, civets, weasels, raccoons, dogs, and bears. At about that time, it divided into groups. One included the cats, hyenas, and civets (pages 214–231). An intermediate group became the weasels (pages 200–202). The third group was represented by an animal, *Cynodictis,* which in late Oligocene times produced a branch that developed into the raccoons (pages 193–196). In early Miocene times, some 10,000,000 years ago, the remaining branch again divided. One branch (pages 189–192) eventually produced the bears and the surviving branch developed into the dogs (pages 131–184).

In early Miocene times, the dog group was represented by a mammal, *Cynodesmus,* which by late Miocene times, or around 9,000,000 years ago, had developed into an animal now called *Tomarctus.* This continued to change in subsequent years, and in early Pleistocene times, or about 1,000,000 years ago, it formed the genus *Canis,* in which we find the wolves, dogs, and coyotes of modern times. For subsequent developments, see back end papers.

Old English Sheep Dog

Canis familiaris metris-optimae · Canidae

DEVELOPED with collie and German shepherd dog from Persian sheep dog, and has not figured prominently in developing other breeds. Not an ancient breed, but known back to 1800. Obviously developed primarily as sheep dogs, but may be excellent household pets in spite of size and possible awkwardness. Excellent sledge dogs and good in obedience and show competition. Height: males, 23½–27 inches; females, 21¾–25¾ inches. Head square, with arched eyebrows; long hair over eyes. Eyes usually dark, but may be blue or pearl; sometimes weak. Ears medium-sized, flat to head, moderately haired for the most part. Neck fairly long and arched, preferably well covered with long hair. Body short, compact, with stout loins and muscular hindquarters. Tail apparently missing or not more than 2 inches long. Forelegs straight and well haired. Feet comparatively small. Coat heavy, shaggy, but not curled; always thoroughly waterproof. Color: gray, blue, or brindle, with or without white at various spots.

Even tempered, intelligent, easily trained, mischievous, and most faithful to masters.

Samoyed · *Canis familiaris intermedius* · Canidae

AN ancient breed, descended from Egyptian house dog, and progenitor of Pomeranian, setters, pointers, and spaniels of many kinds. Samoyeds are recognized as important work dogs, particularly in cold climates as good sledge dogs. Males weigh 50–67 pounds; females, 36–55 pounds. Height: males, 21–23½ inches; females, 19–21 inches. Head powerful, wedge-shaped; tapering foreface. Lips black. Eyes deep and dark and set well apart on head. Ears, usually well rounded at tip, should not be too long or hairy. Neck strong, straight in front, set firmly on compact shoulders. Body not too long. Back strong. Chest deep.

Ribs well sprung. Legs straight, muscular, with good solid bones. Feet well padded. Coat double: outer coat, heavy, thick, and coarse, with straight hairs; undercoat, soft, fluffy, and excellent heat insulator. Breed has remarkable stamina and ability to defend itself. Color white or white and cream.

Intelligent, always alert, and usually most affectionate to all human beings. Some may be strictly 1-man dogs, but many are not.

The Management of Dogs

THE ownership of dogs calls for a 2-way responsibility. Usually the dog accepts its share eagerly. Normally a dog is what its master makes it. Kindness will frequently get greater returns than punishment, and cruelty and neglect breed many undesirable characteristics in a dog exposed to them. Rewards for things well done and denial of privileges for misbehavior, coupled with consistent adherence to reasonable rules, usually bring the best results.

Properly trained dogs are a joy to themselves and to their masters. Seeing Eye dogs may well become a part of the life of the human they serve, but it requires much strict training of intelligent animals before Seeing Eye dogs qualify to serve a sightless person.

Meanness may be bred in dogs that are confined and annoyed when they cannot get back at tormentors. Dogs that are kicked, struck, and beaten learn to fear hands and feet and in confusion may easily bite strangers when they are suddenly approached.

True, a dog will show loyalty to an abusive master, but few things in life can match the love between a boy and a dog. Many dog owners find belonging to a dog training club enjoyable and rewarding.

Giant Schnauzer · *Canis familiaris inostranzewi* · Canidae

DEVELOPED from mastiff, alaunt, and Tibetan mastiff, and progenitor of Doberman Pinscher. It came to America about 1930, became popular at once, and still is. In 3 general sizes, the smallest being of terrier size. Schnauzers were developed as work dogs and as excellent watchdogs. Height: giant schnauzer, 21½–25½ inches; standard schnauzer, 18–20 inches. Giant was developed from the German schnauzer, which was a superior watchdog. Head broad between ears, with flat forehead and well-developed cheeks. Eyes dark and usually oval, medium in size, directed forward. Ears small, V-shaped, moderately thick, forward drooping. Neck not too short, the nape well arched and substantial. Body sinewy, heavy set; moderate chest and strong hips. Tail high and usually cut off at 3rd joint for show purposes. Legs have strongly muscled thighs, short paws, dark nails. Coat short, close, hard, wiry, and shorter on legs, ears, and head. Color usually pepper and salt, black, or black and tan.

The breed ranks near the top in obedience trials, and as retrievers.

Siberian Husky · *Canis familiaris intermedius* · Canidae

LIKE Eskimo, elkhound, chow, and Pomeranian, was developed from Samoyed..Originated in northern Siberia. Was brought to Alaska about 1909 as competitor in sledge-dog races and won immediate fame. Huskies have been used as work dogs, particularly in cold climates. Males weigh 45–60 pounds; females, 35–50 pounds. Height: males, 21–23½ inches; females, from 20–22 inches. Head medium-sized, wide between ears. Jaws strong. Lips dark. Eyes brown or sometimes blue, keen, friendly, often mischievous. Ears medium-sized, erect, high on head,

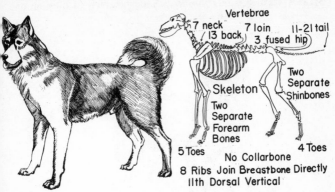

Vertebrae
7 neck 7 loin 11-21 tail
13 back 3 fused hip

Skeleton

Two
Separate
Shinbones

Two
Separate
Forearm
Bones

5 Toes   4 Toes

No Collarbone

8 Ribs Join Breastbone Directly

11th Dorsal Vertical

haired inside, rather soft and rounded at tip. Neck thick, heavy, strong, heavily haired. Body compact, heavily haired, with powerful back and haunches. Tail well haired, held over back or side at rest, arched at work. Legs rather short, strong, straight, not too heavily haired. Coat double: outer coat, thick, soft, and smooth; undercoat, soft and fluffy. Color commonly silver gray or tan and black with white points. May vary in color or may be white.

One of most intelligent breeds. Like children, and make loyal pets but, like others, may develop a dual life and be dangerous on prowl.

Dog Diseases, Parasites, Accidents

IN addition to getting along with man and other animals, a part of a dog's life is involved with diseases, parasites, and accidents. We consider distemper, rabies, pneumonia, fits, and eczema as diseases, and fleas, ticks, mange, worms as parasitic troubles.

From 8–10 weeks of age, puppies are subject to attacks of distemper unless this is prevented by the use of serums. Dogs so attacked have high fever, stop eating, and have diarrhea, but once they have recovered they are immune.

Rabies, the most dangerous of dog diseases, may also be prevented by the use of serums. The disease is caused only by the bite of some rabid animal. The carrier may be a dog, a cat, a squirrel, or other mammal, and dogs may give the disease to humans, to cattle, and to other mammals. Dogs or other animals suspected of rabies should be confined or killed for public safety.

Pneumonia symptoms in a dog are much like those of humans suffering from the same disease. Fits are usually caused by poor care or food. Eczema is caused by mechanical irritations, but is not contagious as is mange.

Parasites are discussed on page 167.

163

St. Bernard · *Canis familiaris inostranzewi* · Canidae

DESCENDED from Great Pyrenees and Tibetan mastiff and related to Newfoundland, which has common stock. Reputed to have saved at least 2,500 lives in the Alps at Hospice of St. Bernard. Inbred there until it lost its vigor, but this was restored with Newfoundland help about 1830. Weight, from 150–250 pounds. Height, from 25–28 inches. Head wide, powerful; wrinkled forehead; nose straight. Eyes dark brown, intelligent, lower lid not completely closed. Ears medium, rather high, with tender flap. Neck high, strong, erect when active, not erect at leisure. Muscular body. Broad shoulders. Broad, straight back. Tail hangs down in repose, with terminal one third tipping upward. Legs strong, straight in front, well covered with hair. Feet broad. Coat of long or of short hairs, dense, tough, and in short-haired type, smooth. Color: red and white or white with red, but usually with white on chest, feet, tail tip, and nose band.

Really beautiful dog. Excellent in obedience classes. Good draft animal, hardy in almost any weather, particularly in winter or in snow.

The Terrier Class

THIS class comprises breeds that are dynamic, persistent, aggressive, willing to take on a fight no matter what the odds may seem to be, and to continue even when the battle goes against them. Often most effective in packs in in-and-out fighting, worrying the game by simultaneous attacks from all angles. Some are small enough to enter into and fight in burrows. Others have good noses and are reasonably good field dogs. Some were bred for pit fighting of other dogs, or for baiting bulls in sports arenas.

Bedlington Terrier · *Canis familiaris leineri* · Canidae

ANCESTRY includes Dinmont terrier, Old English rough terrier, dachshund, beagle, Afghan, Saluki, and Egyptian greyhound, with some greyhound and whippet. Bedlington terriers are bred as fighters of other dogs, badgers, foxes, otters, and other game, and as watchdogs. Males weigh about 24 pounds; females, about 22 pounds. Height, about 15–16 inches, but seems greater. Head narrow-skulled, wedge-shaped. Close-fitting lips. Eyes small, bright, somewhat sunken, appear triangular. Ears moderate, hang flat to cheeks, with 2-inch fringe on edges. Neck long, tapering, somewhat muscular, holding head high. Body deep-chested, muscular, but agile. Broad back. Arched loins. Tail moderate, thick at base, gracefully curved, 9–11 inches long. Legs moderately muscled. Hind legs appear to be the longer. Coat thick, not wiry, brushed toward head; not flat to body. Color: blue and tan, blue, liver, liver and tan or white, or sandy.

Tough, hardy breed, affectionate to humans and often persistently jealous of favors from masters.

165

Bull Terrier · *Canis familiaris inostranzewi* · Canidae

PRODUCED from cross of bulldog and now extinct white English terrier, with alaunt and Tibetan mastiff in remoter ancestry. English terrier and bulldog produced Staffordshire terrier, once known as Yankee terrier, from which evolved standard white bull terrier. Possibly involved in ancestry of Dalmatian. Bull terriers were developed originally as pit fighters with other dogs. Recognized as general breed in 1835; white type recognized as breed in 1860 and colored recognized in 1936. Weight, 25–60 pounds; males average 50 pounds; females, 45 pounds. Head long, widest at ears, with no noticeable brow and little cheek. Muzzle tapers. Eyes small, black, deep-set, close, triangular, alert. Ears small; when erect should not wrinkle skin on top of head. Neck strong, arched, tapers moderately; no loose flesh or skin. Body short, strong, slightly arched, with deep chest. Shoulders slope. Tail short, tapering, set low, not normally held above back level. Legs big boned; front legs straight but not stilted. Feet compact. Coat dense, short, flat, of stiff hairs on tight skin. Color usually white, but other colors are possible.

Bull terriers defend themselves and their masters, but not all of them are friendly.

Cairn Terrier · *Canis familiaris leineri* · Canidae

DEVELOPED from Old English rough terrier, beagle, and dachshund, Afghan, Saluki, and Egyptian greyhound, and related to other terriers more indirectly. Cairn terriers are recognized as superior house pets over a wide area. Also good vermin destroyers. Males weigh about 14 pounds; females, about 13 pounds. Height: males, to 10 inches; females, to 9½ inches; should be two thirds body length. Head is broad, short, heavily haired. Black nose. Eyes dark, wide apart, sunken, covered by shaggy brows. Ears small, pointed, erect, set apart, free of long

hairs. Neck strong, erect, not heavy, with somewhat of a ruff of long hair that makes it appear bigger. Body short, not heavy, to 14–15 inches long. Sloping shoulders. Tail pointed, well haired, not feathered, dark at tip, not curled over back. Legs short, but longer than in Scottish or Sealyham terriers. Forelegs strong, not bowed outward at elbows. Pads thick and strong. Coat hard, weather resistant, of relatively long hairs that smooth down rather well. Colors are practically anything except white.

Active and hardy temperament, with much personality and intelligence. The breed ranks high in obedience contests.

Dog Parasites

Possibly the worst parasites of dogs are mange, fleas, ticks, and worms such as roundworms, tapeworms, hookworms, and whipworms. All of these may be contracted through contact with other animals or with plants. Mange is caused by a mite, and is highly contagious. It is of 2 types, and is normally controlled by washing with green soap and hot water, followed by use of sulfur ointment for at least 3 days. Lice and ticks fasten themselves to dogs and persistently suck the blood, while fleas roam at will from one part of the dog to another, from dog to dog, and many times on to man. Fleas can be controlled by changing the dog's bed frequently, by combing out the fleas, and using a flea powder. In the case of ticks, lice, and chiggers, the parasites can be killed with chloroform on a dab of cotton, and should then be removed with care.

Hookworms are found relatively commonly in the South, especially in hunting dogs. Whipworms cause a rectal infection. Roundworms are treated by giving 2–4 tsp. of mixture of ½ oz. of spigelia, senna, and licorice syrup every morning for 3 days. Tapeworms are treated by giving 1 gram freshly ground areca nut per pound of dog and withholding food for 2 days.

167

ANCESTRY includes Old English rough terrier, dachshund, beagle, Afghan, Saluki, and Egyptian greyhound, and may include some white English terrier. Descendants include wirehaired fox terrier and Sealyham terrier. One of the best-known breeds on a worldwide basis. Once sporting dogs, used to run with a pack of hounds to go into burrow of fox and drive it out. Have rather good noses. Weight of males from 14–18 pounds; female rarely above 16 pounds. Usual height not over 15½ inches. Head 7–7¼ inches long, thin-cheeked, flat, narrow, widest at eyes. Eyes dark, small, circular, mischievous; vision good. Ears small, set high, V-shaped; erect or broken at half length. Neck clean, strong, muscular, of fair length, widest at shoulders. Body about 12 inches from withers to tail. Chest deep, not broad. Back strong and straight. Forelegs straight from any angle; hind legs strong. Best individuals stand reasonably high on toes. Coat smooth, close, with fine, hard hair that clings to skin. Tail is set high, is not curled over back, and may stand erect. Color: white most usual. May be black and white with tan on side of head. Should not be red, blue, or liver.

Tremendous stamina and persistence. Usually intelligent. Rank high in obedience.

Wire-haired Fox Terrier

Canis familiaris leineri · Canidae

DESCENDED from the smooth fox terrier, and the probable progenitor of the Sealyham terrier. Fox terriers have much in common with the black-and-tan or Manchester terriers. General characteristics of size of body and its parts are almost

168

identical with those of the smooth fox terrier, the chief difference being in the coat and possibly in the color. The coat of the wire-haired fox terrier is of a hard, wiry nature but is not shaggy, as in many other terriers. The breed does not confine itself so closely to black and white as does the smooth fox terrier and may be spotted rather than blotched, as is the smooth breed. Both fox terriers are excellent vermin destroyers. They are common in trained-dog acts, and one smooth fox terrier is well known as the featured trademark animal that recognizes his master's voice in an old-fashioned phonograph horn. Another smooth fox terrier, Nornay Saddler, was famous for having won 59 best-in-show awards, a record which in his time had not been matched by any other dog.

Accidents to Dogs

Dogs, like most other animals, suffer from accidents, some of which could be prevented by their masters. For such accidents some regular treatment may sometimes be recommended.

Choking is frequently caused by dogs' bolting their food or by swallowing fractured bones. Chicken bones are not recommended for dogs because they are easily fractured. Dogs vomit freely and frequently, thereby removing the cause of trouble.

Dogs suffer greatly from porcupine quills which, if neglected, may cause serious trouble. Normally the safest treatment is to remove the quills with tweezers, using a quick, direct pull and washing out the wound with iodine or boric acid.

Other common accidents associated with dogs are the stings of bees, the bites of other animals, the swallowing of poisons, and mechanical injuries of many sorts. The treatment of dogs in these instances is essentially the same as the treatment given man. Diarrhea and constipation are usually associated with food habits, although no one cause should be suspected for either. Their treatment is much the same as it is for human beings.

169

Irish Terrier · *Canis familiaris leineri* · Canidae

DEVELOPED from the Old English rough terrier and Irish wolf-hound, with strains of dachshund, beagle, Afghan, and grey-hound. Irish terriers are peppy, popular hunting companions, killers of vermin, retrievers of ducks, woodchuck extermi-nators, and general all-around dogs. Males weigh about 27 pounds; females, about 25 pounds. Height about 18 inches for both. Head is long, flat, narrow between the eyes, with close lips, strong jaws, and usually a blunt nose. Eyes are dark hazel, never light colored, small, lively, unusually intelligent and alert. Ears small, V-shaped, erect, thick, without fringe of hairs. The strong neck widens to the shoulders and is rather erect, but not thick at throat. Body compact, strong, straight, with long, slop-ing shoulders. Tail is usually docked to three fourths normal length and is held erect. Legs are strong and straight, the hind legs powerful. Coat is dense, wiry, and so close that skin can barely be seen when hair is parted. Color is commonly golden red. White on chest is accepted but not favored.

This breed has been used in hunting big game both in the cold North and in the tropics.

Manchester Terrier

Canis familiaris inostranzewi · Canidae

LIKE white English bull terrier, developed from bulldog, alaunt, and Tibetan mastiff, and with schnauzer has contributed to de-velopment of Doberman Pinscher. Formerly known as black-and-tan terrier or as one of the rat terriers. It was produced by crossing a female whippet with a rat terrier and was used for hunting rats and rabbits. Long has been most popular as a house pet and companion, and is among the best and most loyal of

watchdogs. Most affectionate in the family group and often vociferous when strangers approach. Weight of either sex is 12–22 pounds, with toys and standard varieties available. Head narrow, flat, widest behind eyes. Pointed black nose. Eyes dark hazel, not light colored; small, full of life, intelligent. Ears small, erect, thin, close together at base, usually cropped. Body slightly arched, shortened; chest narrow between the legs. Legs straight, strong, often tan colored. Feet compact, with two middle toes in front the longest. Coat close, short, glossy, not soft; may be easily smoothed down. Color usually black and tan, but often a rich mahogany brown, with black predominating. Stands up well in obedience trials and is usually easy to take care of and keep clean.

Dogs and Their Diets

As with men, the diet of dogs has much to do with the happiness they get from life. A wolf can survive comfortably on 1 good meal a week. One good meal, preferably in the evening, is better for a dog than many small meals plus an opportunity to pick up snacks here and there.

Faulty diet in dogs causes unwelcome thinness or corpulence. It may also introduce intestinal and other parasites and cause many skin diseases. Diet should be modified with the conditions under which the dogs live. The nutritional demands of a large, healthy dog confined with little exercise other than an evening's walk on a leash are quite different from those of a farm dog that runs free and wild. If the dog must stay in an apartment, don't feed it as you would a hard-working farm dog.

On the whole, prepared dog food, chosen with care and given so that the dog seems satisfied and neither increases nor decreases its weight conspicuously, may be the best bet. It may appear to be expensive, but usually it does what it purports to do, namely, gives the dog a well-rounded diet suited to its needs.

171

Scottish Terrier · *Canis familiaris leineri* · Canidae

DESCENDED from Old English rough terrier, dachshund, beagle, Afghan, Saluki, and English greyhound. The cairn terrier and West Highland white terrier have closely similar heritage. Popular particularly with Scottish folk at home and abroad. Became officially recognized as a breed in United States in 1883, and during Franklin Roosevelt's administration was represented by Fala as the first dog in the land. Weight to 20 pounds. Height to 10 inches. Head long, of medium width, with short, hard hair. Eyes small, almond-shaped, dark brown to black, set wide apart under brows. Ears small, high, pointed, with short velvety hair. Ears untrimmed. Neck short, thick maned, reaching to sloping shoulders. Front profile erect. Body moderately short; hindquarters muscular. Chest deep and broad and extending to between forelegs. Legs short and heavy and not bowed outward at elbows. Tail, about 7 inches long, is not cut. Main portion of the coat consists of 2-inch harsh, wiry hairs. Color black, brindle, wheaten, or gray. Gait a unique rolling movement.

In general Scottish terriers are full of fun, vigor, and vitality, and ready to meet any situation, whether within the limits of their powers or not.

Sealyham Terrier · *Canis familiaris leineri* · Canidae

DEVELOPED from wire-haired fox terrier through smooth fox terrier, Old English rough terrier, dachshund, beagle, Afghan, Saluki, and Egyptian greyhound. Also some white English terrier, bulldog, mastiff in the line. Primarily used as pets and companions. Much shorter legged than the immediate fox terrier ancestry. Weight: males, to 21 pounds; females, to 20 pounds. Height, 10½ inches. Head long and joined smoothly to the

neck; powerful jaws. Muscular neck, set fairly on shoulders, is, in length, about two thirds the height at shoulders. Body strong. Length of back from shoulders to tail about equals height at shoulders. Tail erect (usually docked) and set somewhat forward of rear profile. Forelegs straight, strong, heavily boned. Large, compact feet. Hindquarters powerful. Coat double: outer coat of hard, wiry hairs; undercoat, soft and fluffy, highly weather resistant. Sealyhams have remarkable stamina and hunting instincts, fighting readily with badger, fox, and otter, and powerful enough to dig into their burrows. They rank high in obedience tests.

Dog Shows and Training Classes

WE cannot recommend too highly that dog owners join obedience training classes, where dogs and their masters are trained to cooperate effectively to the end that both may learn so to act that they are welcome neighbors. While it is exasperating to have your dog "break" in a class demonstration, on the other hand it is a thrill eventually to get the cooperation sought. Since affection for dogs is not determined by financial status or social prestige, a good dog club in an average community is hard to beat as a democratizing agency.

Dog shows are also worth attending, but unless one is willing to spend much time and often considerable money the returns may not be so great as those that come from membership in a training class. Judging may frequently be subjective rather than objective, and it is possible that the financial returns that go with the ribbons won by a kennel may influence decisions through devious and difficult-to-understand channels. I have tried in these pages to give some of the criteria by which dogs are judged in dog shows. The same criteria may be of no use whatever in judging the value of a dog to a boy or girl—or of a child to a dog.

173

Skye Terrier · *Canis familiaris leineri* · Canidae

LIKE most other terriers, developed from Old English rough terrier through dachshund and beagle, Afghan, Saluki, and Egyptian greyhound. Skye terriers have exceptional sight, hearing, and ability to smell. Persistent, diligent hunters, fast workers, good fighters, and fine companions. Height: males, about 9 inches; females, 8½ inches. Over-all length of males, 41 inches; females, 39 inches. Head wide, with close-set, medium-sized hazel eyes. Powerful jaws, black muzzle. Ears not too large; at rest lie flat and straight; erect at outer edges. Neck short, stout, heavily haired. Body long and low, with broad shoulders, deep chest, and well-developed hindquarters. Tail, when hanging, has terminal third perpendicular; is sometimes thrown over back in curve. Legs short, straight, stout. Feet large. Coat double: undercoat soft and woolly; outer coat hard and of straight hairs to 5½ inches long. Color: gray, light blue, or fawn with black "points." Yorkshire terriers have been developed from the Skye terriers and are longer haired.

The Toy Breeds

THIS class includes small animals developed primarily as pets, although many of them are noisy, alert, fearless little dogs that serve as useful watchdogs, calling attention to intruders that they could not possibly hurt. Most are of the lapdog type and affectionate with those with whom they are closely associated. They have been developed in all parts of the world and have often been unduly pampered because of their appealing qualities. In ancient times some of these dogs were popular gifts to royalty, and spent most of their lives amid luxuries that were not shared by larger animals better able to be of real help with man's activities. Frequently the breeds have suffered from too much inbreeding, but some are of surprisingly hardy constitutions in spite of their small size.

Chihuahua · *Canis familiaris leineri* · Canidae

DEVELOPED from Mexican hairless, which descended from Samoyed strain. Chihuahuas are essentially toy pet dogs. Were pets of royalty to Toltec Indians in Mexico, taking part in major ceremonies. Weight ranges from 1–6 pounds, with the best sizes between 2 and 4 pounds. Head has well-rounded dome, lean cheeks and jaws, and moderately short nose. Eyes ruby, set well apart, relatively large. Ears large, thin, erect when alert, and flare at 45° in repose. Neck slopes easily to the lean shoulders and is rather solid, with a ruff of hair. Body length greater than the height, the males having shorter backs than the females. Back is level. Tail medium long, carried curled up or down over the back, and with furry hair. Legs are unusually light boned and relatively fragile. Coat of two types: long-coated and short-coated. Long-coated type has soft, flat, or slightly curled hair, with fringed ears and full, long tail. Smooth-coated type has soft, glossy, close hair, with conspicuous ruff. Short hair on ears and face. In spite of fragile nature, these dogs do not like to be babied.

175

DEVELOPED, like the pug, from Pekingese, Chinese lion dog, Maltese dog, and Egyptian house dogs. One of the group known as "dwarf spaniels." The name "*papillon*" means "butterfly" in French. Was favored breed of royalty for centuries, with popularity spreading from Spain through Italy and France. Papillons are of dainty appearance but in spite of small size are excellent rat killers. Affectionate, alert, adaptable, loyal, good-tempered, spirited, of surprising hardiness, and make superior companions. Head is small, with a moderate muzzle and light hair coloring. Dark brown eyes are large, round, lively, intelligent, set low on the head. Ears are large, round, set low with rounded tips and of fine, leathery texture. Neck is thick and not short, but is lost in the heavy coat. Body is long, with deep chest, curving upward in the loins. Tail is high, carried over the back like a squirrel's, and has a heavy, long plume. Forelegs are straight, rather slender, but plumed to the rear; hind legs well feathered. Feet thin. Coat short and smooth on head, muzzle, and forepart of legs, but much longer and somewhat wavy on most parts of animals. May be of any solid color, or of 2 or even 3 mixed colors.

Pekingese

Pekingese · *Canis familiaris intermedius* · Canidae

DEVELOPED, like pug, from Chinese lion dog, Maltese dog, and Egyptian house dog. Ancestor of Japanese spaniel and its group of toy dogs. Sometimes known as dragon dog, sun dog, or Chinese lion. Brought from China about 1870. Chinese held it as sacred because of supposed resemblance to a lion. In pageants 2 pugs preceded royalty, barking, followed by another pair who held the hem of the monarch's robe. Anyone caught stealing these dogs was sentenced to death. Now popular city pets, they are sometimes called sleeve dogs, since they can be carried up a loose sleeve—maybe. Maximum weight, 14 pounds. Head heavy. Nose broad, short, black; flat wrinkled muzzle. Eyes lustrous, dark, large, and round. Ears heart-shaped, long-feathered, never erect; do not reach to muzzle tip. Neck heavily maned and ruffed. Body heavy in front and broad-chested. Tail set high and lies over the back or over either side, and is heavily feathered. Legs short in front and bowed in the forearm. Coat double: outer coat of coarse but soft, straight hair; undercoat, long and heavy. Any color is accepted, including commonly red, black, fawn, brindle, white, sable. Gait a peculiar rolling movement.

Dogs as Companions

JUST as one cannot measure the value of friends by material things or by services, so the real worth of dogs to man can probably be best measured through the companionship they inspire. Rin Tin Tin and Lassie of the movies have built their reputations on this basis. Ernest Thompson Seton wrote remarkably of his dog friends. Jack London based his *Call of the Wild* on the same theme. We have had *Beautiful Joe* in literature and *The Bar Sinister* in the movies, while Street's *Biscuit Eater* and Kantor's *The Voice of Bugle Ann* have won a place both in literature and in the movies. All these works were based on man's companionship with dogs.

Presidents of the United States have shown deep affection for their canine companions. Washington, Jefferson, Madison, and Monroe were great admirers of foxhounds; Jackson of coon hounds. Cleveland favored field dogs, such as pointers and setters. Coolidge shared the White House with his collie, and Hoover, while President, was very fond of his German shepherd. F. D. R. had his scottie and T. R. and Wilson their airedales. Lincoln and Grant liked just plain "dawgs." History has chronicled such friendships for thousands of years.

Pomeranian · *Canis familiaris intermedius* · Canidae

DEVELOPED with the spaniel group from the Samoyed, a sledge dog. Ancestor of the schipperke and a contributor to the corgi, which has stronger ancestral ties with the collie group. Pomeranians make superior city pets, and while they most obviously enjoy their body comforts, they nevertheless like the outdoors and playing in the snow. Two groups are recognized, one being more than 7 pounds and the other under 7 pounds in weight. Head wedge-shaped and somewhat foxy in general appearance. Eyes medium, oblique, not too far apart, bright, intelligent. Ears small, erect, and have soft hairs. Neck is short, thick-set, and concealed by heavy mane or ruff. Shoulders are clean cut. Body short, compact, with deep chest. Tail held over back and heavily haired. Both front and hind legs are feathered. Front legs are straight. Coat double: outer coat, long and straight; undercoat, soft and fluffy. Color: black, brown, chocolate, red, cream, sable, orange, or bluish. Pomeranians are quick and alert; make splendid show dogs, and are good in obedience trials.

Pug · *Canis familiaris intermedius* · Canidae

DESCENDED, like Pekingese, from Chinese lion dog, Maltese dog, and Egyptian house dog. Pugs came originally from China and were brought to Holland and England by early traders. Have been improved and perfected by breeders in England and America. Popularity has varied over the years. Excellent house dogs with great intelligence, boldness, and loyalty, but not usually friendly with strangers. Weight, 14–18 pounds. Head chunky, with "pug" nose. (Name "pug" comes from resemblance of head to clenched fist of a pugilist.) Face deeply wrinkled; muzzle black and blunt. Eyes round, bright, prominent, of medium size. Ears thin, small, soft, and velvety, and of 2 types, "rose" and "button." Neck short, compact, vertical.

Body short, compact, square, and "cobby." Tail tightly curled over back or hip, and at best is doubly curled. Legs strong, straight, well placed under body; black-nailed, relatively small feet. Coat fine, smooth, of short hairs; glossy, not woolly. Color either a clearly defined black or a silver fawn.

As a rule, people either like or dislike pug dogs, with relatively few who are indifferent, and yet these dogs' affectionate nature warrants friendship.

Non-Sporting Class

THIS seems to be a miscellaneous group, the members of which may or may not fit into the other groups. As a matter of fact, they could easily be so classified. Dalmatians, chows, and bulldogs have plenty of the qualities possessed by members of the working group, and the poodles have excellent records as hunters.

Just "Dawg" Group

While the long-nosed kennel-club breeds look down their noses at these dogs, the mongrel group keep on making friends and influencing people. The mongrels will always be with us, and while they may not win ribbons at bench shows, they will ever continue to win hearts in homes. What more can be asked of a dog?

DESCENDED, like bull terrier and Staffordshire terrier, from bulldog, mastiff, alaunt, and Tibetan mastiff. An American breed of relatively recent development, having attained recognized standing in 1893. For many years it has been acknowledged as one of the most popular breeds in this country. One of the best companions and house dogs, rightly known as the "American gentleman." Originally it weighed more than 32 pounds. Now 3 classes are recognized: under 15 pounds; 15–20 pounds; 20–25 pounds. Head short, flat-topped, with abrupt brow and short muzzle. Eyes dark, wide apart, large, round, alert, intelligent, kind. Ears small, erect, thin, placed on the corners of the skull. Neck of fair length, slightly arched and neatly placed on shoulders. Body short, well knit, compact, and neat in conformation. Tail short, set low, and never held above horizontal. Legs strong, straight, well muscled, set moderately far apart. Coat smooth, satiny, shiny, of short hairs close to skin. Color popularly dark brindle, with showy white patches or contrasting black and white. A lively, determined, and generally able dog.

Bulldog or English Bulldog

Canis familiaris inostranzewi · Canidae

DEVELOPED from mastiff, alaunt, and Tibetan mastiff, and in the ancestry of the bull terrier and Boston terrier. The bulldog, with the lion, is the symbol of the British Empire. The bulldog is also the symbol of Yale and of other colleges in America. Once it was bred primarily for fighting other dogs for wagers, but that was outlawed in 1835. Now the vicious qualities formerly sought have largely vanished, and the dogs may be the most docile of pets. Weight of males is about 50 pounds; of females, about 40 pounds. Head is large, circumference around ears

about equaling height at shoulders. Muzzle short. Cheeks full. Forehead flat. Eyes round, moderate in size, not sunken, and set low down on head, as far as possible from ears. Ears small, thin, folded at back. Neck thick and moderately long. Body thickset, with broad shoulders, short, strong back, and deep chest. Tail set low and extends straight out, then drops; it is never raised over back. Forelegs are straight, stout, and set wide apart, with elbows and compact feet that point straight ahead. Coat smooth, fine, close. Color: brindle, red, fawn, white, black, or pied.

Dogs in Religion and Mythology

APPARENTLY some modern antipathies between nations are deeply rooted and find expression in attitudes toward dogs.

As far back as 4000 B.C. the Egyptians held dogs in high esteem. There were dog cemeteries in later Egyptian cities. Some Egyptian gods had dog heads. Dogs had ceremonial burials and were considered the essence of fidelity.

The Old Testament refers to the dog that in sympathy licked the sores on Lazarus, but for the most part the ancient Hebrews considered dogs unclean, and primarily as scavengers, and dogs were mentioned among the horrors of Hell. Shylock in *The Merchant of Venice*, like many other men, resented being called a "dog."

The Mohammedans and Hindus joined with the Hebrews in considering dogs as unclean, and used the expression "Christian dog" as one of contempt. The Turks, on the other hand, regarded dogs as sacred.

In Asiatic countries, dogs were in many periods held in disrespect by the Chinese and in favor by the Japanese.

American Indians sacrificed dogs to the gods, and ate dog meat to obtain the aggressive spirit of the animals.

Chow Chow · *Canis familiaris intermedius* · Canidae

DEVELOPED, with the Norwegian elkhound and keeshond, the husky and the Eskimo dog, from the Samoyed of the sledge-dog type. Long considered a breed fit for royalty. In A.D. 700 one Chinese emperor's kennel maintained 5,000 chow chows. Have been used as sledge dogs, guardians, retrievers, and of course as companions. Usually form attachments to only a few people. General appearance "cobby." Head broad, large, massive, carried proudly. Large black nose and black tongue. Eyes dark, almond-shaped, deep-set, moderate-sized. Ears small, stiff, round-tipped, wide apart, with forward tilt. Body compact. Chest broad, muscular. Back short, straight, and strong. Tail curled closely over back. Forelegs straight, rather heavy. Feet compact. Coat shining, conspicuously beautiful, abundant, with soft, woolly undercoat. Any color is acceptable in competition, but color is usually a uniform red, blue, or black, lighter on ruff, tail, and rear. The temperament is essentially dignified, aloof, snobbish, sober, and above all independent. Chow chows are alertly active, however, in the interest they show in man's activities.

Dalmatian

Canis familiaris intermedius x *inostranzewi* · Canidae

BASICALLY descended, like pointer, from Spanish spaniel, Italian spaniel, shock dog, and Samoyed, and from bull terrier, which is a descendant of bulldog, mastiff, alaunt, and Tibetan mastiff. Definitely general-purpose dogs, having been used as trackers, hunters, retrievers, gun dogs, shepherds, draft animals, sentries, coach dogs, and circus and stage performers. Rank high in obedience trials, have great endurance and dignity, and are not quarrelsome or usually noisy. Weight, from 35–50 pounds.

Height, 19–25 inches. Head long, pointed, and powerful. Eyes round and bright. Ears of moderate size and set high. Neck long and somewhat arched. Chest deep and capacious. Back powerful, muscular, and slightly arched. Tail strong at base, not too long, uniformly tapering, and preferably spotted. Legs straight, strong, and hardy. Coat short, close, shining, finely haired, with circular black spots on a white ground. In some, the spots are liver or brown in color. As a rule, dogs with spots not joined together are rated higher than those with confused spots.

The Dog Library

FROM the rich literature on dogs, here is a suggested list for a book nucleus for your own library. It will help in many ways.

Ackerman, I. C. and K. Onstott. *Your Dog as a Hobby*. New York City: Harper & Brothers, 1940. 179 pages.

American Kennel Club. *The Complete Dog Book*. Garden City, New York: Garden City Books, 1954. 482 pages.

Baird, Jack. *The Care and Handling of Dogs*. New York City: Permabooks, 1950. 244 pages. Excellent initial book.

Davis, Henry P. *The Modern Dog Encyclopedia*. New York City: Stackpole and Heck, 1949. 626 pages.

Rine, Josephine Z. *The Dog Owner's Manual*. New York City: Tudor Publishing Company, 1944. 446 pages.

Saunders, Blanche. *Training You to Train Your Dog*. Garden City, New York: Doubleday & Company, 1946. 178 pages.

Vesey-Fitzgerald, Brian. *The Book of the Dog*. London, England: Nicholson and Watson, 1948. 1,039 pages.

Whitney, Leon V. *Your Puppy: How To Select, Raise, and Train Him*. Garden City, N.Y.: Hanover House, 1950. 192 pages.

183

Poodle · *Canis familiaris intermedius* · Canidae

DESCENDED through Spanish spaniel, Italian spaniel, and shock dog from Samoyed, and the ancestor of the water spaniel. Here is a dog that is inclined to be ridiculed by those who do not know it, but is held in high regard by those who do. It may seem ridiculous with its fancy haircut, but there are reasons even for this.

Poodles originally were developed as hunters and as retrievers. With their hindquarters heavily covered with hair, their movements through water were restricted, so their owners clipped this part of the body. Their tremendous energy and exceptional intelligence made them ideal companions and food getters for their owners. Not only were poodles used for hunting game, but they were also good at hunting underground fungi—truffles—which had a high market value. Often they were trained to work with dachshunds. The poodles located the truffles and the dachshunds dug them out. Because of their intelligence they have proven to be superior circus dogs, and usually share honors with fox terriers in trained-animal acts.

Poodles are divided into 3 classes: toys weighing under 10 pounds; miniatures, between 10 and 15 pounds; and standards, above 15 pounds. They occur also as curly and corded, the difference being in the nature of the coat. The curly type is by far the more common.

Poodles have large heads with long muzzles, flat cheeks, and moderately domed skulls. Eyes are far apart, oval, and intelligent. Ears are low, close to head, fleshy, and feathered. The neck is strong and erect, with skin snug at throat. Body is deep, short, slightly hollowed, and broad loined. Tail is held high, is docked, never curled, or held over back. Forelegs straight and hind legs well developed. Any solid color is acceptable.

Arctic Fox or Blue Fox · *Alopex lagopus* · Canidae

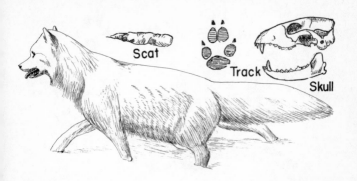

Scat

Track

Skull

WITH the unstable nature of the fur market and the development of artificial substitutes for natural furs, the future of this fur bearer may well become brighter. Decreased demand for hides may relieve trapping pressure and allow populations to return to normal.

Arctic foxes or blue foxes, which are the same species, are found relatively near the Arctic seas, in Iceland, Greenland, and North America from the Gulf of St. Lawrence to southern Alaska. The dominant blue-gray phase, or blue fox, constitutes 50% of the species population in western Greenland and 15% of the Arctic foxes of Baffin Bay and the Canadian Arctic. The blue-gray phase is blue-gray the year round. The recessive white phase is all white in winter and brown in summer, but in mild winters in Iceland there is no seasonal change. Range between the 60th and 75th parallels, N.

Arctic foxes are about 11 inches high at the shoulder, have a 12-inch tail, and are 2½ feet in total length. Both sexes usually are 6–12 pounds but may reach 20 pounds. Arctic foxes are smaller than either the coyote or red fox. The body of the white or Arctic fox is stouter than the red fox's, the muzzle broader and shorter, the ears shorter, more rounded. Eyes small and round. Long, white hairs on the soles of the feet help them to run on ice. The winter coat comes in October and remains until April, then falls off in felty masses. These foxes live well in captivity. Mate in February. Young, 1–14, born 51–52 days later, with about 5 surviving. Pups at birth weigh 2 ounces. Both parents care for young, but family breaks up in fall. Feed on any available animal life, living or dead. May store some uneaten food. Fox liver may be poisonous to man and to other animals.

Respiration rate, 505. Temperature, 101°–106.5° F. Life span, 14 years.

Gray Fox or Tree Fox

Urocyon cinereoargenteus · Canidae

Front Foot   Hind Foot

Tracks

Skull

Scat

BECAUSE this fox has the rather unusual habit of climbing trees, it is sometimes known as the tree fox. Men who enjoy hearing hounds bay as they run a fox are often disappointed when a run is short because the fox is a gray fox and has taken to a tree. Trappers who catch gray foxes instead of red ones are also disappointed, because gray foxes, more southern animals, lack the rich fur of the red ones, having a coat of coarse hair instead. Because the toes of red foxes are well separated by hairs that are less abundant in the gray foxes, the pads are more separated in the tracks of the reds than in those of the grays. The toe and center pads of gray foxes cover practically the whole foot area. The gray foxes favor wooded country, the reds prefer open lands. Some believe that when the grays move into a territory the reds move out.

Gray foxes measure to 40 inches, including a 12-inch tail. Weight, to 40 pounds. The fur is "pepper and salt," black and gray above, with reddish brown along the sides, and gray and tawny beneath. The tail is black marked. Teeth are: I 3/3; C 1/1; P 4/4; M 2/3. Tracks are: F 1½ x 2, 4; H 1¼, 4. A 9-pound gray fox can go through a hole 3⅛ inches in diameter. The fur has 40% the durability of otter and about one fourth the value of red fox.

Gray foxes have an ideal family life. Mating is in January. About 55–63 days later 1–7 young are born, each weighing about 4 ounces and blackish in color. The den is a clean cave. Young take solid food at 6 weeks, and family breaks up in August–September, although parents may stay together through year.

Range is through the United States east of Great Plains, through the Southwest, and along the Pacific Coast to southern Washington. It is being extended northward. Individuals range over 2 square miles. Food about 15–20% plant materials.

Red Fox, Cross Fox, Silver Fox, or Black Fox

Vulpes fulva · Canidae

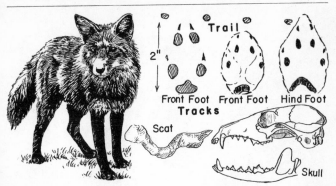

THE red fox, cross fox, silver fox, and black fox are all the same species. All may be represented in a single litter, with the black fox the rarest of the 4. The cross fox is reddish brown, with heavy black markings, the red fox golden brown or reddish above, white beneath, with a white tail tip and black legs. Young red foxes have black on muzzle and back of ears. These foxes have a total length of 41 inches, including a 16-inch tail, and weigh to 14 pounds, the male being the larger. A 10½ pound red fox can go through a hole 3½ inches in diameter. Teeth are I 3/3; C 1/1; P 4/4; M 2/3. Tracks are: F 1¼ x 2, 4; H 1¼ x 2, 4. Durability of fur is 40% that of otter. See also pages 185–186.

Red foxes are found through most of the United States except adjacent to the Gulf Coast, in the extreme Southwest, and through a portion of the Great Plains. They range throughout Canada and Alaska.

Red foxes have provided exhilarating sport for generations. Their skill at confusing their pursuers, their 30-mile per hour speed, their endurance, their threat to poultrymen in the destruction of chickens, their remarkable senses of seeing, smell, and hearing, as well as their unusual intelligence, their value to trappers and what sometimes seems to be their sense of humor, all challenge our interest. They are probably the world's greatest destroyers of mice—the worst enemy of agricultural crops. Unfortunately foxes, like dogs, cats, and other mammals, may carry rabies, which can be fatal to man. One fox farm sold more than 18 million dollars' worth of pelts, and gave permanent employment to 400 persons the year round.

Red foxes are monogamous; mate in late winter. Copulation lasts 15–20 minutes. About 49–56 days later 4–10 blind young are born. At 9 days eyes open. They are independent at 5 months and full grown at 18 months. Temperature, 99°–104.2° F. Life span, 12 years.

187

Kit Fox or Swift Fox · *Vulpes velox* · Canidae

Scat

Skull

Front Foot
Tracks Hind Foot

THE smallest of our North American foxes is the kit fox or swift fox. The kit fox has a total length of 31 inches, including a 12-inch tail. Slender, it stands a foot high at the shoulder and weighs up to 6 pounds. It is gray to pale yellowish brown, with black on each side of the snout and at the tip of the tail. It has unusually large ears somewhat like those of the coyote. Teeth are: I 3/3; C 1/1; P 4/4; M 2/3—a formula similar to that of the red fox and gray fox. Tracks are: F 1¾ x 1½, 4; H 1¾ x 1¼, 4. They are possibly larger than those of the gray fox, but definitely smaller than those of the red fox. The stride (distance between footprints in a walking animal) of a gray fox may be 10–16 inches, while that of a kit fox usually would not exceed 10 inches. The den of a kit fox is at the end of a burrow to 9 feet long and to 5 feet below the surface. The entrance may be only 8 inches across.

Kit foxes range largely through Montana, Wyoming, Colorado, New Mexico, Arizona, Nevada, southern California, and extreme western portions of North Dakota, Nebraska, Kansas, Oklahoma, and Texas. In some of these border areas the animals are extremely rare if not now completely gone.

The pelts are of little or no commercial value. Since kit foxes take poisoned baits more readily than do most of their associates, they are among the first of the so-called "vermin" to disappear following intensive poisoning campaigns.

Kit foxes feed largely on mice, gophers, and other small mammals, and because of this, from an agricultural standpoint, are essentially useful. They are shy and almost wholly nocturnal, spending much time underground. In February, or later, 4–7 pups are born. They are cared for by both parents, nurse about 10 weeks, and remain with the family for some months.

Some authors recognize the kit as *Vulpes macrotis* and the swift fox as *Vulpes velox*. Others consider both as *Vulpes velox*.

188

Black Bear, Brown Bear, or Cinnamon Bear
Euarctos americanus · Ursidae

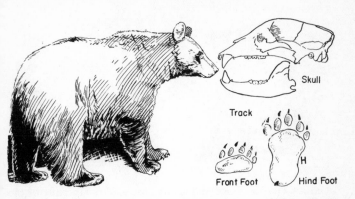

Skull

Track

Front Foot

Hind Foot

H

ANY animal that can reach a weight of 300 pounds, be potentially dangerous to man and yet survive civilization in considerable numbers in such heavily populated states as New York and Pennsylvania, must have tremendous reproductive powers or be a past master at survival techniques. Black bears have only 1–4 young, and they bear these only every other year, so their reproductive capacity is low in comparison with most other mammals. The key to their survival, then, lies largely in their ability to avoid their chief enemy, man.

Black bears were found originally throughout most of North America except eastern Oregon, Washington, California, Nevada, and western Utah. Ten or more subspecies have been recognized, all found in wooded areas and often surprisingly close to centers of human population, such as New York City.

Black bears have a length of to 6 feet and a shoulder height of to 3 feet. They are black or cinnamon, with a white throat, the all-brown bear being a color phase of the black bear. They have long snouts, flat feet, and short tail. Teeth are: I 3/3; C 1/1; P 4/4; M 2/3. Tracks are: F 3 x 4, 5; H 4 x 7, 5. The fur has a durability of 85% that of otter. They may hibernate in deep winter, when the 1–4 cubs are born 7 months after the June mating. Parents separate after the mating. At birth, cubs are blind, practically helpless, and weigh about 8 ounces each. They remain with the mother at least through the first fall. They climb trees readily.

Black bears feed on flesh, fish, carrion, fruits, and vegetables, and may range over a 30-mile territory. They should not be exterminated, as they are a valuable game species. Temperature, 88°–102° F. Life span, if the bear is lucky, may be to 25 years.

Grizzly Bear · *Ursus horribilis* · Ursidae

Skull

Hind Foot

Tracks

Front Foot

ORIGINALLY this huge animal was found through most of the western half of the United States and the western third of Canada. Now, except in parks, it has almost completely vanished as a wild animal of the United States. Tourists can still see some grizzlies free and wild, however, most commonly in Yellowstone Park. The bears favor rough country. Some consider the Alaskan brown bear to be a subspecies of the grizzly, but the U. S. National Museum recognizes the Alaskan brown bear as being one of some 75 species of the genus *Ursus*.

Grizzly bears have a length of to 8½ feet and shoulder height of to 4 feet. They appear high shouldered. They average about 900 pounds in weight, but individuals of 1,150 pounds have been known. Females are slightly smaller. Sexes are colored alike a yellowish brown. Teeth are: I 3/3; C 1/1; P 4/4; M 2/3. Tracks are: F 4 x 6, 5; H 5 x 12, 5. In a grizzly track, the 5 claws show more clearly than do those of the black bear. In a tree scratched by a grizzly, 5 claw marks show, instead of the 4 of a black bear.

Grizzlies probably pair for the season, and 180–236 days after the mating 1–4 cubs are born. They weigh 1½ pounds at birth, and are 8 inches long. They remain with the mother the first summer and breed when 3 years old. At maturity, young are born every other year. There may be a life span of to 31 years. Grizzlies as adults do not climb trees.

Grizzlies feed on gophers and ground squirrels, fish, snakes, birds, grass, fruits, and vegetables. They kill deer and may develop a habit of killing stock, such as sheep, goats, cattle, hogs, and horses. Some show a preference for sheep and horses. This habit of killing stock, plus their direct potential danger to man, has resulted in the grizzlies' almost complete extermination from the United States. Their flesh is considered edible and the pelts may bring $100 for use as rugs.

Alaskan Brown Bear or Kodiak Bear

Ursus middendorffi · Ursidae

THIS bear is justly referred to as "our largest carnivore." Since it is believed that some reach a weight of 1,500 pounds, the animals have few competitors in their class. This particular species is known on Kodiak Island in Alaska and on some adjacent islands, but not on the mainland. It has been contended that there are 8 species of Alaskan brown bears, but some of these so closely resemble some grizzlies that it may be that they are all 1 species.

Alaskan brown bears, or Kodiak bears as they may be called, reach a length of 8 feet, stand to 4½ feet high at the shoulder, and, as already stated, weigh to 1,500 pounds. A 7-year male of medium size weighs to 1,000 pounds, while a female of the same age may not exceed 700 pounds. Teeth are I 3/3; C 1/1; P 4/4; M 2/3. Tracks are, for mature males: F 8 x 9, 5; H 10½ x 16, 5, with the pad of the hind foot occupying most of the tracks. The long, curved claws do not appear so conspicuously in the tracks as might be expected. Females' tracks are about one third the size of those of the males.

From 1 to 3 cubs, each about the size of a rat and weighing 1½ pounds, and with eyes closed, are born in January or February, 210–250 days after the mating takes place. The cubs leave the den in 3–4 months, and stay with the mother through the second summer. Some authorities say that the young breed at 2 years of age, while others insist that breeding is delayed until 6 years. Mature females breed every 2–3 years.

The gait of an Alaskan brown bear, which most of us have observed only through movies, has been described as something between that of a camel and a giraffe. The food has been described as follows: spring, roots; June–July, reed grass and horsetail; August–September, berries and ground squirrels; with young caribou, hares, sheep, and salmon in season. Hibernate. Temperature, 98.6°–100.4° F. Life span, in captivity, is known to be to 34 years.

191

Polar Bear · *Thalarctos maritimus* · Ursidae

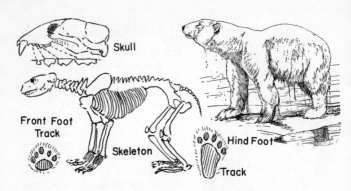

Skull

Front Foot Track

Skeleton

Hind Foot Track

THE species name *maritimus* is most appropriate for this, the most marine of all our bears. Most of us will see polar bears only in zoos, where they are relatively common and almost invariably the center of attention. Normally these bears live through Arctic America near the sea. They have been reported swimming vigorously 200 miles from land, but whether this was near floating ice does not appear in the references.

Polar bears are to 11 feet long and weigh to 1,700 pounds, the average male weighing 900 pounds and the average female 700 pounds. The sexes are colored alike a uniform white with a yellow tinge. Some brown may appear in summer, and the young may be whiter than the adults. The shoulder height is to 5 feet. Teeth are: I 3/3, C 1/1, P 4/4, M 2/3. Tracks are: F 9 x 9, 5; H 9 x 12, 5; not well defined due to the fact that except for small pads the soles are well haired and the toes may make little impression and the claws none.

It is believed that polar bears may scent food or enemies as much as 20 miles away. Normally, they will not attack man, but when forced to be they are powerful fighters. They feed on a great variety of animal matter and sometimes graze on grass much as does a hog. In winter, the females hibernate but the males do not.

Courtship takes place in midsummer, but for most of the year the sexes live apart. By November the females dig a den in hard-packed snow and begin hibernation. From 1–4 cubs are born 8–9 months after the mating. They are rat size and practically naked; respiration rate, 700. The mother remains in the den with the young, nursing them until March, when the family takes to the sea. The young leave the mother when 10 months old and may themselves breed when 2½–4 years of age. A mature female usually breeds every other year. Temperature, 99°–100.2° F. The life span of zoo specimens has been recorded as to 33½ years.

Ring-tailed Cat, Cacomistle, or Civet Cat

Bassariscus astutus · Procyonidae

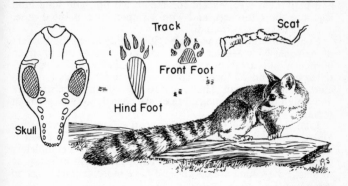

THE name "civet cat" is sometimes improperly applied to this animal, which is found in wooded and rocky areas in 3 recognized subspecies. One subspecies ranges from Oregon through California. A second is found in Nevada, and the third in Arizona, New Mexico, Colorado, and Utah, east through Texas and rarely to Alabama. All range south into Mexico. Nocturnal in their habits, they are seen rarely. Because of the value of their fur and their reputation as raiders of chicken coops, they are trapped regularly. During the day, they sleep safely in their dens, which are among rocks or in holes in trees.

The ring-tailed cats are sleek and graceful. They are to 32 inches long, including a 17-inch tail. They weigh to 2½ pounds. The sexes are colored alike. The tail bands are black and white. The general color is a brownish gray, lighter beneath, with a whitish snout and dark spots in front of each eye. Teeth are: I 3/3, C 1/1, P 4/4, M 2/2. Tracks are: F 1 x 1, 5; H 1 x 1, 5, and in walking the hind foot may be placed where the front foot was. The claws show only rarely and then under ideal conditions. The fur has 40% the durability of otter.

Ring-tailed cats feed on small mammals, birds, and fruit, and in turn are preyed upon by horned owls. Their coiled scats are often full of bones of their prey. They make excellent ratters and useful pets.

In May or June the 1–5 young are born in the home den. Their eyes are closed and their ears hardly visible. They weigh about 1 ounce and are covered with a white fuzz. At 3 weeks they eat meat brought by either parent, at 2 months they join the parents on trips; at 4 months they are weaned, and at 4½ months have reached adult size. The sexes congregate at different times of the year, but the animals are not normally social. In the trade ring-tailed cat fur is known as "California mink" or "civet cat." There is no scientific basis for either name.

Ring-tailed cats have been known to live 8 years in captivity.

Coati or Coatimundi · *Nasua narica* · Procyonidae

IMAGINE a brown, short-haired raccoon with a slender tail that is usually held erect except for the curled tip, with long hind legs and short forelegs, and with a rather long, pointed nose, and you have a coatimundi.

Coatis are found in the United States only along the borders of Arizona, New Mexico, and Texas and close to the Mexican border. While a raccoon is about 30 inches long and a ring-tailed cat about 32 inches, coatis are over 50 inches long, including the 2-foot tail. They stand to a foot high at the shoulder and weigh up to 25 pounds. Males are considerably larger than females.

Like that of the raccoon, the coati's face has contrasting black and gray markings. Also as in the raccoon, the tail is ringed with dark bands, except that it is not always completely encircled by them. In general the color is reddish brown-gray to black; the young are darker and have more distinct rings on the tail.

Coatis climb trees readily, their long tails serving as excellent balancing organs. They feed on almost any available plant or

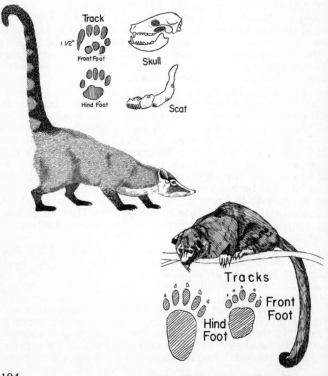

Track
1 1/2"
Front Foot
Hind Foot
Skull
Scat

Tracks
Front Foot
Hind Foot

Kinkajou

nimal matter, enjoying insects, worms, mice, birds, fruits, and plant tissues. They are normally friendly to those whom they know, make excellent pets, but when cornered can be formidable fighters, using their long, sharp-edged fangs as weapons.

Coatis are active most of the day and night, except for the hours around noon and midnight. When the light is poor for their purposes, the coatis just take it easy and sleep. Male coatis are rather solitary animals, but the females may live together with other females and their young. The young, usually from 4–6, are born in spring or early summer 77 days after the mating has taken place. The very young animals are practically hairless.

Kinkajou or Honey Bear · *Potos flavus* · Procyonidae

MEXICANS sometimes call kinkajous "monkey lions." The powerful, slender, prehensile tail and the ability of the animals to use this tail in traveling through the treetops account for the "monkey" part of the name. The "lion" part is more difficult to understand, since the kinkajous are usually rather friendly animals that may have fed on animals generations ago but now favor plant materials, such as juicy fruits. The front feet are used to carry the food to the mouth and to hold it there, much as is the case with monkeys. When tamed, they make superior pets.

Kinkajous have bodies about 1 foot long and tails to about 18 inches long. They stand about 10 inches high at the shoulder. Body is rather slender. Hind legs are the longer. Pads of feet are naked. Eyes are large, dark, and sparkle in the short face. Ears are small and round. Color is dark gold to brown. The fur is soft, woolly, and unfortunately popular as an adornment for women.

The name "honey bear" comes from the manner in which the kinkajou seems to express its satisfaction when it is eating a juicy fruit, sticking out its tongue and smacking its lips when pleased.

Two–4 young, covered with soft, black, fluffy fur and about the size of newborn kittens, represent a litter. At 10 days they open their eyes and at 7 weeks they are able to hang safely by their tails.

Kinkajous have lived in an apparently healthy state in captivity for 19 years. One pair which had lived together for 9 years bore their first litter of young when they themselves were 12½ years old. Temperature, 97°–99° F.

The kinkajou bears the generic name of *Potos,* and some South American natives give it the common name of *potto*. It should not be confused with the African lemur, also called potto, described on page 51.

Besides eating fruit, kinkajous feed readily on birds, small mammals, and other animals.

Raccoon · *Procyon lotor* · Procyonidae

Tracks

Front Foot

Hind Foot

Sku...

Scat

Trail

HERE is a wild animal with a valuable fur pelt, with a reputation for destroying corn, chickens, and other agricultural crop
and so capable of taking care of itself in the face of civilizatio
that it can be found successfully raiding garbage pails we
within the limits of cities of considerable size.

Raccoons range in and near wooded areas from the Gulf
St. Lawrence to southeastern British Columbia, south to th
Gulf of Mexico and South America. They are not found in th
northern Rockies or in the drier parts of the Great Basin, i
cluding much of Montana, Idaho, Wyoming, Utah, Nevada
Colorado, or New Mexico.

Raccoons are to 30 inches long, including a 10-inch bush
and ringed tail. They weigh to 25 pounds. The sexes are supe
ficially alike. The fur is long, of excellent quality, having
durability 65% that of otter. The hairs are mostly gray, brow
and black, with dull brown at the base. There is a conspicuou
black band across the face and eyes. A 10-pound raccoon ca
go through a hole 3½ inches in diameter.

The fur is known commercially as "Alaska bear" or "Alask
sable." Teeth are: I 3/3, C 1/1, P 4/4, M 3/2. Tracks are
F 2½ x 3, 5; H 2½ x 4, 5; L 20. Suitable woodland of 200 acre
can support a raccoon population which will give a sustaine
yield of 1 raccoon a year, for which appropriate den trees mus
be left standing. A full meal for a raccoon is ½ pound of fis
or the equivalent. Food also includes crayfish, birds and the
eggs, corn, and vegetables. Food is not stored but is frequentl
"washed" before being eaten. The dens are not kept clean
Raccoons may carry rabies, are desperate fighters when cor
nered, but tame easily when young. Probably monogamou
Mate in January to June, after hibernation ends, and 1–6 blin
young are born 60–73 days later. At 19 days, eyes open. The
suckle for 2 months, and remain in family circle a year, whe
they breed. Respiration rate, 395. Temperature, 95.6°
100.2° F. Life expectancy, to 13 years.

Giant Panda · *Aeoloropus melanoleucus* · Aeoloropidae

To many Americans, the giant panda is probably the most popular of all zoo animals. It even seems to take joy in amusing the human beings who stand outside the pen and watch what is going on inside.

Giant pandas are native of western China near the border of Tibet, at elevations of 6,000–12,000 feet, where dense bamboo forests prevail. They have been known to zoologists since 1869, but the first one was brought to an American zoo in 1937. Their nearest relatives probably are the raccoons.

These pandas have a head and body length of 4–5 feet, and a tail about 5 inches long. The head is large and somewhat bearlike. It is white except for the black at the muzzle tip, around the eyes, and on the ears. The body is white, but the animal seems to be wearing black stockings, with the front pair extending up to and around the neck. Weight, to around 300 pounds. Fur is thick and dense, claws long, and feet flat like those of a bear.

Giant pandas probably do not hibernate but remain active through the year. They probably mate in spring, and the 1–2 cubs are born in January. They weigh only a few pounds at birth, the normal size being about 3 pounds. By the end of the following year they weigh up to 70 pounds, having gained an average of 5 pounds a month during the first year. They probably become sexually mature in from 4–10 years, but this is not definitely known. During the breeding season the males often roar loudly.

The food of giant pandas is almost wholly plant materials, bamboo sprouts being a favorite. They must feed from 10–12 hours a day to get enough plant food to maintain health and assure normal growth. In captivity, they are fed vegetables, cereals, milk, and of course cod-liver oil, which is a standard diet element for many zoo animals from overseas. Orange juice also helps to keep the pandas in good condition most of the time.

197

Marten or Sable · *Martes americana* · Mustelidae

A marten, or sable, looks and acts somewhat like an enormous red squirrel which is 2 feet long and conspicuously slender.

Martens range normally through wooded Canada and Alaska and south to West Virginia and Colorado, with isolated colonies in central California and northern New Mexico.

Martens weigh up to 4 pounds, but this weight does not seem to limit their activities, and they speed through the treetops with all the confidence of a squirrel. However, squirrels lose their celebrated confidence when pursued by a marten, and they are lucky if they do not lost their lives shortly.

Martens are a rich brown with an irregular white or yellowish patch on the throat. The ears are pointed and white or dull inside. Teeth are: I 3/3; C 1/1; P 4/4; M 1/2. Tracks are: F 1⅝ x 2, 5; H 1⅝ x 3, 5; Sp 6–10; L 10–48. Thick pads of hair conceal the details of the tracks in winter. The nail tracks and those of some toes may not show.

Generally considered as rare mammals, martens are confined rather definitely to heavily wooded country. They hunt day or night tirelessly through the treetops for their food, which may be squirrels, birds, mice, eggs, or any other animal they can capture in the trees or on the ground. They do not hibernate and are as relentless in their squirrel hunts in winter as in summer. The fur is so valuable that the animals have been trapped almost to extinction. Its durability is 60% that of otter. In the best marten country, 6 animals per square mile is a high population. They are among the most valuable of mice controls.

Martens mate, possibly monogamously, in July or August. There is a delayed fertilization of the egg and the 1–5 blind young are born 255–285 days after the mating. The den is a grass-lined hollow in a tree or burrow. Eyes of young open at 39 days. They are nursed for 6 weeks, stay with mother 3 months, when mature size is reached. Life expectancy, to 17 years.

Fisher or Pekan · *Martes pennanti* · Mustelidae

Trail

Front Foot

Track

Hind Foot

Scat

WHILE a marten has a total length of about 2 feet and weighs up to 4 pounds, its larger relative, the fisher or pekan, is 3 feet long, and weighs to 18 pounds. The length of the tail is to 14 inches. Female fishers are much smaller than the males, weighing up to 6 pounds.

Fishers range through heavily wooded country across most of southern Canada, south into New England and New York, and in the West south into western Montana and western Washington, Oregon, and California.

Fishers are dark brown to almost black, with the legs and tail tip black. They resemble a slender, short-legged black cat, and while they may be active in treetops are less so than are the martens. They are much more slender and short-legged than any fox. When disturbed, the fisher, like most other weasels, can give off a most offensive odor.

Fisher fur is one of the most valuable. Single pelts have brought to $150, and over a 70-year period the harvest from the entire range has averaged between 8,000 and 9,000 pelts a year. In some states, the fishers enjoy complete protection, but suitable range is decreasing with the advance of human populations. Pelts of females are worth about twice those of males.

Teeth are: I 3/3; C 1/1; P 4/4; M 1/2. Tracks are: F 2½ x 3¼, 5; H 1¼ x 2, 5; Sp 8; L 36. Fishers feed on squirrels, mice, porcupines, raccoons, and rabbits, captured by tireless pursuit. Food may be stored. Fishers do not burrow. They may follow regular beats. They can swim if necessary.

Mating is in April, and 1–5 blind young are born about 50 weeks later. Within a week a new mating has taken place. Eyes of young open at 7 weeks. They stay in den to 3 months. They are reared by mother alone, using series of dens high in hollow trees with entrance 4–5 feet above ground. Family breaks up in fall. Fishers range over 8–10 mile territory.

199

Bonaparte Weasel, Ermine, or Short-tailed Weasel
Mustela erminea · Mustelidae

Trail

Tracks

Hind Foot

Front Foot

PRESIDENT THEODORE ROOSEVELT is credited with helping establish the expression "weasel words" in the dictionary. It is a term designed to take the strength out of a statement without seeming to destroy it completely, much as weasels are reputed to suck the contents of an egg without breaking it.

Bonaparte weasels range from south of the Great Lakes almost to the northern border of the continent, west to the Pacific, and south in the highlands into Wyoming and central California. Closely related species extend the range greatly.

While weasels are reputed to suck blood from their victims, an examination of 500 stomachs of this species gives no evidence of blood-sucking. Examination of 360 stomachs showed that 96.8% had fed on only such mammals as field mice, rabbits, deer mice, shrews, rats, and chipmunks, all archenemies of farmers. And yet Pennsylvania has spent as much as $80,000 a year in bounties on weasels, with no evidence of change in population other than an increase in the number of weasels submitted for the bounty. The name "ermine" is used in the fur trade to cover a number of Old World and New World species.

A male Bonaparte weasel is 14 inches long, including a 3½ inch tail; a female, 9 inches long. Weight, to 3½ ounces. In summer they are brown above and white beneath; in winter, all white except for black on tail tip. Teeth are: I 3/3, C 1/1, P 3/3, M 1/2. Tracks are: F 1 x 1, 4; H 1½ x 1, 4; Sp 3; L to 72. Tail track shows. The 5th toe rarely shows.

Bonaparte weasels are active night and day, but mostly at night, the year round. They molt in spring and fall. Mating takes place in July, and the 6–13 blind young are born in a fur-and feather-lined nest in a cave or hollow log 9–10 months later. Young weigh ¹⁄₁₄ ounce at first; appear naked. At 4 weeks eyes open. They are weaned at 5 weeks. In 7 weeks young males are larger than their mothers. Males breed at 1 year; females may breed their first summer. Both parents care for young and will defend them with their lives. Population varies in 4–7 year cycles. Respiration rate, 5,000.

Least Weasel · *Mustela rixosa* · Mustelidae

THIS little demon is the archenemy of mice, shrews, and similar small mammals, as well as of insects, and apparently will not let superior size frighten it from making an attack and a kill. It follows its prey by scent, swims easily when necessary, and once it is on the trail of a luckless mouse it usually persists until the mouse has gone to its fathers.

Least weasels are found in woods, lawns, and waste areas from Hudson Bay to Alaska and south to Pennsylvania and Montana, with related species extending the range farther south.

Male least weasels are from 7–9 inches long, including the 1½ inch tail. They weigh from 1–2½ ounces. Females measure 6½–9 inches. In all of these weasels the tail does not exceed one fourth the combined length of the body and head, and the tail has but a few black hairs at the tip. In summer, the upper parts are brown and the under parts, including the forefeet and much of the hind feet, white. In winter the animals are all white in most parts of the range. In the East some of the upper parts may remain brown. Some researchers contend that the white fur of the least weasel will fluoresce a vivid lavender under ultraviolet light. This is not the case with related species.

Teeth are: I 3/3, C 1/1, P 3/3, M 1/2. Tracks are: F ¾ x ¾, 5; H ¾ x 1, 5; Sp 2½; L 24. There is little evidence of a tail mark. The hind-foot tracks are frequently exactly superimposed on those made by the front feet. Temperature, 101°–108° F.

From 3–10 young are born in a den which is usually underground. The nest is commonly lined with mouse fur and is usually well ventilated. The mother alone cares for the young, which surprisingly enough may be born in almost any month of the year. Food may be stored, but not in the nest. Few animals are more valuable as mice destroyers.

Long-tailed Weasel

Mustela frenata longicauda · Mustelidae

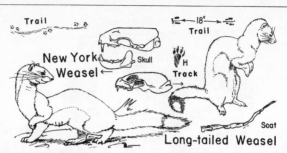

New York Weasel

Long-tailed Weasel

SUBSPECIES of *Mustela frenata* include the long-tailed weasel and the New York weasel, *Mustela f. noveboracensis.* Found throughout United States except for northern Maine, western Arizona, and southeastern California; also in southwestern Canada and in Mexico.

Whereas the male New York weasel is 16.3 inches long, including a 5.8 inch tail, the male long-tailed weasel is 18 inches long, including a 6.6 inch tail. Weight, to 14 ounces. Females are smaller. Both subspecies are white in winter. These weasels, weighing about ½ pound, can go through a hole ⅞ inch in diameter.

Teeth are: I 3/3, C1/1, P 3/3, M 1/2. Tracks: F 1 x 1½, 5; H 1 x 1½, 5; Sp 3, L 50. The 5th toe rarely shows in the track except under unusually good conditions.

Food is mostly mice, rabbits, chipmunks, squirrels, birds, snakes, and insects. A long-tailed weasel can hold a half-pound rabbit above the ground. These weasels can climb readily, chasing chipmunks and red squirrels out to the ends of smaller branches in pursuit. They are usually solitary. When excited, they give off a strong, unpleasant odor. When cornered or in defense of a recent kill, they have been known to attack men or dogs. They are often seen hunting in daytime. They kill usually by a vicious bite at the base of the skull. They do not suck blood. Populations vary over periods of 4–7 years. Their destruction of rodents should more than make up for their occasional attacks on poultry, even though these may be tragic at times. Fur is brown under ultraviolet light.

Mating takes place in July or August, and 4–9 blind young are born from 220–337 days later, or in spring. There is a delay in the egg fertilization. Young weigh about ⅛ ounce, and are practically naked. At 3 weeks, solid food may be taken; at 37 days, the eyes open and nursing ends, and at 7–8 weeks, hunting may begin. Males bring food to young. Females breed the first year, but males breed first at about 11 months. Pulse, 172–192. Long-tailed weasels have lived for 5 years in captivity.

Mink · *Mustela vison* · Mustelidae

MINK coats have figured prominently in the world of female fashions. Mink represents luxury to the average person. In the past, superior pelts have brought as high as $25, but with the manufacture of synthetic imitations that are automatically mothproof, the price of mink may fall and the fortunes of the animals may rise, with the trappers going on relief.

Range through most of North America except the extreme North, the Southwest, and Mexico. Excellent swimmers and favor wooded waterways in marshlands. Go considerable distances from water. To 28 inches long, of which 8 inches is tail. They weigh to 3½ pounds, with the females one half to three fourths the size of males.

Fur uniformly dark brown, except for mutations, which are unusual. Minks of Labrador are the darkest and those of Alaska are largest. Teeth are: I 3/3, C 1/1, P 3/3, M 1/2. Tracks are: F 1½ x 1½, 4; H 1½ x 1½, 4; Sp 5; L 24. In most cases a tail drag shows and usually the hind-foot tracks are in front of or superimposed on those of the front feet.

Muskrats, birds, frogs, snakes, and fish, with small aquatic animals, make up the mink's diet. In winter they pursue and kill rabbits on land.

Breeding takes place in February or March, the male mating with more than one female. Female in heat 2 days. Copulation lasts ½–2½ hours. Male usually stays with 1 female after the young are born, and helps in their care and feeding. Young numbering 3–8 are born 45–60 days after the mating, are blind from 3½–5 weeks, and leave den at 6–8 weeks, after being weaned at 5 weeks. In captivity they live to 10 years. Both sexes breed at 1 year of age, and the males fight fiercely for domination. Food may be stored in or near the den. The home range of a female is about 20 acres, with that of the male somewhat larger.

Black-footed Ferret · *Mustela nigripes* · Mustelidae

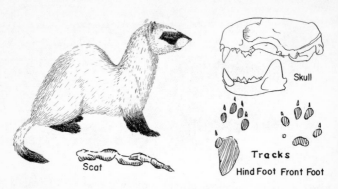

Skull

Scat

Tracks

Hind Foot   Front Foot

THE fate of many predatory animals often depends not on the predators themselves, but on the animals or plants on which they feed. This seems to be especially true of the black-footed ferret, which formerly thrived in territory that supported prairie dogs. With the disappearance of prairie dogs owing to the activities of agriculture, the ferrets that fed on them, and in some degree kept them under control, have declined in numbers. It seems reasonable to assume that this species may well become extinct in our time.

Formerly the black-footed ferret ranged from western and northern Texas through the western parts of Kansas, Nebraska, and the Dakotas and the eastern parts of New Mexico, Colorado, Wyoming, and Montana. The range extends into Canada a short distance north of Montana and North Dakota. Ferrets are found in the Rockies up to elevations of 10,500 feet.

These ferrets measure to 2 feet, including a 6-inch tail. They weigh about 1½ pounds, the female being the lighter. They are a yellow buff in color, lighter beneath. The feet, tail tip, and a patch across the eyes are black. Teeth are: I 3/3, C 1/1, P 3/3, M 1/2. Tracks are: F 1½ x 1½, 5; H 2 x 1½, 5; Sp 4.

Little seems to be known about the life history, and unless it is learned in the relatively near future it may never be known. Mothers and young have been seen working together in late summer, and a nursing female has been captured in July. Aside from that, little information has been recorded.

The poisoning campaign waged against prairie dogs may have exterminated some ferrets. Without the prairie dogs to give them food and burrows in which to live and to rear young, the ferrets face a losing battle. Before it is too late, the story of these vanishing mammals should be sought by all naturalists who have the opportunity to observe prairie dog towns and the associated black-footed ferret.

Polecat · *Mustela putorius* · Mustelidae
Domestic Ferret or Fitchet · *Mustela fure* · Mustelidae

THE polecat is a native of Europe where in the wild state it has become one of the rarer mammals. The American variety, *Mustela fure,* is known as the domestic ferret. Because of the foul odor of the creatures, the term "polecat" has been turned into an expression of repugnance and disgust applied to persons whose habits are considered blatantly offensive. In America it is also loosely applied to the skunks (pages 208–210).

The polecat has a total length of to 27 inches, of which 6 is the tail. The body is long and thin, the head massive. Legs short. Ears short, rounded, and light colored. Nose moderately pointed and light colored. The area around the eyes is dark and the general color of the long fur is a dark brown to black. The domestic ferret may be lighter in color and even white, with the typical red eyes of albinos. Ferrets apparently originated in Africa, were introduced into Spain, and from there spread through Europe and the civilized world.

Ferrets are raised for use as rat destroyers and in driving rabbits from their burrows, where they may be shot or caught in bags at the entrance. When used for rabbit hunting, the ferrets are frequently muzzled to keep them from killing the rabbits in the burrows and then staying in the burrows to rest. Wild polecats often raise havoc in poultry yards or pigeon lofts, and will sometimes raid beehives for the honey, which they enjoy. Teeth are: I 3/3, C 1/1, P 3/3, M 1/2. A full-grown male weighs as much as 5 pounds, but the average is 3 pounds. Pulse, 216–242. Temperature, 100°–109° F.

In the wild state, male polecats desert their families after the mating season, which may be twice a year. The mother alone protects the 5–8 young which make up the normal litter. Young polecats are excessively playful. Young are born in a sheltered den commonly under a large rock, the entrance to which is far from obvious. Their eyes are closed for the first 2 weeks of their lives.

Wolverine, Skunk Bear, Carcajou, or Glutton

Gulo luscus · Mustelidae

PROBABLY few animals of the wild have been more roundly cussed than have wolverines—and with ample reason. Few animals can be more exasperating. Wolverines seem bent on fouling or destroying everything useful they can find. If they cannot eat cached food, they render it unfit for human consumption, and do so apparently with malice aforethought. Their one saving grace seems to be their fur. It is ideal for the front of a hood or parka worn by a man who must survive rugged winter weather, as the frost from his breath does not readily collect on it. The fur is also worn around the wrists.

Wolverines originally ranged from southern Quebec across wooded Canada and in the West south into Colorado and even to southern California. At present their presence is rather closely confined to the Hudson Bay area and Alaska.

Wolverines are to nearly 4 feet long, including a 9-inch tail. They stand to 14 inches high and weigh more than 40 pounds. They are dark brown with a pale band along the sides, have a bushy tail, small ears close to the head, strong, sharp teeth, and powerful claws. Teeth are: I 3/3, C 1/1, P 4/4, M 1/2. Tracks are: F 4½ x 3, 5; H 3½ x 3¾, 5; L 36.

Wolverines are powerful enough to kill mountain sheep or even moose or elk that are hampered by the snow. They can drive bears or cougars from their kills and kill porcupines without trouble. They rob traps shamelessly and all too effectively. They can drag a carcass three times their own weight for a mile over rather rough terrain.

Wolverines mate during a short period, from February through April, after which the pair separates. In a carefully hidden den, some 60 days later, 2–4 young are born. They nurse for 8–9 weeks and are two thirds grown by fall, at which time the family breaks up for good. In captivity, wolverines have lived for 13 years.

Badger · *Taxidea taxus* · Mustelidae

Tracks

Front Foot   Hind Foot

Skull   Trail   Scat

So common a practice was it among so-called "sportsmen" to tease and worry a badger before killing it, presumably to see it defend itself, that the term "badger" has come to be used for teasing and worrying anything. The badger has never lost face in such situations and remains an outstanding example of courage and fighting ability in the face of odds.

Badgers live normally in dry, open country where the soil is such that it can be burrowed into successfully. In loose soil they can burrow rapidly enough to catch prairie dogs and ground squirrels underground. This ability provides a ready escape for a badger surprised away from its natural den or burrow. For defending itself, the badger is armed with strong teeth and front claws and an effective scent gland to the rear, which may be even more effective if gas warfare is in order.

Badgers are 30 inches long, including a 5½ inch tail; weigh to 24 pounds, although average is 13 pounds. Sexes superficially alike in size and color; are a grizzled gray and black. Hairs are gray at base, then gray white, then black, and then silver tipped. Teeth are: I 3/3, C 1/1, P 3/3, M 1/2. Tracks are: F 2 x 3, 5; H 2 x 2, 5; Sp 7. Nail marks of the front foot tracks are more conspicuous.

Badgers serve a most useful function in keeping down numbers of ground squirrels. Range matched rather closely that of these animals, extending approximately from Ohio south of Great Lakes to central Saskatchewan and southwestward into Mexico. Southeastern boundary extended from Iowa to central Texas and the Gulf Coast. Recently numbers have been greatly reduced.

Badgers can swim or climb, but are best at burrowing. A full meal for a badger is about ⅓ pound of ground squirrel. They keep dens clean.

Badgers probably pair, since both parents care for the young. Mating is in fall, and young are born 6 months later. Young, 1–5, are blind and furred at birth, open eyes at 4–6 weeks, are weaned at 6 weeks. The family breaks up late in the summer. Badgers have lived 13 years in captivity.

Spotted Skunk or Civet · *Spilogale putorius* · Mustelidae

IF we measured skunks by their size, the little spotted skunk would not be too important, but that is not the quality by which most of us measure skunks. When it comes to the question of producing a foul odor, these skunks are as good—or as bad—as the next one. They are excellent killers of rats and mice and good insect destroyers. They are known to carry rabies and to kill chickens and game, but these characteristics are hardly limited to skunks of this or of any other kind. They are found in most of the United States west of the Mississippi, except Montana and most of Wyoming, and also occur along the Gulf Coast and up the southern Appalachian highlands.

The little spotted skunk has a total length of 22½ inches, of which nearly 9 inches is tail. There are 4 longitudinal white stripes on the back, sides, and tail, but they do not appear to be clean cut and continuous, as they are in the common striped skunk. The weight is up to 3 pounds, the females being about three fourths the size and weight of the males. Teeth are: I 3/3, C 1/1, P 3/3, M 1/2. Tracks are: F 1 x 1½, 5; H 1 x 1¼, 5; Sp 5. The combinations of imprints found in a skunk trail are most confusing and may remind one of squirrel tracks, cat tracks, or other tracks of the same general size. These skunks can swim, burrow, climb, run, or walk slowly, and are excellent with their scent gun.

In late winter 1 male may mate with many females. By mid-spring the litters of 2–10 young are born in a den or hidden cavity, which may be shared with other skunks. A young spotted skunk weighs ⅓ ounce, is about 4 inches long, opens its eyes at 32 days, is weaned at about 56 days, and at about 100 days is full grown. The female assumes all responsibilities for the young. The fur is of relatively poor quality but of an attractive pattern.

208

Striped Skunk · *Mephitis mephitis* · Mustelidae

SKUNKS have paved the way to college for many a farm-boy trapper and have kept many an underprivileged man off relief and able to preserve pride in his independence. They were first protected by law in one state because of their recognized service in destroying insects that ravaged hop plants, and ever since have enjoyed and deserved some protection for the good they do in killing mice and insects. More than 400 stomach analyses indicate that nearly half of skunks' food is insects, ⅕ fruits and berries, ⅛ mice. They are particularly destructive of potato beetles, white grubs, and eggs of turtles that destroy ducks.

These skunks are to 30 inches long, including a 7½ inch tail, and weigh to 10 pounds; the females to 8 pounds. A 3¾ pound skunk can go through a hole 2¾ inches in diameter. The fur is of fine quality, with a durability of 70% that of otter, and is sold under the trade names of "Alaskan sable" or "black marten." It is black or black and white. Teeth are: I 3/3, C 1/1, P 3/3, M 1/2. Tracks are: F 1½ x 2, 5; H 1½ x 2½, 5; Sp 10. Pulse, 144–192. Temperature, 99°–101° F.

Striped skunks are found in woods and plains, either near to or remote from towns, where there is loose soil. They range through the southern half of Canada south through most of the United States except southern Florida and parts of the Coastal Plain.

Skunks, unfortunately, are destroyed in great numbers by automobiles. They protect themselves largely by using their effective scent. This is ejected from glands near the tail and can be directed accurately for 12 feet. Skunks usually stamp the ground in anger before throwing their scent.

Mating is in early spring. One male in captivity serves 6 females. In 51 days 4–10 naked, blind young are born in a den which may be shared with other animals. Eyes open in 3 weeks. Nursing is for 6–7 weeks. Male may rejoin family when young are well developed.

Hooded Skunk · *Mephitis macroura* · Mustelidae
Hognose Skunk · *Conepatus mesoleucus* · Mustelidae

Hognose Skunk

Skull

Track

2"

Hind Foot   Front Foot

Hooded Skunk

Scat

HOODED skunks are found within the limits of the United States only close to the Mexican border of Arizona and the extreme southwest corner of New Mexico. They are found south through central Mexico. They are of primary interest, probably, to zoologists. They are to 31 inches long, about the size of striped skunks, but the tail is longer than the head and body and there is often a ruff of hair at the nape of the neck. The back is black and white. The teeth and tracks are like those of the striped skunk and the habits are probably the same.

Hooded skunks are animals of desert lands. They can dig readily, using their claws or the bare snout in turning up soil over a considerable area in search of food. They might be characterized as the "diggin'est" of all the skunks.

Hognose skunks are found from southern Texas through most of New Mexico to southeastern Arizona, and in southern Colorado, in wooded areas at high elevations. They may possibly exist in Kansas and Oklahoma. They are our largest skunks, having a total length of 33 inches, including a 14-inch tail. Weight, to 10 pounds. The back is all white. The claws are longer and larger than those of the striped skunk. Teeth are: I 3/3, C 1/1, P 2/3, M 1/2. Note that in this skunk there are 3 teeth behind the canine tooth on each side of the upper jaw, instead of 4, as is the case in members of the genus *Mephitis*. The all-white back is of course an easier character to recognize in the field, since few would care to try to examine the teeth of a large skunk if the skunk were alive and able to protect itself. One of the common names of this skunk is "white-backed skunk." It might also be called the "white-tailed skunk," since its tail is wholly white and not black and white. There may be a few black hairs on the tail, but they are hardly noticeable.

Otter or River Otter · *Lutra canadensis* · Mustelidae

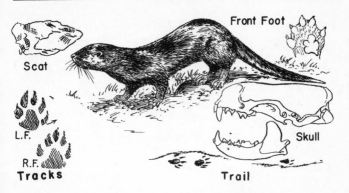

Front Foot

Scat

L.F.

R.F.

Tracks

Skull

Trail

ON land, in the water, in a zoo, or in the wild, an otter is an animal that most people enjoy observing. At play or in search of food in the water, it is a superlative swimmer. Sliding down a hill covered with snow, it makes one laugh in glee. At rest on land, it is a thing of graceful beauty. Dead, its skin is practically tops both in beauty and in quality—characters which are not always found together.

Otters are found in relatively wild country near good-sized waterways, through all except the northernmost parts of Canada and Alaska south through most of the United States, except areas in the Southwest.

Otters are to 5 feet long, including a 1-foot tail. They stand to 10 inches high at the shoulder and weigh to 30 pounds, so they are rather substantial creatures. Females are about two thirds the size of males. Otters' feet are webbed and the soles of their feet are hairy. There are 5 toes on each foot. The tail is strong and muscular and usually makes a trough in the trail. The fur is a rich, glossy brown but the lips and cheeks are of a lighter brown. Teeth are: I 3/3, C 1/1, P 4/3, M 1/2. Tracks are: F 3½ x 3½, 5; H 3¼ x 3¼, 5; Sp 8; L 30. The toe marks are not always conspicuous, partly because of the web between the toes. The fur is considered the standard of perfection on the basis of durability. Temperature, 101° F.

Otters feed largely on fish, but they may kill muskrats, young beaver, ducks, poultry, and birds. When disturbed, they give off an offensive odor.

Otters probably mate for life. They begin breeding at 1 year of age. From 288–380 days after the mating, 1–4 blind young are born, from February to April or earlier. The pups weigh to 6 ounces at 10 days and are black. Eyes open at 25–35 days. The young nurse for 4 months but may leave den with mother in less than 3 months. Family is together a year, both parents caring for young. May live 19 years.

Sea Otter · *Enhydra lutris* · Mustelidae

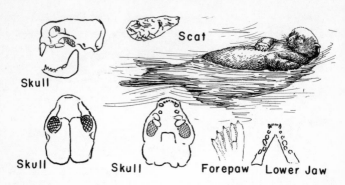

THE United States owes much to this animal, since the value of its fur provided one incentive for the development of our Northwest. Incidentally, too, it encouraged Russians to push down our Alaskan coast before that territory became the property of the United States. Its fur was the badge of royalty in China and Russia, and 1 pelt was sold in the London market for $2,500. The fur is 80% that of otter in excellence and durability. It is of a deep velvety brown, with a frosting of white guard hairs. About 1900 the animals had disappeared in American waters. Rigid protection was given them in 1912, and by 1938 a few appeared as far south as southern California. They are truly a species resurrected.

Sea otters are to 5 feet long, including a 1-foot tail. They weigh to 85 pounds. The hind feet are broadly webbed and haired on both sides. Teeth are: I 3/2, C 1/1, P 3/3, M 1/2. Tracks are: F 4 x 4; H 6 x 6, 5 (?). Weight, to 75 pounds. Females, much smaller. It should be noted that sea otters and hognose skunks have a total of 32 teeth; the weasels, 34; the river otter, 36, and the wolverine, marten, and fisher, 38.

Sea otters obtain food from the sea bottom by diving to depths of as much as 300 feet.

Young are born at any month of the year, 8–9 months after the mating which is preceded by elaborate courtship. Young are born often at sea, with eyes open and with fully developed teeth. They are able to get about well. They may nurse for a year, and are held in the mother's arms as they sleep and as she swims on her back. The mother mourns separation tremendously. Young may not reach full size for 4 years. The family may stay together for years, possibly forming the basis of a herd. The young breed at 1 year of age.

The story of the abundance of sea otters is a perfect example of what can and has been done in the conservation of a valuable renewable natural resource that came near to vanishing forever.

Mongoose · *Herpestes auropunctatus* · Herpestidae

THE movies, a rare trip outside of continental North America, or the reading of Rudyard Kipling's "Rikki-tikki-tavi," provides most of us with our introduction to the mongooses. The animals scuttle across roads in Hawaii and Jamaica much as do woodchucks in the eastern United States, but, unlike the woodchucks, they seek flesh for food, not plants. While they have been widely introduced to cut down rat populations, they have also done much to keep chickens out of many a family's stewpot.

Mongooses are chiefly Asiatic and African, but 1 species lives in Spain. They cannot legally be brought into the United States.

The Javan mongoose, *H. auropunctatus,* is to 18 inches long, with a 15-inch tail added on. Mongooses have 5-toed feet with long, retractile claws, are grayish brown, lighter beneath, and can stand erect on hind legs.

Mongooses are great snake destroyers, killing venomous snakes by a quick bite in the neck just after the snake has struck. Their agility protects them from being bitten. They are easily tamed, and become affectionate pets. In Hawaii, newborn young are found in all months except October, November, and December. There are 2–3 litters a year, with 2–3 young to a litter. The young are born in a den hole and are protected by the mother until about one fourth grown. Life span, to 8 years.

Among the different mongooses are the striped-necked group, including the striped-necked mongoose of India and the crab-eating mongoose of China and Malaya. Among those without a neck stripe are the Indian mongoose, *H. edwardsii,* to 33 inches long, and the Javan mongoose, *H. auropunctatus,* also to 33 inches long. The water mongoose of Borneo and lower Malaya is 26 inches long and has faint markings on the neck.

Mongooses were brought into Hawaii in 1884 and promptly wiped out many of the island's ground-nesting birds (fortunately they cannot climb, but where they left off introduced rats took over). They were introduced into Jamaica in 1872. There are records of rabies being carried by mongooses in Puerto Rico.

Domestic Cats · *Felis catus* · Felidae

As with the dogs, in describing the cats, we give general information on certain pages, in addition to the specific information about different breeds. Accordingly we consider the care and feeding of cats on this page, reproduction in cats on page 217, the ancestry of cats on page 219, and the economics of cats on page 221. Show points are included in individual descriptions.

The appetite of a cat, like the appetite of humans, is not a good measure of its food needs. Cats feeding largely on beef may become constipated; those on fish and liver, low in disease resistance; those feeding too largely on fruits and vegetables, troubled with skin diseases and low in stamina. Cats cannot digest bones and stale meat as can dogs. Horse meat may be a good staple diet, with liver, heart, or kidneys once a week, and milk at most times. Cereals should be kept in low proportion. Canned food should be kept at a minimum. Cats should be given a box of sand to use, and this should be kept clean. To save furniture, they should be given and trained to use a scratching post. They should not be sprayed with DDT powders, unless of course you wish to get rid of your cat.

Manx Cat · *Felis catus* · Felidae

MANX cats probably came to England and America from the Isle of Man, but are reported to have developed from cats that came ashore with wrecks of the Spanish Armada in 1588. The Manx breed first appeared in America about 1820. They are intelligent animals and are easily trained.

The Manx cat's back is short, the hindquarters unusually high. The gait is a sort of hop, but these cats have excellent speed if necessary. Tail is absent, but there is a depression in back of spine where tail should be. Head is round and full, face broad. The coat varies in different Manx cats, but in general is double, with long top hairs, and shorter hairs forming a dense undercoat. The undercoat causes the outer coat to stand out like a rabbit's fur. In cat shows, Manx cats are judged like the long-haired breeds discussed later. In color, Manx cats may be either solid or "tabby" (diversified), without prejudice to the show value of the animal. Important in judging are the body proportions suggested above; namely, short back, absence of tail, long hind legs, and proper head.

Siamese Cat, Sacred Cat, Temple Cat, or Royal Cat
Felis catus · Felidae

Skull

IN Burma and Thailand this cat was known as the "Temple Cat" for more than 200 years. Siamese cats were introduced into England in 1884 and into America in 1894, and are now more numerous outside of Thailand than they are in that country.

Siamese cats are always trim in appearance. Length, including tail, about 21 inches. Head wedge-shaped. Legs thin, with the hind ones the longer. Ears broad at base, pointed, and rather large. Tail thin and of moderate length. Fur short, sleek, and close to the body. Eyes deep and slanting. These cats are nervous, graceful, and quick acting.

There are 3 types: *Seal-point:* light fawn-colored body. Ears and mask dark brown to black, as are legs, paws, and tail. Eyes almond-shaped, deep sapphire blue. *Blue-point:* body shades into blue on back and is glacial white below. Tail, legs, ears, face, blue. *Chocolate-point:* body ivory, and "points," such as ears, feet, and tail, chocolate.

Siamese cats are generally independent with strangers. The kittens are born white, getting mature color in 3–6 months.

Burmese Cat · *Felis catus* · Felidae

BURMESE cats may be the oldest of all breeds. In Burma they were originally owned by the priests and the wealthy, and each cat had its own servant. The cats could not be bought in Burma at the time when they enjoyed their highest favor. They are ordinarily more gentle and lovable than are the Siamese cats. They are easily house broken and not unusually destructive.

This breed is much like the Siamese breed, and is considered by many as being simply a variation of the Siamese cat. Coat is unusually smooth and velvety brown. Fur is short, close, chocolate or sable brown. Eyes are yellow, orange, or golden. The absence of dark "points" distinguishes this cat from the Siamese cat.

Probably the royal cat of Burma, which had long hair and bushy tail, interbred with the Siamese cat when Burma was conquered some 300 years ago. The modern Burmese cat is the result of the cross. The Siamese cat of the modern cat fanciers is descended from the pure Siamese breed of old.

Abyssinian Cat · *Felis catus* · Felidae

ABYSSINIAN cats are of Egyptian origin and were probably associated with the Egyptian goddess Bast, which gave cats the name of "puss." The goddess had the body of a human and the head of a cat. Abyssinian cats are rare in the United States, where they were introduced in Washington, D.C., about 1936, but are relatively common in England.

In the Abyssinian cat the head is pointed and the tail long and tapering. Coat is gray-brown or red-brown, with 2–3 black or dark brown bands on each hair and a spot of dark brown or

black at the end of the hair, producing a mottled effect. Thus the color of the cats is basically ruddy brown or silver, but with black and brown ticking. Belly and forelegs are lighter brown, with dark stripe running down spine to end of tail. The hair is short.

Abyssinian cats have lithe bodies and long, slender, and graceful legs. Ears long-pointed. Voice soft and weak. Eyes large and bright, and yellow, green, or hazel in color.

These cats are quiet and extremely dignified animals. They are highly sensitive and need a reasonable amount of liberty.

Reproduction of Domestic Cats

DOMESTIC cats breed at 10 months or younger, usually cease after 14 years, have lived to 31 years. Height of breeding, February–March, but may extend, at 10-day intervals, from December to August. Females in prime 2–8 years; males, 3–14 years. Heat is preceded by 2–3 days of excessive playfulness. Heat may last 2–21 days. Copulation may be repeated at 15–30 minute intervals at height. Gestation, 56–65 days, with 62–63 normal. Litters, 1–8; young and old females have smaller litters. Mother can nurse only 8. Nursing continuous first day, may last 2 months, but declines after 4–6 weeks. Female 6 weeks pregnant may mate and produce litter of mixed sizes. Kittens blind 10 days, develop milk teeth between 4 days and 5 weeks, and permanent teeth 4–7 months. Incisors appear first; 2nd upper molars appear last. Male and female kittens grow equally first 2 months, then males develop more rapidly. Females may best be spayed at 4 months and males castrated between 3 and 6 months. In feline genetics, tabby is usually dominant over black, short hair over long hair, and short tail over normal tail. Pulse, 110–140. Temperature, 100°–102° F.

Long-haired Persian-Angora Cats · *Felis catus* · Felidae

Leg Bones

Track

1"

Front Foot

ANGORA cats originally came from Turkey and had a long head, long body, long tail, and long hair on the stomach. These characteristics have given way to the dominant shorter structures of the Persian, and now the 2 are considered as 1 owing to interbreeding. The many current differences are largely in coloring.

These cats are compact bodied, with round head, short, stocky legs, fluffy tail, and long, silky hair, but not so long as in the original Angora. The voice is soft and well modulated and the animals are not normally aggressive. They are more or less indolent, are graceful, and are affectionate to owners but reserved with strangers. From these cats have developed many breeds, some of which have official recognition, while others are not well defined officially or otherwise.

The Maine coon cat is probably descended from Persian cats that crossed with the short-haired cats of Maine at the time of the French Revolution. The Persians were brought to America by the followers of the unfortunate Marie Antoinette. The Pekingese-Persian has developed superficial characters similar to those of the Pekingese dogs. It is gaining recognition.

Short-haired Cats · *Felis catus* · Felidae

ON pages 218–221 are considered some of the common and uncommon short-haired cats. We illustrate 4 of these. The common domestic alley or house cat may be descended from the Kaffir cat of Africa or the wild cat of Europe, or a combination of the two. It may also have been crossed with the yaguarundi of America (page 228), which figured in the development of the Paraguayan cat, but this is questioned by some. Our domestic cat is a mixture of many cats. It may have blood of

218

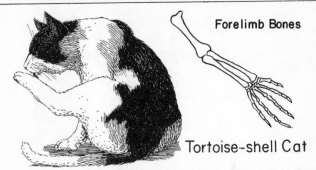

Forelimb Bones

Tortoise-shell Cat

the stiff, wiry-haired Mombas cat of East Africa, the close, scanty-haired Paraguayan cat of South America, the Egyptian cat of Africa, and the wild cat of Europe.

A typical short-haired cat has a body about 2 feet 5 inches long, including a 9-inch tail. The tail is tapered and held on the level. The chest is deep. The hair is well compacted and uniform in length. The voice is far from meek and mild during breeding or fighting.

The tortoiseshell is a breed with well-defined and broken patches of bright orange, cream, and black. The nose is half orange and half black. The eyes are deep copper and orange. No tabby markings. Male tortoiseshells are rare and usually sterile.

Ancestry and History of Domestic Cats

As we have seen, modern domestic cats trace their ancestry to many parts of the world. Long-haired cats probably derive originally from Pallas cat of northern Asia; short-haired, probably from Kaffir cat of Africa. Very likely first domestication was in Egypt about 1300 B.C., but some records point to about 2400 B.C. Cats are not mentioned in the Bible and were probably not domesticated in Europe until the beginning of the Christian era. They were venerated in Egypt, where the city of Bubastis was dedicated to cat worship. To this city 700,000 persons came in one year to worship cats. Cat goddess Bast was goddess of the hunt, of love, and of pleasure. Naturally, therefore, abuse of cats was severely punished in ancient Egypt. Many cat mummies have been found there, but no cat remains in ruins of Pompeii or of Herculaneum. In medieval Europe cats were feared, hated, associated with the devil, darkness, sin, and witches; in England, they were tortured by roasting in cages before slow fires. Few animals have been more hated, worshiped, petted, abused, and feared by mankind than have cats.

219

Silver and Tabby Cats · *Felis catus* · Felidae

Silver

Tabby

Skeleton

Russian Blue Cat

AMONG the silver cats 3 types are recognized: the chinchillas, shaded silvers, and smoke groups.

In chinchillas, the hair of the undercoat is pure white and the coat of the back, head, tail, and flanks black-tipped, to give a silver effect. Legs may be shaded, but chin, ear tufts, chest, and stomach are pure white. Eyes are green. Rims of eyes, nose, and lips outlined in black. The center of the nose is brick red.

In shaded silvers, the animals are darker, without markings, but shaded down sides, face, and tail from dark above to white on chest, chin, belly, and underside of tail. Otherwise coloring is as in chinchilla.

In smokes, the color should be black shading to smoke, with white undercoat. Ears, nose, legs, paws, tail, and mask black. Eyes bright copper or orange and ear tufts light silver.

In the tabbies, we have, among others, the blue-cream, brown tabby, red tabby, and silver tabby. In the blue-cream, the blue and cream should be in well-defined patches. Eyes should be copper or orange. In the brown tabby, the basic color is tawny, with black markings in broad lines. Barrings on tail. Legs should have bracelets meeting body markings. Swirls on cheeks and sides are unbroken. Black down back. Eyes copper.

The red tabby is basically red, with deeper-toned markings as in the brown tabby. Eyes copper or deep orange.

220

The silver tabby is basically silver, with darker markings as in the brown tabby. Eyes green or hazel.

In the solid-color groups we have black, red, cream, white, and blue cats. For show purposes, a black cat must be intense black from hair roots to tips, with no suggestion of brown at the tips or of gray beneath. Eyes should be deep orange or copper, according to the standards.

Red cats should be a deep, brilliant red, without shadings or markings. Lips and chin are similarly colored. Eyes deep copper or orange.

Cream cats are a uniform cream color throughout, with no variation from bases to tips of the hairs. Eyes deep orange or copper.

In white cats, no colored hairs are allowed; hairs should be wholly white. Eyes blue or rich orange.

Blue cats, similarly, should be blue, not drab, throughout. Light blue is preferred. Eyes bright orange or copper.

Russian blue cats are seldom seen in America, but are common in England. They have short, thick, sleek, bright blue fur, vivid green eyes, and long neck, legs, and body. Blue is not a common mammal color.

Economics of Domestic Cats

CATS were probably originally domesticated to destroy rats and mice that damaged food useful to man. They still perform that function, and a breed has been developed that can live in commercial refrigerators at 6° F. These, of course, can control rats that have adjusted themselves to live in similar circumstances. Cats have commercial value to pet fanciers just as rare stamps and glassware have value. They are useful in medicine in study of disease, diet, physiological behavior, and mammalian anatomy, and have some value for sale in this field. Cat fur, known as "genet," has some value as trimming for women's attire. Cats are known to carry hydrophobia and other diseases as do dogs, cows, and other mammals. Cats that have returned to the wild state as feral animals are among the worst enemies of small wildlife. Individual cats have been known to kill 4 rabbits in 1 day; 100 chickens in a season; 40 turkeys in a few days. One well-fed cat was known to have killed 58 songbirds in 1 season. By New York State law, a cat found hunting or killing any bird protected by law, or with a dead bird of a protected species, may be killed by any holder of a hunting license, or by a game protector or peace officer.

African Lion · *Felis leo* · Felidae

Skull

THE "king of beasts" has been much misunderstood. Some writers picture the beast as vicious, brave, and crafty; others describe it as cowardly, lazy, and stupid. Probably the truth lies somewhere between these extremes. Everyone recognizes that an animal whose length is 8 feet and whose weight is nearly 600 pounds, with powerful muscles and sharp teeth and claws, must be treated with respect.

While lions originally were found in Europe, Asia, and Africa, they are now confined in the wild state to southern and central Africa, and their range is constantly being reduced. They breed readily in captivity. Caged lions eat 100 pounds of meat a week.

Lions live most of their lives in a group or "pride" of other lions. The members of the group work together in reasonable harmony for their own protection, in food getting, and to some extent in the rearing of the young.

Male lions stand to 4 feet high at the shoulder and have a total length of 11 feet, including a 3-foot tail. Lionesses are possibly a foot shorter and rarely weigh up to 300 pounds. Males, when mature, may develop heavy manes. In old animals, the mane may be black; in young, it is light. The mane appears at 3 years of age. Lions can run 100 feet at 60 m.p.h., can leap a 12-foot fence or 40 feet on the level. Respiration, 10. Pulse, 40–50.

Lions may pair for a year or more. They have a 2-week mating period. Young, 4–6, spotted, and size of large house cats, are born 108 days after the mating. They nurse for 3 months. Young females may die at teething time. Young can climb trees until half grown but cannot kill for selves for first year. Cubs' eyes are closed for about 6 days. Lions are in their prime at 5–6 years, and may live to 30 years.

Tiger · *Felis tigris* · Felidae

Front Foot
Track

TIGERS range through much of Asia, from Siberia and northern China to Malaya and west through India, and on Java and Sumatra. Siberian tigers are 13 feet long, weigh to 650 pounds, stand 3 feet at shoulder, have grayish to brownish stripes and rich, thick hair. Tigers of India are about 6½ feet long plus a 3-foot tail, and weigh to over 500 pounds. The females are smaller than the males. Normal color is fawn with black stripes and white beneath. White tigers are known. Pulse, 64.

Natives of Africa and of Asia sometimes are better than Americans in recognizing the role of predators in controlling destructive plant eaters, and give some protection to tigers and lions that kill deer and pigs that destroy the crops of farmers. Yet 1 tiger was known to have killed 213 humans. Bengal sometimes loses 60,000 farm animals a year to tigers, and in certain districts more than 300 humans a year have been slain by them. One tiger was reported to have killed 80 men in 1 year. Old tigresses, however, apparently are the most dangerous to man.

Male tiger is reported to roar when hit by bullet, while tigress keeps quiet. Males have long hair on cheeks, but no mane.

Tigers have no fixed mating period, but the adults pair, breeding in alternate years. Fifteen weeks and 4 days after the mating, 2–6 young are born, with sexes evenly divided. Young are blind 2 weeks, weigh 2–3 pounds each; at 6 weeks follow mother, and at 7 months can kill independently. Mature at 3 years. Family together 2 years. Captive animals have lived to 25 years.

A zoo tiger needs 10 pounds of meat a day to survive.

Tigers have bred with leopards and with lions, producing young. A female lion bred to a male tiger produces a *tiglon*. While both lions and tigers may appear to be loyal to their mates, the males of both may be polygamous.

223

Leopard · *Felis pardus* · Felidae

LEOPARDS have a wide range in the warmer and colder parts of the Eastern Hemisphere. They may be found from the Black Sea to Siberia and through most of Africa. Formerly they ranged through Europe to Spain and Great Britain. They favor tree-covered country and are at home high in trees as well as on the ground. They are more savage and probably more dangerous than either the lions or tigers. Presumably leopards are also more intelligent than lions or tigers. Black leopards, or "panthers," are found only in Asia. African leopards have smaller, more solid spots than others.

Leopards catch their prey by dropping on it from trees, by short, fast pursuit, or by stealth. The prey is seized by the throat and torn with the powerful claws.

Male leopards have a body to 57 inches long and a tail to 38 inches. They weigh to 200 pounds. Females are smaller, some totaling no more than 4½ feet. They are tawny yellow above and whitish beneath, with numerous dark to black spots resembling a cat's footprints over the body. These spots are smaller on the head. The fur is of good quality and has a durability of 75% that of otter. Leopards can swim well, can leap upward 10 feet, and can run up a smooth-trunked tree as easily as can a monkey, and turn on an attacker. A group of leopards is known as a *leap*.

Leopards feed on many animals, such as deer, monkeys, sheep, goats, hogs, and antelope, but they seem to like dogs best of all, and will sometimes stalk them in broad daylight. They will commonly drag their prey into a treetop, where it cannot be reached easily by many competitors.

In the spring, some 3 months after the breeding time, from 2–4 cubs or kittens are born. Rarely are there 5 in a litter. The family may remain together until the young are full grown. While the adults sometimes hunt in pairs, they more commonly do this singly. Life span, to 23 years.

224

Jaguar or American Leopard · *Felis onca* · Felidae

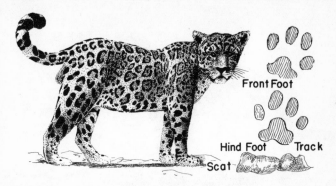

Front Foot

Hind Foot   Track

Scat

THE heaviest of the American cats is the jaguar or American leopard. Jaguars weigh up to 300 pounds, or 100 pounds more than a cougar. The average male jaguar is about 7½ feet long and 28 inches high at the shoulder; female, about 1 foot shorter. The tail is just over 2 feet long, and is proportionately shorter than the African leopard's. The basic color is yellow above and white beneath, with an abundance of black spots, ½–1 inch across, often in groups of 4 or 5 around a central spot, but varying greatly in different parts of the body. The claws are strong and retractile.

Jaguars range in jungles from Texas south to Paraguay, and they may sometimes be found in open country where food is abundant. Like leopards, jaguars can climb trees readily and can pursue their prey in water, over open country, or through dense brush. Jaguars feed on cattle, pigs, sheep, horses, tapirs, fish, alligators, and turtles. They have been known to attack men without too much provocation, and to kill and eat human beings. While they are larger than cougars, apparently cougars can whip them in a free-for-all fight.

Jaguar pelts are valuable, for the fur is of excellent quality. The animals are hunted relentlessly for sport, for their pelts, but especially for self-protection or for protection of herds of domestic grazing animals.

Jaguars definitely pair at the January breeding time. The 2–4 kits are born about 100 days after the mating, are well furred, and have their eyes closed. In the tropics, young are born at any time of the year. Though both parents assist in their care, the mother assumes the main responsibility for rearing the young, who stay with her for about 2 years, when a new litter takes their place.

Teeth are: I 3/3, C 1/1, P 3/2, M 1/1. Tracks are: F 4 x 4¾, 4; H 3 x 3, 4.

Life span, to 22 years.

Ocelot · *Felis pardalis* · Felidae

Track

Front Foot

Hind Foot

Scat

NOT infrequently this relatively small, wild cat is caught young and tamed to serve as an intriguing but rather demanding pet. It is an American animal, ranging from the southern United States to Paraguay. There is evidence that in the past it may have ranged as far north as Ohio.

Ocelots have a total length of 3 feet, including a 15-inch tail. They weigh to 35 pounds, are slender, well proportioned, and agile. They are grayish yellow with large, black-bordered spots. Ears black; upper cheeks white. Spots on opposite sides of the animals do not match. Tail ringed. Hair soft but not thick, and varies greatly in different animals. Teeth are: I 3/3, C 1/1, P 3/2, M 1/1. Tracks are: F 2 x 2, 4; H 2½ x 2½, 4.

Ocelots are flesh eaters, requiring 5 pounds of meat a day. Food includes mammals, birds, reptiles, and amphibians. Important in the diet are monkeys, kids, shoats, and lambs. Ocelots do not attack man, but put up a fearful fight if cornered. Prey is seized by the neck and held to the ground until it dies. Prey may also be caught in the trees. Ocelots are at home in the most rugged and densely wooded country. They hunt mostly at night, and a pair on a hunting expedition often keep in touch with each other by mewing calls.

Breeding probably takes place in June or July, or in the tropics at almost any time. A den in a hollow log or rock pile is well lined with soft bedding material. There, about 3 months after the mating, 2 blind young are born. They have the general markings of the adults. Full-grown ocelots have definite spots for depositing their excreta, and use these spots repeatedly.

Ocelots' greatest threat to man is as killers of poultry.

The allied margay is 18 inches long, including an 8-inch tail, and is marked with black lines and bands. It ranges from Mexico to Peru.

226

Cougar, Panther, Puma, or Mountain Lion

Felis couguar · Felidae

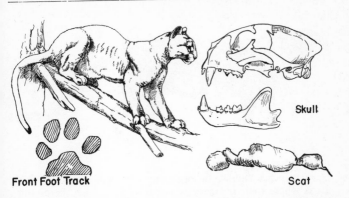

Skull

Front Foot Track

Scat

To avoid confusion, it might be well to add the common name of "painter" to the list given above. To yell "like a painter" is a common expression with some folk, and of course refers to the hideous sounds produced by cougars. Sometimes the calls are like those of a child or woman in distress, and they are often highly disturbing to the listener.

Cougars have ranged through most of the forested Americas. Now they range from Quebec to Vancouver Island and south to Patagonia, with isolated groups in Florida. Probably there are few east of the Rockies and north of the Gulf States.

A full-grown cougar measures 9 feet, including the 3-foot tail. It weighs to 200 pounds, the weight representing primarily the powerful muscles that enable the animal to make its living. Cougars are a yellowish brown above and whitish beneath. The nose, ears, and head are small. Ears are held erect and head is round. Whiskers prominent. Fur short, close, and uniform. Teeth are: I 3/3, C 1/1, P 3/2, M 1/1. Tracks are: F 3 x 3½, 4; H 3 x 3, 4; Sp 15. Pulse, 60. Temperature, 100°–103° F.

Cougars need 7–8 pounds of flesh for a meal, can drag a 900-pound moose 300 feet on snow, can jump up 15 feet and down 60 feet in safety. They may range over 20 miles in a night in a claimed territory 60 miles across. The kill is made by a surprise spring and breaking the neck of the prey. They have served a useful function in keeping down numbers of plant eaters.

Cougars definitely pair. Litter of 1–5 blind kittens is born at any time of year, 91 days after the mating. Eyes open at 9 days. Kits crawl at 7 weeks, suck meat at 9 weeks, eat meat and are weaned at 3 months. Stay with mother 1–2 years. Both parents care for young. Life expectancy, to 20 years. They should not be completely wiped out of existence for many reasons.

Yaguarundi, Eyra, or Otter Cat

Felis yaguarundi · Felidae

YAGUARUNDIS (eyras, or otter cats) probably exist in many areas where their presence is not suspected. They favor thick brushland, which hides them effectively, and they may live much of their time in or close to water, where one would not suspect a cat to be.

Yaguarundis are active day or night, on the ground, in water, or trees, in almost any season of the year. They feed on mammals, birds, reptiles, amphibia, insects, and of course fish, which they catch with little difficulty. They are particularly useful in keeping a check on the abundance of mice and rats that feed on crops in rice fields. The only places where they can be found free and wild in the United States are the extreme southern tip of Texas and the southwest corner of New Mexico. They extend into Mexico along both coasts. Guaymas, Mexico, is about as far north as they get on the Pacific Coast.

A yaguarundi has a length of 50 inches, including the slender 21-inch tail. Yaguarundis stand 12 inches high at the shoulder, weigh to 20 pounds, and are about twice the size of an ordinary house cat. There are 2 color phases: one, brownish red, with white throat and lips, often referred to as the eyra; and the other a solid gray that may be darker in winter. If caught young, they make colorful pets of limited dependability. Their fur is of little value in comparison with that of other cats. Teeth are: I 3/3, C 1/1, P 3/2, M 1/1. Tracks are: F 1¾ x 1½, 4; H 1½ x 1¼, 4.

Yaguarundis breed at any time of year and a litter of young may include representatives of both color phases. This refutes any contention that the 2 phases are distinct species. The young have been found at various times of the year between August and March, indicating a long period during which breeding may take place.

The impression one gets when he sees a yaguarundi, either as a pet or in the field, is that it is an extremely long, long-tailed cat of unusual size.

228

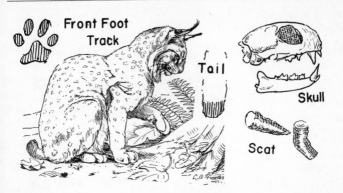

THE Canada lynx and bobcat may easily be confused in some respects. Males of each species weigh about 40 pounds (females are smaller). They are about the same total length, 3½ feet. The Canada lynx, however, has much larger paws and most conspicuous ear tufts, and its tail is black-tipped, not dark-barred. In the field, it is safer to try to observe the tail and ear tips than the feet, although an encounter with either animal usually results in nothing but the retreat of the cat, unless it is prevented from doing so by a trap or the terrain.

The Canada lynx is gray with brown mottlings, and in general is lighter colored than the bobcat. Its fur is long and loose —exceptionally long on the lower cheeks. The lynxes feed on small mammals, particularly rabbits, and their abundance varies over a 7–10 year cycle, largely because of a similar variation in the abundance of snowshoe rabbits, their chief source of food supply. They commonly capture rabbits by lying in wait over a well-used trail. They can follow prey successfully on the ground by scent, and they can swim well if necessary. They serve as a most useful check on the abundance of destructive rabbits. Their fur makes an excellent robe but has low durability, only 25% that of otter. Canada lynxes may be tireless walkers, but cannot continue at galloping speed for long. Teeth are: I 3/3, C 1/1, P 3/2, M 1/1. Tracks are: F 3¾ x 3¾, 4; H 3 x 3, 4; Sp 10. In winter, in deep snow, the toe marks usually do not show. It should be noted that these tracks are approximately the size of those of a cougar.

Female lynxes may breed at 1 year of age. The 1–4 kits are born 2–3 months after the mating, which takes place probably in March. They are blind, furred, and heavily spotted or blotched. Young open their eyes at 10 days. They follow the mother at 2 months. The family stays together until the middle of the winter or the following spring. The mother assumes responsibility for rearing the young. Life span, to 11 years.

Bobcat, Wildcat, or Bay Lynx · *Lynx rufus* · Felidae

Skull

Tail

Trail

Scat

Track

THE word "lynx" may well be confusing when we remember that both the Canada lynx and the bobcat belong to the genus *Lynx,* and that the bobcat is just as properly known as the bay lynx as *Lynx canadensis* is known as the Canada lynx. On the preceding page I have pointed out some of the differences as to which there can be little controversy. To repeat, the tip of the bobcat's tail is not solid black and the ears are not conspicuously tufted, in contrast with these characters in the Canada lynx.

The bobcat is found over all of the United States except the region that is popularly known as the corn belt. Bobcats are found in open country, in thickets, in swamps, and on farmlands, while Canada lynxes are rather closely confined to forested areas.

Bobcats measure a total of more than 3 feet, including a 6-inch tail. They stand to 23 inches at the shoulder and weigh to 40 pounds. They are reddish brown with black spots, lighter beneath. A full meal for a bobcat is about ¼ pound of rat. Bobcats serve as one of the best checks on the multiplication of rabbits, the archenemies of orchardists. Like those of the Canada Lynx, bobcat numbers vary with the abundance of snowshoe rabbits. Bobcats may kill some small stock. One study states that 44.5% of their food is harmful animals, 20.5% helpful animals, 16% vegetables, and 3%'birds.

Teeth are: I 3/3, C 1/1, P 3/2, M 1/1. Tracks are: F 1¾ x 1¾, 4; H 1¾ x 2, 4; Sp 7; L 60.

Bobcats breed at 1 year of age, usually in late winter. Young kits, 1–4 to the litter, are born blind 63 days after the mating and weigh 12 ounces each. Eyes open at 10 days. They nurse 2 months. They run with the parents at least for the first season. By the first fall the young may weigh to 12 pounds. In captivity, bobcats have lived for 15 years.

230

Imagine a mammal that in 2 seconds can reach a speed of 45 miles an hour and then travel at 50 miles an hour for 500 yards. This sounds like an advertisement for gasoline or some new-model car, but such is the speed of the cheetah. Throughout the ages, men have used cheetahs in the so-called sport of capturing large game. They have even used them to work in harmony with other animals in this sport. Usually the cheetahs are hooded like falcons and freed on their own when the game is in sight. They are guided in their quest by sight instead of by scent. Cheetahs, if surprised, can take to a tree like the average house cat. If stroked, they purr like a cat, and they often sharpen their claws by scratching on trees. Like some cats, they have regular scratching posts which they patronize, and hunters who wish to capture them set nooses at such points with good success. Animals to be trained for use in capturing game are caught young and trained early. They have long been the pride of their owners, who are usually among the royalty, or other wealthy people.

Cheetahs are to 7 feet long, including the tail. They weigh to 100 pounds, have rounded heads, rounded feet, extremely long legs, short manes, and claws that are only partly retractile. The over-all impression they give is dominated by their abnormally long legs. Cheetahs are basically brown, with solid black spots. They have bluish streaks on the side of the face. Their fur is soft, and not woolly like a cat's, but more like that of some dogs.

Cheetahs are represented by at least 3 species. The Asiatic cheetah, *A. venatica,* and the African cheetah, *A. jubatus,* are spotted. The African *A. rex* is striped. *A. jubatus* ranges from India to the Caspian Sea and south into Africa to the northern Transvaal and Cape Colony. Cheetahs are essentially animals of the open country. There are 2–4 silky young, blue gray above and tawny beneath. Cheetahs have lived to 16 years.

231

ORDER PINNIPEDIA
(*sometimes in order Carnivora*)
Seals and Walruses
Alaska Fur Seal, Sea Bear

Callorhinus alascanus · Otariidae

Cow

Bull

THE family Otariidae includes the sea lions and Steller sea lions (p. 233) and the fur seals. The genus *Callorhinus* includes the Alaska fur seal (males to 700 pounds), the Southern fur seal (males to 450 pounds; females to 125 pounds); and the South African cape seal (males to 800 pounds).

Many an American woman's claim to social eminence has been strengthened by the possession of a coat made from the hide of an Alaska fur seal. Were it not for the practical application of sensible conservation practices, the Alaska fur seal would be no more.

Alaska fur seals range from the Pribilof Islands south to California. They were nearly exterminated twice, once by American hunters and once by Russians. Now harvested under international agreement, 30,000 surplus animals are killed by American hunters every year. The profits are shared internationally. They feed largely on fish at night, to 50 miles offshore, preferring surface temperatures of 47°–52° F., and can submerge safely for 15 minutes. Except at breeding time, they remain at sea.

Males (bulls) are to 18 feet long, with 2-inch tails; females (cows) are to 50 inches long. Ears 2–9 inches long. Eyes large and watery, with dark irises. Bulls are black with gray cape; cows gray. Young (pups) are black. Teeth are: I 3/2, C 1/1, P 4/4, M 1/1 or 2/1. Temperature, 100°–103° F.

In April–May, bulls come ashore and defend territory 75–250 feet square. They may not eat for more than 2 months at mating time. Cows join them over 6-week period (June–July), enter harem of to 40 cows, in 2–48 hours give birth to pup, and remate. Gestation, 330 days. Virgin 2-year cows come ashore in August and mate. Pups, cows, and bulls leave in August. Cows bear young at 3 years. Bulls mature at 6. Life span, 20 years.

Steller Sea Lion · *Eumetopias jubata* · Otariidae

Forelimb Bones

STELLER sea lions range along whole Pacific Coast of United States, Canada, and Alaska, usually close to rocky shores. Bull Steller sea lion is to 13 feet long and to 1 ton in weight. Cow is to 8 feet long, weighs to 600 pounds. Hind flippers can flex forward. Forelimbs and hind limbs nearly equal.

Smaller California sea lion, *Zalophus californicus* (to 600 pounds, with prominent crest), ranges along Pacific Coast north to San Francisco.

Teeth of Steller sea lion: I 3/2, C 1/1, P 4/4, M 1/1; of California sea lion, I 3/2, C 1/1, P 4/4, M 2/1.

Hair and pelts of sea lions have little value. California sea lions make intelligent and popular circus performers as "trained seals," of particular value in balancing acts. Both species are protected by law and popular with tourists, but fishermen under some conditions may legally control those that destroy their nets.

Food of Steller sea lions is largely crustaceans and small fishes. They sometimes feed on cuttlefish, which may color excrement red. Some sea lions can move over land as rapidly as can man.

One bull has harem of 10–15 cows, which he defends. Cows give birth to 1 pup on coming ashore in breeding season, and immediately mate. Courtship of caressing of neck and mouth precedes mating. Pup weighs 50 pounds at birth, is to 43 inches long, and chocolate brown; learns to swim within a week, and may be guarded by bull and cow. After breeding season there is usually a southern migration. Young reach breeding age at about 3 years. Temperature, 100° F. Life span may be more than 19 years.

Here is an example of an animal of little direct economic value, except possibly as fertilizer or dog food, with some economic handicaps as a destroyer of fish and fish nets, which nevertheless enjoys reasonable legal protection largely because its behavior is interesting to man.

233

Walrus · *Odobenus rosmarus* · Odobenidae

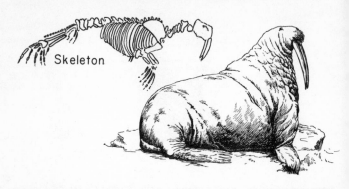

Skeleton

THE Atlantic walrus, *O. rosmarus,* ranges along the Arctic Atlantic shores south to the Gulf of St. Lawrence. The Pacific walrus, *O. divergens,* ranges along the Arctic Pacific shores of Asia and America south to the Pribilof Islands. Both species make northern migrations in May through July and southern migrations in the fall.

A bull walrus is to 16 feet long and weighs to 3,000 pounds. A cow measures 8 feet and weighs to 1 ton. Both are almost hairless, but cow may have haired upper lip. Tail 4 inches long and 6 inches wide at base. There are no outside ears. Shoulder height is to 4 feet. Muzzle short and mouth wide, with 2 protruding tusks. Tusks of cow more curved in the middle and more slender than those of bull. Hide wrinkled and from ½ inch to 3 inches thick.

Walruses are found in noisy herds of more than 100 animals. They commonly feed standing on their heads in water to 300 feet deep. They live largely on mollusks grubbed from bottom with tusks. In captivity, are fed small fishes. They may inflate the neck and float erect in the water while they sleep. An excited herd may be heard more than a mile away.

A single walrus may yield 1 ton of oil. Hide makes best-known buffing leather. Take is regulated to protect supply to natives. Natives use walrus flesh for food, intestines for glass, oil for light, tusks for ornaments, equipment, and trade.

Normally, sexes remain apart except that young may be with mother for 2 years. Mating takes place in May and June, with young born 330–360 days later. Young may ride on the neck of the mother. Calf is to 4 feet long, gray, and with no protruding tusks. Nursing may last 2 years until calf has 2–4 inch tusks and can dig its own food. Bulls mature at 5–6 years, cows, at 4–5 years. Teeth of calf are: I 2/2, C 1/1, P 3/3, M 2/1. Teeth of adult are: I 1/0, C 1/1, P 3/3, M 0/0. Temperature, 101° F.

Harbor Seal · *Phoca vitulina* · Phocidae

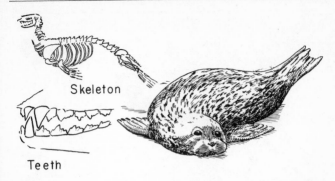

Skeleton

Teeth

HARBOR seals, often known as common seals, are often found in harbors, along shores, in bays, or on the ice. In salt water, they occur in the Atlantic north of Florida and Spain, in the Black Sea and the Mediterranean, and in the Pacific south to California from Alaska and the Pribilofs. They sometimes ascend rivers beyond tidewater and into fresh water. They are commonly known as the hair seals or earless seals, a group to which the harp seals, gray seals, bearded seals, and hooded seals belong.

Harbor seals are to 6 feet long. Old bulls weigh to 300 pounds. Tail 1 inch long. Color cream or yellow gray to dark brown, with brown or blackish patches. Skull pointed, and they may be described as dog-faced. There are no external ears. Neck short and heavy. There are 7 neck vertebrae, 15 back vertebrae, 5 loin vertebrae, 4 hip vertebrae, and 11–15 tail vertebrae. Teeth are: I 3/2, C 1/1, P 4/4, M 1/1. Pulse, 10–140.

These seals have little if any value as to their fur, hides, or oil. Fur durability is 25% that of otter, and since herds are small it is not economical to make great hunts. Someone has said that the flesh tastes like "asafetida flavored with onions." Eskimos like it.

These seals can speed to 10 m.p.h. in water and 3 m.p.h. on land, can dive to 240 feet, sleep underwater 15 minutes. They require 10 pounds of fish a day to live. About 95% of their food is fish. When swimming, they surface at 5–6 minute intervals.

When coming ashore, cows and pups precede the bulls. Sexes are mixed in winter. Bulls fight in August, breed promiscuously in September. Pups, 1–2, born in water 280 days after the mating. Pups may be white at birth or grow white coat soon; are suckled for 2 months, are 3 feet long by September, and sexually mature in 2–3 years. Grow for 3 years. Life span, to 19 years.

Harp Seal, Saddle-backed Seal, or Greenland Seal
Phoca groenlandica · Phocidae

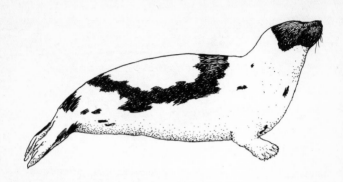

EACH year more than 100,000 harp seals are harvested for the sake of their hides and oil. Their fur is of little or no value. Probably the oil and hides they yield compensate for the fish they eat. These seals form great herds which make their harvest profitable. The animals are gentle, affectionate, and most unsuspicious. Some herds may number 500,000. Some authorities claim that fish comprises about 50% of their total food.

These seals are found in Arctic waters of both the Atlantic and the Pacific. On the Atlantic Coast, they have ranged south to Pennsylvania rivers. They are occasionally found in western Arctic waters around the delta of the Mackenzie River. They migrate with the seasons.

Bulls weigh to 800 pounds, often much less. A 3-year-old animal sometimes weighs to 400 pounds. Cows weigh to 300 pounds. They have a maximum length of 7 feet, and they are relatively slender. The first toes of the flippers are not longer than the second ones. Bulls are light gray or yellowish white, with black face and brown bands forming over shoulder to make a saddle or harp. Cows are a dull white, sometimes with obscure markings. Teeth are: I 3/2, C 1/1, P 4/4, M 1/1.

Mating occurs both in the water and on land. It begins at 3 years of age for the cow and at 4 for the bull. Breeding grounds are most commonly in Gulf of St. Lawrence, east of Greenland, or east of Newfoundland. Pups, single or twins, each weighing 9–12 pounds, are born in March, with white coat and dark muzzle. They are unable to swim. Weigh to 80 pounds at 2 weeks, at which time cow leaves pup and joins bull in water and mates. Deserted pup is called a "beater"; at 3–4 weeks it begins to swim. Pup doubles weight first 5 days. Seals' milk has 12 times the fat and 3–4 times the protein of domestic cows' milk, but no sugar. Adults may swim at 20 m.p.h. May submerge for 20 minutes, sometimes to 200-foot depth.

236

FOUND in Arctic waters, usually near ice floes, or near land, from Alaska to Newfoundland. Two subspecies, the Atlantic and the Pacific, with cranial differences, are recognized.

Bearded seal bulls are to 12 feet long; cows, to 8 feet. Bulls weigh to 1,000 pounds. The coarse, flattened bristles in clumps on either side of the mouth give the animal its name. Flippers are square-tipped. May appear black when wet but are gray to yellow, blotched with black on the back and beneath. These seals are relatively solitary, and any group is usually a family group. Food is largely mollusks gathered from bottom, with sensitive beard as exploratory agent. Seals probably harbor more than their share of intestinal parasites. The liver is supposed to be poisonous. Fur is of little value. If meat is eaten by natives, it may cause trichinosis. Seals are valuable to natives primarily because of their very thick skin, from which heavy harpoon lines and dog harnesses are made. The hides also find many other uses as leather, where strength and weight are required.

Bearded seals breed in early summer months, June or July. Some 11 months after the mating, in May or June, 1 pup is born. It is nearly 4½ feet long, has a curly gray coat, gives a highly pitched, whistling cry. The pup nurses for a rather long period. The cow has 4 mammillae instead of the 2 customary with seals. Temperature, 99°–100° F.

The feeding habits are much like those of walruses, and the long nursing period of the young bearded seal is also like that of the walrus. The animals are not found in great herds, as are the walruses, the fur seals, and the harp seals.

Gray Seal · *Halichoerus grypus* · Phocidae

THIS is more a European than an American species, though in 1933 one was found off the coast of New Jersey. It is rare anywhere along the coast of North America but relatively common off European coasts. It is a North Atlantic species. It is gregarious.

Gray seal bulls are 12 feet long and weigh to 600 pounds. The cows are to 7 feet long and are lighter in weight than the bulls. The bulls have longer jaws than the cows. The color is from a plain ash to a dusky gray, with obscure dark spots above and on the sides. They are often silvery. The skin, particularly of the bull, has the odor of tar. Teeth are: I 3/2, C 1/1, P 3/3, M 2/2. All upper teeth are hooked and *single* pointed. The lower molars are notched at the base.

These seals can dive to 240 feet, expelling to 90% of the air in the lungs in a dive. They can drop the heartbeat from 100 to 10 per minute and maintain that rate for 20 minutes. They are relatively insensitive to increase of carbon dioxide in the blood. They have no great economic importance. They feed wholly on fish.

In August, the bulls go ashore and defend a territory of about one tenth of an acre. They mate with any cow that comes into the territory, but the cows are not kept in a harem and may shift from place to place. Breeding is in September and October, at which times the bulls have longer hair on their necks. One pup is born, 11½ months after the mating, a few hours after cows come ashore. Pup is white, woolly. It is kept hidden in a cave by cow for 3 weeks, then weaned. At 6 weeks the pup sheds the white coat. From 6–6½ weeks it is a dappled yellow. At 6½ months the second coat is shed. Nursing lasts at least 2 weeks. There is a difference in the breeding season in the Old and New World, or at least in parts of the Old World and the New World. In the Baltic and in America, the breeding season is such that the pups are born in January or February. Off the British Isles, the breeding season is such that the young are born in autumn. These seals have been known to live for 18 years.

Hooded Seal · *Cystophora cristata* · Phocidae

FROM Newfoundland to Greenland and south to New England, or occasionally even on the Florida coast, hooded seals may be found. They spend their summers in Greenland, where, for the most part, they rear the young. In the North Atlantic these are perhaps the commonest and most abundant seals. While they occupy much the same territory as the harp seals, the herds do not commonly mix.

Hooded seal bulls are to 10½ feet long and weigh to 1,000 pounds. The cows weigh to 900 pounds. More common weights are, for bulls, 850 pounds; cows, 400 pounds. The animals are blue gray above and lighter beneath. They may have white or light-colored spots on the sides. The cows are paler than the bulls. The muzzle is black. The forepart of the top of the head is inflatable, giving the seal the appearance that suggested the name "hooded seal" or "bladdernose." The cow's hood is smaller than that of the bull. Teeth are: I 2/1, C 1/1, P 4/4, M 1/1.

Generally these seals are rather solitary and the bulls are quarrelsome. Angered bulls can leap their length out of water, and they may inflate their hoods so that they are 7 inches long and 6 inches wide. Getting these measurements cannot be considered a simple pastime. The call is a loud bark, usually given under stress of excitement.

Hooded seals feed largely on fish. They have been hunted so strenuously that their role in general marine economy is small. Potentially they should yield good oil and good leather.

One pup is born sometime in the February–May season. It weighs about 30 pounds, increases about 4 pounds a day for 8 days under protection of bulls and cows. At about 3 weeks the pup is deserted and the cow mates again. Small young are called "graybacks"; the older ones may be confused with gray seals and harbor seals.

239

Elephant Seal or Sea Elephant

· *Mirounga angustirostris* · Phocidae

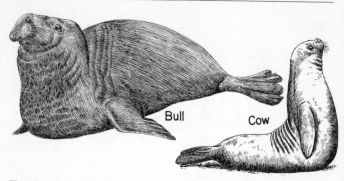

Bull

Cow

THE Northern elephant seal has been found along our Pacific Coast from Baja California, Mexico, to Marin County, California, and north on offshore islands to Prince of Wales Island, Alaska. The Southern elephant seal is more or less confined to Campbell Island, 300 miles south of New Zealand. The animals have been hunted relentlessly for use in making oil and dog food. They now have reasonable protection and need not become extinct.

A bull elephant seal is to 18 feet long and weighs to nearly 3 tons. Cows are to 9 feet long. A bull may have a girth of 20 feet and a height at the shoulder of 5 feet. Bulls are pale brown to gray, and cows are gray all over; cows are gray all over. There is no external ear. The flippers are large, the eyes dark brown, the snout to 10 inches by 6 inches, and inflatable. Teeth are: I 2/1, C 1/1, P 4/4, M 1/1.

Elephant seals feed at night and sleep by day. They go inland to 700 yards from the shore, at a speed of to 5 m.p.h. They can submerge for 12 minutes. On land, they can throw pebbles with their flippers with surprising accuracy. The animals may visit the breeding ground twice a year, once to mate and once to molt.

On the breeding ground, at breeding season in December through March, 1 bull maintains a harem of to 50 cows, but more commonly from 12–20. Bulls often engage in terrific battles with other males, trumpeting violently as they fight. During breeding season bulls often go without eating for 2 months. About 50 weeks after the mating, from February to June, 1–2 pups are born, in the North. Pups are to 2½ feet long and black at birth. They are nursed for 6 weeks. They molt at the end of the first month. Cows that have become pregnant develop a gray mask. A nursing cow may be accompanied by a yearling, indicating that the mother and young remain together at least more than a year.

240

ORDER TUBULIDENTATA (*Aardvarks*)

Aardvark · *Orycteropus afra* · Orycteropodidae

IT is quite probable that crossword puzzles, books, and zoos, rather than free wild animals in the field, have provided most of us with our introduction to the aardvark. Aardvarks are also known as "earth pigs" and "ant bears."

They have a total length of 6 feet or more, of which about 4 feet is the bulky piglike body. They stand about 2 feet high at the shoulder and weigh about 100 pounds. Head is long and thin, with the end of the snout enlarged and mobile. Eyes small. Ears large, pointed, narrow, and erect. Legs strong. Forefeet have 4 long, strong-clawed toes; hind feet have 5 similar toes. With these armed toes and strong legs, the aardvark can quickly dig into the ground for protection or for food. Skin thick, and makes excellent leather. Hair soft, scanty, and reddish brown. Flesh is fatty but is a favored food of the natives. Aardvarks are strictly nocturnal. They give off an odor of rotten fruit which attracts hordes of flies. In nature they feed wholly on insects, particularly ants and termites, and because of this are highly useful animals. In zoos they thrive on ground meat, eggs, and milk.

Two species of aardvark are to be found in Africa, from the Cape of Good Hope through South Africa and up the east coast to Ethiopia and Egypt.

Aardvarks were formerly considered members of the group Edentata (pages 66–68). Like the anteaters and armadillos, they lack teeth on the front of their jaws. They have no canines and no incisors, and the teeth they have have no enamel and no roots. They have numerous milk teeth. Approaching maturity, they have 8–10 teeth on each side of the upper jaw and 8 on each side of the lower jaw, but with age these become reduced to 5 on each side of each jaw. The teeth are made of tiny tubes that radiate from a central area, and give the group the name Tubulidentata.

One young is born between May and July. Life span may be 10 years.

241

ORDER PROBOSCIDAE (*Elephants*)
Indian Elephant · *Elephas indicus* · Elephantidae

Molar

Fore Foot Bones

FORMERLY there were some 300 species of animals in the order Proboscidae. Now there are but two (pages 242–243). In living elephants there is a long, prehensile trunk or snout. All toes have heavy nails. Upper incisors appear as tusks and new molars replace old ones from the rear as the older ones wear away. The mammary glands are near the front legs and the testes are abdominal. The brain is well developed.

Indian elephants weigh to 6 tons and stand to 10 feet at shoulder. The females are smaller. There are 4 nails on the hind feet and 5 on the front feet. The trunk is smooth. Ears one third size of those of African elephant. Grinding surface of the molars is shown in sketch. Cow Asiatic elephants sometimes tuskless and Ceylon elephants generally tuskless. Tusks are to 9 feet long and weigh 150 pounds. Brain weighs to 10 pounds. The pulse of a standing elephant in daytime is 42–46; at night, 30–37; lying, 35–47. The skin temperature is 84°–86° F., body temperature, 97.6° F. The heat production of 2,000 calories per square inch of surface per day is greater than in any other known animal. Hearing is acute. The maximum speed is 24½ m.p.h. Respiration rate, 155. Pulse, 22–53.

A single Indian elephant is born 18–24 months after the mating. It weighs about 200 pounds at birth, and stands about 3 feet high. Cows can breed at 8 years, bulls at 11 years, and full growth is reached at 25 years. Life span may be to 84 years, but this is unusual.

Indian elephants occur naturally in southern Asia, India, Burma, Thailand, French Indo-China, Malay Peninsula, and Sumatra. They have been widely used in Asia, and to some extent in Africa, as draft animals, in which capacity their intelligence is important. They are the common circus-performing elephants. Machines are replacing their use as draft animals. In wild, herds of to 50 may have 1 or more males.

242

African Elephant · *Loxodonta africanus* · Elephantidae

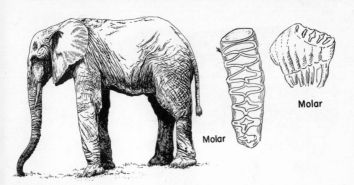

Molar

Molar

AFRICAN elephants are found or have been found throughout Central Africa and south to the Cape of Good Hope. They are not found in the Sahara or north of it. Elephant ancestors date back to Eocene times. In Upper Eocene and Lower Oligocene eras, they were represented by *Moeritherium;* in Oligocene, by *Palaeomastodon;* in Pliocene, by *Mastodon.*

Bulls weigh to 13,000 pounds, have a length of to 12 feet, and stand to 13 feet high at the shoulder. Skin is black and nearly an inch thick. Ears to 5 feet from top to bottom, and to 4 feet wide. Eyes small and well protected with lids. Eyesight is poor. Hearing is only fair, but the sense of smell is well developed. Trunk measures to 98 inches. There are nails on 3 toes on the hind feet and 4 on the front feet. Tusks to 10 feet, 2½ inches long, and weigh to 226½ pounds.

Females usually first mate between 18 and 21 years of age. A female may bear 4–5 calves in a lifetime and one was reputed to have borne a calf at 61 years of age. Bulls do not mature sexually until about 21 years old.

African elephants do not submit to domestication as do Indian elephants. They may do great damage to crops. Jumbo, the famous circus elephant, was an African elephant. At 26 years of age he stood 11 feet, 2 inches, at the shoulder, and weighed 6½ tons.

The molar of an African elephant is shown in the sketch. Molars are important in determining age. The first molar appears during the second week after birth, is complete, and ready for use at 3 months, and shed at 3 years; second molar is in use at 2 years and shed at 6 years; third molar appears at 2 years, is in use at 5 years, and shed at 9 years. These are all milk teeth. First permanent molar, the fourth grinder, appears at 6 years and is shed at 20–25 years; second true molar appears at 20 years and is shed at 60 years; third and last molar appears at 40–50 years.

ORDER HYRACOIDEA (*Coneys*)

Coney · *Hyrax syriacus* · Procaviidae

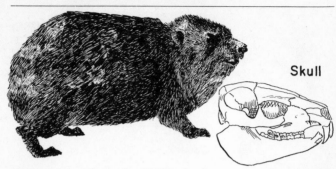

Skull

ACCORDING to Proverbs 30:26, the "coneys are but a feeble folk, yet make their homes in the rocks." Psalms 104:18 suggests the "rocks for the coneys," and Leviticus 11:5 and Deuteronomy 14:7 declare the coney to be unclean and unfit for human food because "he cheweth the cud but divideth not the hoof."

Arabs are reputed to prize flesh as food. Coneys do live in holes in rock piles, but also in treetops. They do not chew cud, but do have tiny hoofs on their small feet, with 4 toes in front and 3 toes in back. Inner toes of hind feet are clawed and pads of feet are usually moist and soft.

The Bible shows no more confusion about these animals than do modern zoologists, who seem to have placed them not only among the hoofed animals but also among the rodents. We call them the Hyracoidea. This order includes only the one family, Procaviidae, and the one genus, *Hyrax*, in which there are at least 14 distinct species. Most important of these are the tree hyrax, *H. arborea*, a tree dweller of eastern and southern Africa, and the cape hyrax, *H. capensis*, of eastern and southern Africa and Asia Minor. Syrian hyrax (pictured above) lives in rocky terrain in regions around the Red Sea, and in Ethiopia.

Generally speaking, Syrian hyraxes are indeed "feeble folk," taking refuge quickly from their many enemies. They vary in size, but are usually about 1 foot long. Some of them are nearly as high at the shoulder as they are long. Ears and tail short. Snout sharp. Nostrils extend beyond the jaws. Eyes small, round, and dark. They feed almost wholly on plant material. In captivity, they may thrive on rice, bread, biscuits, fruits, vegetables, and eggs. In general, they are like dark-gray woodchucks with no obvious tail.

The related male tree hyraxes may howl far into the night at some seasons of the year. The 1–3 young are born fully haired and with their eyes open. The blood resembles that of elephants more closely than any other group.

244

ORDER SIRENIA (*Sea Cows and Dugongs*)

Sea Cow or Manatee · *Trichechus manatus* · Trichechidae

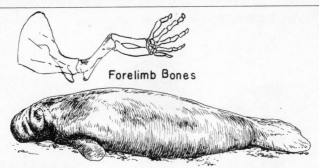

Forelimb Bones

THE order Sirenia is represented today by the dugongs of the Pacific and the manatees of the Atlantic. Like the whales, they have several pairs of molars and oblique diaphragms. Their stomachs have certain similarities to those of the cud-chewers. Like the elephants, they have mammary glands near their forelimbs. Their molars wear as do the molars of elephants, and much of their general bone anatomy is like that of elephants. They are neither whales, elephants, nor wholly like our cud-chewers, so we put them in a class by themselves, the Sirenia. The forelimbs are modified into flippers. There are no external hind limbs, but the rear is reduced into a tail useful in aquatic living. The nostrils have valves, but in many ways are like those of the average grazing mammal. The upper lip of the Pacific dugong is not divided; that of the Atlantic manatee is.

A bull Florida manatee is 12 feet long and weighs more than 1,300 pounds. The cow measures to 7 feet. Color lead gray. They rest in water with arched backs, can spend nearly 4 minutes underwater safely, have excellent sense of touch but poor senses of smell and sight. In water temperature of 78° F., they have a body temperature of 100° F. Pulse, 50–60.

Food, exclusively succulent plants collected mostly at night; in captivity, thrive on loaf of bread a day. Hide makes superior valve leather and flesh is excellent food. Breast meat is white and that of pelvic region red.

Manatees breed in shallow water in the United States, around the Florida coast. About 162 days after the mating 1–2 calves, each weighing 40–60 pounds, are born. These must be allowed to surface to breathe every 3–4 minutes; are nursed 18 months. They remain 2 years or thereabouts with the cow.

About 1768 the Russians, to the shame of the human race, wiped out completely the 25-foot Steller sea cow. It had been described only three decades earlier. To our disgrace, others of the group were seriously decimated. The Florida manatee is becoming rare in spite of protection.

245

ORDER PERISSODACTYLA
(*Odd-toed Hoofed Mammals*)
(*Tapirs, Rhinoceroses, and Horses*)

Malay Tapir · *Tapirella indicus* · Tapiridae

Forelimb Bones

THE most obvious character of the order Perissodactyla, to which the tapirs belong, is the odd number of toes, with the middle toe dominant. These animals also have molars suitable for grinding plant material high in silica content. The stomach is simple and not of the ruminant type. Tapirs have 4 toes on the front feet and 3 on the hind feet.

The genus *Tapirella* is represented by animals living in Borneo, Sumatra, and the Malay Peninsula. The Malay tapir is to 8 feet long from the tip of the nose to the root of the 1-foot tail. The head, neck, and limbs are brownish black and the back and sides grayish white. Young Malay tapirs are spotted and striped with white or fawn color on a dark background. They lose their spots and stripes when they reach the age of about 6 months. An adult Malay tapir stands to 3½ feet high at the shoulder and weighs to about 500 pounds. As in the other tapirs, there is a short, somewhat elephantlike snout, which is movable.

Tapirs are generally defenseless but will fight with what they have to defend their young. They are usually solitary creatures, and any aggregation or herd is probably a family group. Young are born, 1 to a litter, from 392–405 days after the mating takes place. If tapirs are caught young, they make good pets, and will follow their masters around much as do dogs. They will wander all over towns where they are given adequate protection. They favor a temperature of 70° F., but do well where the climate is ordinarily much warmer than that. They must have plenty of exercise and warmth to continue to live, and a few days that are unduly cold may be fatal to them.

Tapirs normally feed wholly on plants, but in captivity will eat potatoes, bread, vegetables, green and dry hay, and similar plant food. They are preyed upon by all of the large flesh eaters, and about their only protection is escape through the dense jungles in which they live.

Amazon Tapir · *Tapirella americanus* · Tapiridae

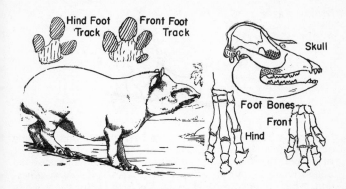

AMERICAN tapirs, such as the Amazon tapirs, are smaller than the Malay tapirs. American tapirs are about 6 feet long and 3 feet high at the shoulder. They are dark brown or black with a grayish tinge on the head and chest. The tail is not more than 3 inches long. They may urinate backward between their hind legs as they flee, thus leaving a trail that may be followed by friend or foe.

In Central America, in the mountains up to 6,000 feet above sea level, is found the giant Central American tapir *Tapirella bairdii*, which is 6 feet long and weighs up to 600 pounds. It is brown to black, with some white on the throat, chest, and face.

The mountain tapir of Ecuador and Columbia is found in mountains to 8,000-foot elevation. It has a rounded head and hair that is to an inch in length.

When pursued, tapirs usually escape in any available direction rather than following some established trail. They normally make their way to water as quickly as possible and swim underwater for surprising distances to escape their enemies.

In America, the greatest enemies of tapirs, besides men, are the jaguars and the alligators. In anger, tapirs may give a hissing cry, but they do not usually fight back effectively except in defense of their young.

Unfortunately for the tapirs, their flesh is excellent food for man. It is much like beef. Their hides, too, make a reasonably good leather, but it is apt to be hard and stiff when dry, and soft and spongy when wet. It is therefore not suitable as leather for shoes.

Tapirs of Asia and of America sprang from a common ancestor that was once abundant at least through the Northern Hemisphere. It is interesting that the survivor groups are now so widely separated geographically.

Life span, to 9 years.

247

Indian Rhinoceros · *Rhinoceros unicornis* · Rhinoceridae

Skull

Fore Foot Bones

IMAGINE a huge animal more than 30 feet long and standing nearly 18 feet high at the shoulder, and with one of the meanest of tempers. You will have to do this in imagination, because the huge ancestor of our present-day rhinoceroses, the *Baluchitherium,* which roamed through Asia, has long been extinct. Only its bones have been left to tell us that it did once exist. It may not be too long before we have to depend on our imaginations to picture even our present-day rhinoceroses, because some of the species are now perilously near the vanishing point, and as civilization advances (if it does), the lands on which our rhinoceroses depend will be used for other purposes and the rhinos will vanish.

The Indian rhinoceros is the largest of the Asiatic species. Unlike its hornless *Baluchitherium* ancestor, this animal has a single "horn." It is 10½ feet long, stands 5 feet 9 inches at the shoulder, has a 2-foot 5-inch tail, and a 1-foot horn. The so-called "horn" of all rhinoceroses is not truly a horn, but a modified bunch of hairs. Natives believe that the horn has mystical powers in romance, and that mixed with poison it will render the poison harmless. For this reason many prominent rulers drank from cups made of rhinoceros horns. Whether this also stimulated their amatory instincts and thus served a double purpose, we do not know.

Asia has supported the 1-horned rhinoceros of Java, the small rhinoceros of Sumatra, and the 2-horned rhinoceros of Sumatra, Thailand, and Malaya.

The Indian rhinoceros and the Javan rhinoceros both have a pair of broad incisors on the upper jaw and a pair of sharp-edged, pointed tusks on the lower jaw. In addition they have molars, as indicated in the drawing. Eyes small. Nostrils wide. Tongue harsh. There is a double fold of skin on the forequarters and on the rear quarters. The skin is hard and thick on the back and soft and thin on the under parts. Color of Indian rhinoceroses is an earthy brown above and somewhat pinkish beneath. There is but 1 young born at a time. Gestation is 19 months. Pulse, 44. Temperature, 100°–101° F. The animals have been known to live for 47 years.

African Rhinoceros or Black Rhinoceros

Diceros bicornis · Rhinoceridae

THE common rhinoceros of Africa is the 2-horned black rhinoceros. It ranged from Ethiopia to the Cape of Good Hope. It is more than 12 feet long, stands 4 feet, 9 inches, at the shoulder, has a 2½ foot tail, and 2 horns, the longer being 1 foot, 4 inches long. A black rhinoceros weighs to 3 tons. As in the Indian rhinoceros, the horn is an aggregation of hairs rather than a true horn, which continue to grow through the life of the animal. The record horn for a black rhinoceros is 4 feet, 5 inches long.

The black rhinoceros makes a track to 9½ inches across. Black rhinoceroses are relatively solitary animals, but an aggregation of them is—appropriately—called a *crash* rather than a herd. The behavior of rhinoceroses is most unpredictable. Rhinos may, without warning, attack a locomotive or an automobile, sometimes with disastrous results to both conveyance and animal. The hide of a black rhinoceros is to ¾ inch thick. When dried, it makes a superior shield for use in native warfare. Rhinos have excellent senses of hearing and smell, but a very poor sense of sight. There has been much discussion as to why a rhinoceros charges, whether it is because of fear, anger, curiosity, or for protection of the young. Whatever the cause may be, man should do all he can to avoid it, because it is a fearful thing to face. Rhinoceroses charge at a speed of 28 miles per hour through tall grass. They love to wallow in mud, like hogs. One may range over a territory 10 miles across. Black rhinoceroses breed at any time of the year. Usually 1 calf, weighing to about 75 pounds, is born 18 months after the mating. The calf nurses for nearly 2 years; during this period the cow will not mate again. Thus a cow might normally bear 1 calf every 3½ years. Life span in captivity, to 50 years.

WHILE the tapirs and the rhinoceroses have more than 1 toe on each foot, members of the Equidae family, such as zebras, horses, and ponies, have but 1. As described on page 257, the horse has evolved through the ages from a 5-toed animal to the modern 1-toed creature. As shown in the picture on that page, the single toe represents the ultimate in specialization for a foot, and possibly the ultimate in effectiveness for covering hard ground at great speed. The parts of a horse are shown on page 252, how to judge the age of a horse on page 253, the gaits of horses on pages 254 and 255, and the skeleton of a horse on page 256. On page 251 we give the essence of the biology of a horse, on page 253 the care of horses; on page 255 their relation to man, and on page 257 the evolution of horses.

Zebras are natives of Africa. Wild zebras stand 4 feet at the withers, are white with black stripes. Burchell's zebras stand 4½ feet high, have white legs, and head and body striped brown over sorrel. Zebras feed in herds. They are favored food for lions. They can speed to 40 m.p.h., and give a peculiar neigh. They have a gestation period of 11–12 months, and their life span is to 25 years.

Ass, Donkey, or Burro · *Equus asinus* · Equidae

THESE animals were once wild in Africa and Asia, but have been domesticated for thousands of years. In height at withers, they vary from 2½–5 feet. They have long ears, sparsely haired tails, deep-set eyes, coarse, wiry, uneven manes, medium-length legs and small feet, and are variously colored— commonly white on the nose, belly, and flanks.

Male donkeys are *jacks;* females are *jennets.* The largest domestic jacks are the Poitou. Others are the large Majorcas,

medium Andalusians, and small Maltese. A jack mated to a
mare produces a *mule;* a stallion with a jennet produces a *hinny*.
Gestation, 348–377 days. Body temperature, 98.5° F. Pulse,
40–56 per minute. A pack burro can carry 250 pounds for days
with little forage. Burros do better in warm climates than in
cold ones. Their endurance, surefootedness, and persistence
make them useful on trails and in mines. Their ability in
negotiating mountain trails with heavy loads assures them a
usefulness to man for a long time to come, both in war and in
peace. An aggregation of donkeys is a *pace*.

The Life History of Horses

HORSES just born are *foals;* when weaned from their mothers,
they are *weanlings*. A young female is a *filly;* a young male a
colt. The age of race horses is reckoned from the first day of the
year in which they were foaled. A mature male horse is a *stallion*. A male castrated before it is mature is a *gelding;* one castrated after maturity is a *stag*. A mature female is a *mare;* one
with nursing young is a *brood mare*. A *foal* is born to a mare
11–12 months after she is bred to a stallion. Horses should not
be worked until 2 years old. A mare is ordinarily in heat 5–7
days, may be bred at 12–24 months, but ordinarily not until 3
years old. A mare is normally in heat starting 9 days after she
has borne a foal; the heat period at this time is only about 4 days
long, but of great effectiveness. A mare carrying a mule foal has
a longer pregnancy than if she is carrying a horse. A filly can be
bred at 1 year of age, but preferably should not be bred until 3
years old. A young stallion should be bred to 4–5 mares at 2
years of age so that his breeding capacity may be determined.
At 3 years he may serve up to 25 mares, but not more than one
a day. He may be worked up to 90 mares a season, with 2 services a day, in the height of the breeding season.
   Life span, to 35 or possibly even 50 years.

251

DOMESTIC HORSE

Percheron Horse · *Equus caballus* · Equidae

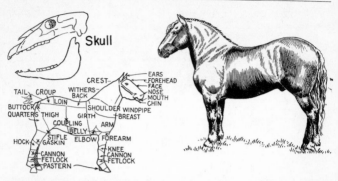

Skull

CREST
WITHERS
BACK
TAIL CROUP
LOIN
BUTTOCK
QUARTERS THIGH
COUPLING
BELLY
STIFLE
GASKIN
HOCK
CANNON
FETLOCK
PASTERN
SHOULDER
GIRTH
ARM
ELBOW
FOREARM
KNEE
CANNON
FETLOCK
EARS
FOREHEAD
FACE
NOSE
MOUTH
CHIN
WINDPIPE
BREAST

HORSES are bred for work, speed, general uses, sport, and recreation. Percherons are bred for work. They have a maximum height at the withers of 17 hands, or 68 inches. May weigh 1 ton in 3 years. Types that are short-legged, compact, and rugged are favored. The back should be short and the back and rump broad. Loins should be smooth and well muscled. Accepted colors are gray, roan, or brown, but dappled black and gray is typical. Chestnut is typical of the Suffolk breed. Percheron's body less blocky than that of Belgian, and legs less feathered than in the long-legged Clydesdale or the short-legged Shire.

This breed was produced in Le Perche district of France, near Paris. It is reputed to have been developed by Crusaders, who needed sturdy horses to carry armored knights. Percherons were long popular in America when horses found greater use on farms than is now the case. Make excellent workers in the mud. Have been used in serum production. Are of recognized intelligence, patience, and willingness. Sometimes clumsy in harness.

Morgan Horse · *Equus caballus* · Equidae

MORGAN horses are of the general-purpose type, to be used both as carriage horses and as general farm animals. Are usually bay, stand to 14 hands (56 inches) at withers. Weigh about 1,000 pounds. Have unusual endurance. Legs short and well muscled. Back short. They have long, sloping shoulders. Well ribbed. Feet small and well shaped. Mane long. Legs dark. Ears small. They are even-tempered and respond quickly to driver's commands.

Breed descended from famous stallion, Justin Morgan, which was foaled in 1793 and died in 1821 in Vermont, whence it had come from Massachusetts. Breed has held trotting and running records. One famous horse of the breed, named Gladstone, was foaled in 1913. It worked on a farm through the haying season, entered saddle and endurance competition, and beat

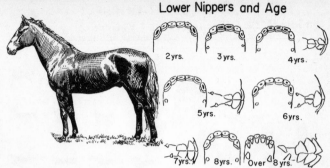

horses weighing 200 pounds more. At one time the general qualities of the Morgan horse were nearly lost to specialization, but these have been regained.

The Age and Care of Horses

A HORSE'S age is told best by examining its teeth. Suggestions as to how this may be done are given in the sketches above. It should be noted that the teeth of horses appear according to the following time schedule: 1st incisors, 2.2–3 years; 2nd incisors, 3.5–4 years; 3rd incisors, 4.2–5 years in stallions, 3.5–5 years, and usually absent, in mares; 1st premolars, 4–5 years; 2nd premolars, 2–2.5 years; 3rd premolars, 3–3.5 years; 4th premolars, 4–4.5 years; 1st molars, .5–1 year; 2nd molars, 1.5–2.2 years; 3rd molars, 3.5–4.5 years.

Young horses should grow steadily the first 2 years. Wholesome growth is stimulated by wise feeding. Oats are popular horse feed because hulls add bulk and prevent gorging. After being worked, horses should be given a small drink of water, rested, watered again, and then fed. In pasture, horses leave manure in special places where they do not feed, but they will eat grass growing from cow droppings. Eat grass closer than cattle but not so close as sheep. When confined, need abundant roughage. Respiration, 8–16. Respiration rate, 130. Heartbeat, 23–45 per minute. Temperature, 100.2° F.

A male donkey crossed with a female horse produces a mule; about 44% of mules are males, none of which are fertile. Copulation of horses may last 10–30 minutes, as compared with seconds for sheep, rabbits, goats, and cattle, and to 2 hours for cats, minks, dogs, ferrets, and swine. This is about the same time as for foxes.

In some parts of the world mares' milk is used as a food for human consumption. Like milk of donkeys and hippopotami, it is over 90% water. Mammal milk which is normally in the 80% bracket, so far as water is concerned, is found in zebras, sheep, pigs, llamas, foxes, cats, bison, buffalo. In the 70% category is the milk of rats, rabbits, elephants, dogs. In the 60% category is the milk of anteaters, deer, and whales. In the 40% category are dolphins. Domestic cow's milk, about 87% water.

Saddle Horse · *Equus caballus* · Equidae

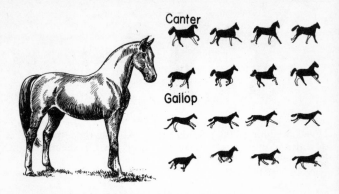

Canter

Gallop

IT is not improbable that saddle horses, a breed developed in part for pleasure, may outlast those breeds developed for performing labor or for general farm purposes. The gas engine has replaced the grass engine in many places. These saddle animals, however, will long continue to be useful in exploring, in police work, in shows, and for those who love association with horseflesh.

Saddle horses stand 14–16 hands (64 inches) high at the withers. They weigh from 950–1,250 pounds. Accepted colors are bay, brown, black, or chestnut. The stride is generally short. The animals should be able to take a variety of gaits when commanded. There should be spirit, style, and prompt obedience to orders.

The breed is of American origin and was first developed by plantation supervisors in the South, particularly in Virginia, Kentucky, and Tennessee. In the North, saddle horses were developed with a greater variety of gaits, including the canter, walk, and trot. Some of these gaits have no real practical usefulness.

Thoroughbred Horse · *Equus caballus* · Equidae

MEN will probably always like to race horses. It is a primitive instinct that is not and will not be lost easily. Thoroughbreds, representing the best in racing stock, thus are likely to find a place for themselves in man's scheme of things indefinitely. Men and women will bet on a horse race whether it is fixed or not, and men who would not know how to harness a workhorse will long engage in juggling the odds on races. The widespread love of racing will keep thoroughbreds important to society and will keep many people poor.

Thoroughbreds stand from 14½–16½ hands (66 inches) high at the withers. They weigh from 900–1,100 pounds. Legs long

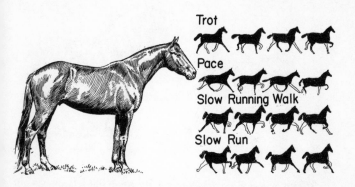

Trot

Pace

Slow Running Walk

Slow Run

and slender. Neck light. Color usually bay or brown, although there are some blacks, grays, and chestnuts. Thoroughbreds are restless and generally nervous. They are usually beloved by their masters and get the best of care. Crossed with other breeds of horses, the thoroughbred contributes speed and endurance to polo ponies, saddle horses, and hunters. The breed was developed for racing in England. Records of ancestry are available for more than 200 years.

Horses and Man

HORSES have inspired a substantial literature and many special terms in the language. Since a horse is mounted from the left side, that is called the "nigh" side, while the right side is the "off" side. "Giddap" is derived from "get up." A pair of usually well-matched horses, driven abreast, is known as a "span." When 2 horses are driven one behind the other, it is called a "tandem."

Horses produce great quantities of serum used by man in the treatment of diseases. Horseflesh is sometimes eaten by man, and is important in the commercial food for dogs. There were approximately 19 million horses on United States farms in 1910; 19,700,000 in 1920; 10 million in 1940; 5 million in 1950, and 3 million in 1954. Obviously the horse as a farm animal is on the way out. Land used formerly to grow food for horses will in the future be available to produce food for man. With a steadily increasing world population of men and a steadily decreasing acreage of good farm land, there must be an ever increasing competition in land use between humans and other animals. In such a race the horse must inevitably lose in the long run.

Shetland Pony · *Equus caballus* · Equidae

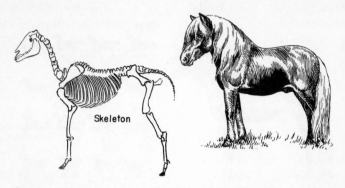

Skeleton

SHETLAND ponies were developed in the Shetland Islands, which lie off the mainland to the northeast of Scotland. Introduced into more favorable regions, they tend to increase in size. They came to America for use as pets, as circus performers, and as draft animals in mines. A small pony can haul ½ ton of coal in a mine 20–30 miles a day. A 3-foot pony can carry a full-grown man with ease, and as a pack animal it can carry loads of 120–140 pounds and still stay good tempered.

A Shetland pony is not accepted for registration in shows if it stands more than 46 inches high at the withers. A mature stallion weighs 370–400 pounds. Ponies have short, straight legs, well-rounded bodies, broad backs, heavy manes, thick, full tails, and short necks, and carry their heads well.

Ponies can subsist on forage which would not support the average horse, and are therefore useful on marginal lands where much is expected from little. They develop heavy coats in winter and can survive severe winter weather in the open where other horses would succumb.

Mustang · *Equus caballus* · Equidae

THE Wild West, Indians, and cowboys are conspicuously identified with the horse. As the old activities of the West diminish in their natural setting, they have been perpetuated by rodeos and the entertainment industry. These pageants would be impossible without a bucking bronco. The word "bronco" means wild and rough, and that ably describes the mustang, which is of Moorish origin, and the Indian pony, which is probably of Norman origin. These tough beasts of burden became the cow pony, without which the cattle range of the past and of the present would be well-nigh impossible. Probably so long as men raise cattle in open country they will ride herd on those cattle on tough mustang ponies.

256

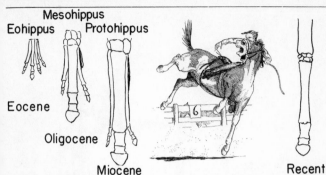

Mesohippus
Eohippus   Protohippus

Eocene

Oligocene

Miocene   Recent

The mustangs, or broncos, have extraordinary strength and endurance. They may be ridden day after day over rough country unshod, carrying a man and a heavy saddle, and still survive. They stand to 14 hands high at the withers, have a deep, compact body, and muscular legs. The Indian pony of the Northwest is not so fast, is more compact, and stands to 13 hands high at the withers. Great numbers of wild horses are herded up and killed for dog meat.

The Ancestry of Horses

It is believed that horses developed in early Eocene times from the small *Eohippus,* which had 4 toes on the forefeet and 3 toes plus 2 splints on the hind feet. In the late Eocene, the collie-sized *Orohippus,* with somewhat similar toes, appeared. Then in the Oligocene came the *Mesohippus,* with 3 toes on each foot, the side toes touching the ground on the hind feet. Later, in Miocene times, came the 3-toed *Merychippus* and *Protohippus,* none of whose toes touched the ground. In the Pliocene, the evolution was continued, and we had the 1-toed *Pliohippus,* in which the splints of the second and fourth toes remained off the ground. About Pleistocene times, along came the modern horse *Equus,* with its single toe, possibly best typified by a dancing mustang giving his all to maintain his independence. What the mode will be in another, subsequent epoch remains to be seen. Possibly just a picture in a book or a few specimens in a museum? We hope that that is not the fate of one of man's best friends.

Undoubtedly in the near future a number of recognized breeds of horses will disappear except as curiosities, but it is doubtful that men will ever completely discontinue using horses as racing animals, as serum factories, and as welcome companions, even though their maintenance may cause more personal inconvenience and sometimes more expense than does a gasoline engine.

257

Mule · *Equus asinus* crossed with *Equus caballus* · Equidae

It is a stock joke that a mule is an animal that has no future, since it is normally sterile and must be produced by crossing a male jackass with a female horse. The reverse mating of a stallion with a jennet or female ass produces a *hinny,* which lacks the good qualities of the mule. It is quite possible that mules will last as long as some of their progenitors because of their great usefulness as draft animals, their endurance and ability to live on relatively poor fare. An aggregation of mules is a *barren.*

A mule retains the long ears, small feet, sparse tail, and bray of the father jackass, together with the size and strength of the horse mother.

Statistics of various types of mules are somewhat as follows: draft mules stand 16 hands (64 inches) high at the withers and weigh a ton or more. Farm mules weigh about 1,100 pounds and stand 15 hands high at the withers. Mining mules weigh from 600–1,300 pounds and stand 12–16 hands (48–64 inches) high at the withers.

Mules sometimes evince more sense than horses, as they are less inclined to eat or drink when they are tired or exhausted and when this might cause trouble. However, when they are rested they should, of course, be supplied with ample food.

Mules should not be put to hard work until 4 years of age, and many not until 8 years old. Mules usually lack the nervous impatience of their mothers, but those most nearly like their mothers are considered to be superior. Just as the number of horses has been and is on the decline, so is the number of mules to be found on farms in the United States. From 4 million in 1910 they rose to 5½ million in 1920. Since then they have shown a steady decline to 3 million in 1945, 2 million in 1950, and just more than a million in 1955.

ORDER ARTIODACTYLA
(*Even-toed Hoofed Mammals*)

THE animals of this group have 2 or rarely 4 toes on each foot, with each toe usually sheathed in a nail-like hoof. All but the pigs and their group have a reduced number of teeth and a 4-compartment stomach, useful to them in chewing the cud. There are 2 suborders. In the pig and pig ally group (pages 259–268), the canines are enlarged into tusks, there are no horns or antlers, and there are from 38–44 teeth. In the other group, the ruminants (pages 269–313), the canines are absent or small, there may be horns or antlers, the stomach is 4-parted, and there are 32 teeth.

Pigmy Hippopotamus
Hippopotamus liberiensis · Hippopotamidae

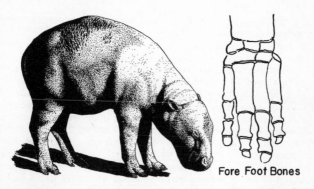

Fore Foot Bones

THE Liberian or pigmy hippopotamus is less than 6 feet long and 2½ feet high, making it much smaller than its larger relative. Pigmy hippopotamuses weigh about 400 pounds, are greenish black above and yellowish green beneath. They are shiny in appearance. They have a 5-inch tail. Eyes and ears are small and the nostrils large. Toes are sharp nailed and well separated. Eyes are dark brown.

These animals live in West Africa, particularly in Liberia, and are not well known. Instead of gathering in herds, as do the other hippos, they usually are found singly or in pairs in the forest, instead of in the water, sleeping by day and feeding on plants for the most part at night. They are not unduly vicious animals, and in zoos become adjusted rather easily to the situation in which they find themselves. The first of these hippos was captured alive in 1912.

A single young pygmy hippopotamus is born from 7–8 months after the mating takes place. Life span, to 35 years.

Hippopotamus or River Horse

Hippopotamus amphibius · Hippopotamidae

Skull

CIRCUS posters have made much of the enormous mouths of the hippopotamuses, which, though represented as being a part of the show, can usually be seen only in the side show at so much extra. They formerly ranged from Egypt to the Cape of Good Hope and north of Zululand, but are now restricted to the river areas south of 17° north latitude.

A hippopotamus measures 17 feet from snout to tail tip and about the same around the middle. The males are larger than the females and weigh to 4 tons on the hoof, but much less in the water, of course. Possibly the buoyancy of the water is one reason why these animals spend so much time in it. They have the power to float or sink at will and can safely stay underwater for a half hour. The mouth is to 2 feet wide and is conspicuous because of the enormous tusks, some of which are to 9¾ inches in circumference. The lower canines are 2 feet long and weigh to 7 pounds. The large nostrils are at the top of the blunt nose, where they can reach the air without exposing much of the animal. The ears are set high and far back on the head; they are to 4 inches long and resemble those of a pig. The eyes are set high and far back just in front of the ears.

Hippopotamus flesh is used as food by the natives. One animal yields to 200 pounds of fat. This is prized as food by the Arabs. The hide makes excellent soup. The teeth give superior ivory. The animals do serious damage to crops. It is not surprising, under these conditions, that they are prized as catches by some natives.

Hippopotamuses are found in rivers and muddy-bottomed lakes and lagoons. Bulls may live solitary lives or in a herd. One young born 234–243 days after the mating. It weighs to 60 pounds, is 3 feet long and 1½ feet high. It walks 5 minutes after birth. Eats solid food at 18 months. Female may bear at 7½ years. Life span, to 49 years.

Collared Peccary, Javelina, or Musk Hog

Pecari tajacu · Tayassuidae

Skull

Front Foot Hind Foot

Tracks

Dung Trail

PECCARIES originally ranged from Arkansas to Patagonia. In the United States they are now limited to the southern parts of Texas, Arizona, and New Mexico. They extend on into Mexico, favoring marshy woodlands where the soil is soft and can be easily rooted in. They also like nut groves and cultivated lands. They readily feed on a variety of roots, fruits, and other plant parts. Nuts, grain, and vegetables naturally find favor with them. They are found usually in pairs, not in droves of to hundreds of animals, as are the white-lipped peccaries, which are larger, and live in Central and South America.

The collared peccaries or javelinas (pronounced "hav-a-leen-a") are to 38 inches long, with a height of to 20 inches at the shoulder and a weight of to 65 pounds. They are blackish brown with yellowish brown mixed with white on the flanks, and a broad, whitish stripe around the shoulders and neck that looks like a collar. The name "musk hog" comes from a large gland on the back that looks like a navel. This is lacking in domestic pigs. Teeth are: I 2/3, C 1/1, P 3/3, M 3/3. There are 3 hind toes, but 1 does not show in the tracks. Tracks are: F 1½ x 1½, 2; 1¼ x 1¼, 2; L 120. These are smaller than those of the domestic pig. Speed is to 11 m.p.h. Can defend themselves well against dogs. A herd of peccaries (usually not of this species) is known as a *sounder*.

The flesh of javelinas is good for food, and the hide has some value. Each year thousands are shipped into the United States for their flesh and hides.

We do not know whether these peccaries are polygamous. They breed at any time of the year. The 1–2 young are born, usually in a cave or hollow log, 112–116 days after the mating. Young may be well haired, spotted, and striped when born. They follow the mother within 2 or 3 days.

261

European Wild Boar · *Sus scrofa* · Suidae

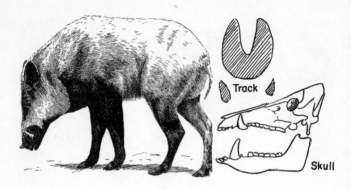

Track

Skull

THIS is the same species and genus as the domestic pig. The family Suidae, to which they belong, is European, while the Tayassuidae, to which the peccaries belong, is American. Wild boars originally were found from India to western Europe, and in Africa, with some variation, of course, over the range, and many closely related species.

The presence of the musk gland, the straight, downward-pointing tusks in the upper jaw, and the absence of a small outer hoof on the hind feet distinguish the peccaries from the pigs. Neither they nor the hippopotamuses chew the cud.

European wild boars have been hunted in Europe from time immemorial for sport, for flesh, and for the protection of crops. They have been introduced into America for hunting and provide an exciting and dangerous sport. They have become established in Tennessee, North Carolina, and New Hampshire, and on Santa Cruz Island off the coast of California.

Wild boars stand to 3 feet high at the shoulder and have a head and body length of nearly 5 feet. They weigh more than 350 pounds and have long, sharp tusks that are to more than a foot long. When angered, they are formidable adversaries for any animal to take on. They are pale gray to blackish. The term "wild boar" is applied to both the boar and the sow. The boar breeds freely with domestic swine. There are 3–12 little pigs born 112–115 days after the mating takes place. The piglets have dark stripes and spots in lengthwise lines, and are active almost immediately. Groups of sows and piglets are known as *sounders,* but the family obligations fall on the sows because the boars go off in their own separate groups once the mating season has passed.

When the family breaks up, the animals may do some minor migrating. Wild boars have been found swimming strongly in the sea a full mile from shore.

Domestic Swine. Berkshire Swine · *Sus scrofa* · Suidae

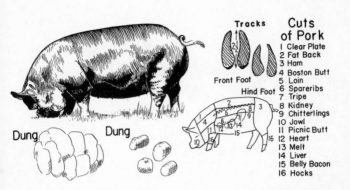

Tracks

Front Foot

Hind Foot

Dung

Dung

Cuts of Pork

1 Clear Plate
2 Fat Back
3 Ham
4 Boston Butt
5 Loin
6 Spareribs
7 Tripe
8 Kidney
9 Chitterlings
10 Jowl
11 Picnic Butt
12 Heart
13 Melt
14 Liver
15 Belly Bacon
16 Hocks

IN our treatment of domestic swine we show the parts and tracks of a hog on page 263, the teeth at different ages on pages 264–267, and the bones of the foreleg on page 268, and discuss the general life history on page 265, and the management of swine on page 267.

The popularity of the different breeds of swine varies in different countries and in different parts of countries. This variation is based on available food, nature of the market, climate, and so on. In America, swine rank as follows: Durocs first, Polands second, Berkshires third, with the other breeds varying greatly. Swine have been domesticated in China since 2900 B.C. Like horses, they have probably lived on the earth from 3–6 million years. They are bred to serve certain purposes, such as bacon production, pork production, or general production of both pork and bacon.

The Berkshire breed originated in Berks County, England. It was first brought to the United States, to New Jersey, in 1823. In 1838 it was introduced into Canada, and during many of its earlier years it had few rivals in popularity, and figured rather prominently in the rural economics of the times. Its popularity then and now has been warranted by its record.

Berkshire swine are generally black with 4 white feet, white nose, and white tail tip. Nose is short and turned upward. Face is dish-shaped. Ears stand erect. The breed is rated by some as being of the lard type, but its flesh is good and it produces superior backs, shoulders, and hams, if not the best bacon. The breed matures early, fattens early and easily, and is an economical converter of feed into good pork.

Yorkshire Swine · *Sus scrofa* · Suidae

Incisors at Birth

At 1 month

Molars at 1 month

ONE of the largest of all breeds of swine is the Yorkshire. Yorkshires have long, narrow, deep bodies, usually without wrinkles, and are white. The head is short and the face is dished. Ears are erect. Sides are long and smooth, as one would expect of a hog of the bacon-producing type. The quality of the bacon produced is probably this breed's greatest claim to fame. Another good bacon type is the Tamworth hog. It has a long, narrow red body, long head, and unusually long snout.

The Yorkshire breed originated in County York in England and was developed by factory workers who used kitchen wastes to raise pork for home consumption. It was introduced into the United States in 1841 and into Canada in 1886. The breed does well in close quarters and so was ideal for factory workers. Even to the superficial observer, the bacon type of hog, such as the Yorkshire or Tamworth, differs greatly from any of the lard or general-purpose breeds. Whereas the Yorkshire is lean and thin, the Chester White, for example, is a large, heavy animal. Both are white.

Chester White Swine · *Sus scrofa* · Suidae

THIS breed was developed in the counties of Chester and Delaware near Philadelphia, Pennsylvania, from white hogs which had been brought there in 1820. Swine with Chinese strains were bred to the Chester County Whites. One of the desirable qualities of the breed is that the sows make excellent mothers, producing large litters and raising them to maturity and to large size quickly and with relatively little loss. The breed requires relatively little care and thrives on a minimum of food as compared with some other breeds.

The Chester White breed is of the pork type. The face is straight, not dished. Ears droop, point forward, and break one half to one third the distance from the tip to the base. Legs are strong. The ideal show animal should have no black whatsoever.

264

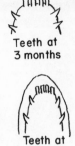

Teeth at
3 months

Teeth at
9 months

Nomenclature and Biology of Swine

SWINE just born are *pigs;* when weaned, they are *shoats.* A young female is a *gilt;* a mature female, a *sow.* Mature males are *boars,* and castrated males are *barrows.* Sows should be 1 year old before being allowed to bear young, but may be bred at 4 months, though they should not be. Young are born 112 days after the mating. Young pigs are called *farrows,* and to bring forth is *to farrow.* If care is taken, sows may produce 2 litters a year. Young pigs usually run with the sow from 10–12 weeks. If 2 litters are being raised, young should be weaned at 8 weeks, being allowed to return to sow only to relieve udders temporarily. Sows are in heat for 2–4 days every 9–12 days, unless mated. They can breed for 6 years. Cleanliness pays in rearing young pigs. Pulse, 55–86. Temperature, 101°–103.5° F. Respiration rate, 220. An adult pig is often referred to as a *hog.* A second-year boar is a *hogget* (this name is also applied to a second-year male sheep). Life expectancy, to 27 years.

In general, American breeds of swine have a lower fertility rate than do the English bacon breeds. Average litter sizes for American breeds are as follows: Chester White, 9.78; Poland China, 7.9; Duroc Jersey, 9.8; Berkshire, 8.22. If a gilt is bred at about 180 pounds in weight, she should usually bear young when about 12 months of age and should be ready to be bred from 3 to 5 days after the weaning. Usually the whole litter is born within an hour, the longest interval commonly preceding the birth of the last young one. Unwatched sows may eat their young and the afterbirth unless they have had a suitable diet of proteins and minerals before farrowing.

Boars may be used sparingly at 8–9 months of age and normally should not be allowed a service oftener than once a day, or for more than 15 times the first season. This may be increased to 30 times for year-old boars and to 60 times for 2- or 3-year-old boars. It is not good practice to run young boars with a group of older sows.

Teeth at
1 year

THE Duroc Jersey breed is characterized by being red and having rather long legs and heavy bones. In general appearance, because of their redness, they rather resemble the Tamworth breed which, as stated, is a bacon type of hog.

This breed was developed in the United States by crossing Durocs that had been grown in New York State with Jerseys that had been developed in New Jersey. The earliest record of the breed is for 1832, and until 1875 it was the commonest breed in New York State, Vermont, and Connecticut. After that they became popular in the Middle West in the corn belt territory. The breed is more popular in the United States and Canada than elsewhere in the world. It has excellent grazing ability and can thrive in open range because of this. It also is hardy enough to stand severe winter weather, and this adds to its popularity where housing and shelter are at a premium. In other words, the breed is excellent when it comes to taking care of itself, thus leaving the farmer time to attend to other matters. In Canada, the breed is popular in Alberta and southwestern Ontario.

Hampshire Swine · *Sus scrofa* · Suidae

THESE medium-sized hogs are generally smaller than Duroc Jerseys or Chester Whites. Their most conspicuous feature is the white belt, which is from 4–12 inches wide and runs around the shoulders to include the forelegs. Because of this band the hogs are sometimes called by the common name "belted swine." They are also called "thin rind swine." This last refers to the nature of the bacon, in all probability.

The head of Hampshires is narrow. Face straight and smooth. Eyes bright. Ears medium and directed slightly outward and forward. Chest large and deep. Back of medium width. Jowls light. Legs of medium size and weight.

266

Teeth at Maturity

At 6 months, boars and sows should weigh about 140 pounds each; at 18 months, boars 350 pounds and sows 325; at 2 years and over, boars 450 pounds and sows 400 pounds. These swine are quiet, docile, and easy to handle. Their strong points are that they dress out superior carcasses, are among the most prolific of all breeds, and make good mothers.

Management of Swine

To manage swine it is rather important to be able to tell their age. Pigs' teeth are shown in the illustrations (pages 264–267). In summary, pigs have 6 incisors on each jaw, the outer pairs being present at birth. Center pairs appear at 3 months, and remaining pairs at 4 months. At 6–10 months, outer pairs are replaced by permanents; at 20–24, intermediates, and at 30–36, middles are replaced. Pigs grow more rapidly than cattle, breed earlier, and eat less roughage. They need 8½ gallons of water daily, plus good pasturage, grain, skimmed milk, and whey. Growing pigs need salt and alfalfa hay. Brood sows must have exercise, freedom from parasites, good pasturage, and good treatment. In winter, sows may be fed corn with alfalfa hay. With good care some may reach to 400 pounds in 1 year. Boars should not be allowed to become too fat. Summer pasturage and 1 pound of grain a day should be adequate. Sows with new litters should have only warm water the first day and warm, thin foods for 4–5 days. Fattening pigs is a science and a gift, and success varies with the availability of suitable pasture, food, and care at strategic times in the lives of the young and the old. Each pig-growing area has its own problems, the solution of which probably is well understood by the local agricultural college, which should be consulted.

Poland China Swine · *Sus scrofa* · Suidae

Bones of Front Feet

POLAND China swine were developed in Butler and Warren counties, Ohio, probably by the introduction of Russian-strain hogs into the herds of Ohio swine. The animals are medium-sized and are essentially an all-purpose type, with the emphasis on the production of fat carcasses.

The obvious field character by which these animals may be recognized is the general black color, accompanied by 6 white "points": namely, the face, tail tip, and 4 feet. In addition the slightly dished face may be recognized, and the full jowl which one somehow associates with fat hogs.

At 1 year, boars of this breed should weigh 400 pounds and sows 350 pounds. At 18 months, boars should weigh 500 pounds and sows 450 pounds. At 2 years and over, boars should weigh 600 pounds and sows to 500 pounds. These large weights are produced at a relatively early age, shortening the normal time to market.

One of the great weaknesses of the breed is the low reproductive rate, due in part, of course, to the relatively small litters. In spite of this shortcoming, Poland China swine have ranked second in popularity to the Duroc Jerseys in the corn belt states of the United States.

The Ruminants

ON pages 259–268 we have considered the 3 families of the even-toed hoofed mammals which are not ruminants; that is, do not chew a cud. These are sometimes grouped in a sub-order, the Bunodontia, the members of which have no horns or antlers, have enlarged curved canine tusks, and 38–44 teeth. The remaining animals covered in this book belong to another suborder, the Pecora, or ruminants, in which there are no ca-nines, or only small ones, and in which the stomach has 3 or 4 parts (see page 282) and the animals chew the cud. In this group, we recognize these families: the Camelidae (camels and llamas), Cervidae (deer), Giraffidae (giraffes), Antilocapridae (pronghorns), Bovidae (cattle, goats, and sheep).

Arabian Camel or Dromedary
Camelus dromedarius · Camelidae

CAMELS originated in North America and their group spread over the world. They are now represented by the camels of Africa and Asia and by the llama and alpaca group, to be found in South America and discussed on pages 271–272.

Height at shoulder 7 feet. Can hold eyes 9 feet above ground. Legs and neck long. Feet 2-toed, with undivided soles and hoofs on upper surface. Prominent knee pads. Tail short. Hair thickest on head, neck, hump, and thighs. One hump. Three chambers in the stomach, with the usual psalterium of the ruminant stomach missing, but the rumen and reticulum supplied with many water cells. Eyes have heavy lashes. Ears haired. Nostrils closable. Sight keen. Ability to smell excessively good.

With 1 drink of 15 gallons of water, can carry 400–600 pounds for 30 miles a day to 4 days, or 1,300 pounds to 10 days for shorter distances. Can carry 600 pounds at 2½ miles an hour. Can go 9 days without a drink. Temperature, 100° F. Life span, to 25 years.

Six camels can draw as heavy a load in carts as can 3 6-mule teams, and do this over terrain that even mules could not negotiate.

In winter, camels can root beneath the snow for their food, but this, of course, is a more common practice with the Bactrian than with the Arabian camel.

Camels provide flesh that is used as food by the natives. Their hides are used in making leather. Their hair makes superior fabrics, light in weight and highly durable. To some degree they provide companionship to their masters, but they frequently try to take a bite out of passing humans with their teeth. Naturally this is not always appreciated.

Bactrian Camel · *Camelus bactrianus* · Camelidae

BACTRIAN camels are now confined to the deserts of central Asia, although they are natives of the steppes of eastern Asia.

Bactrian camels have shorter legs than the dromedary or Arabian camels, and therefore are not so tall. They have 2 humps instead of 1, a heavier coat of fur, and harder and shorter feet that make it possible to negotiate rougher country. They are more docile, easier to ride, and slower. They never need shelter in the most bitter weather, and can stand the roughest traveling.

The Bactrian camel can begin to earn its living at 4 years and can continue a useful existence until 30 years or older, which is longer than for the Arabian camel. During the 3 months of the rutting season, male camels may not eat. A single calf is born from 45–56 weeks after the mating. The calf has a soft fleece, a gentle *bah*, and lacks the knee pads of the adults. It goes to pasture when 1 day old. Mothers may mourn loss of young for 3 months. Full growth is attained at 5 years. A female may breed every alternate year and produce to 12 young in a lifetime. Life expectancy, from 17–50 years.

Bactrian camels are almost essential to man for survival in the rugged regions where they live. Not only do they supply necessary transportation, but they can exist on little food. Bactrian camels can and will drink brackish and even salt water, and if forced by hunger will eat fish, flesh, bones, and skin. They will thrive on salty plants that will be wholly rejected by other grazing mammals.

Bactrian camels, like other camels, provide milk for their masters. The milk is commonly fermented to produce *kumis*, a beverage which is a common and apparently pleasing drink to the natives.

Arabian and Bactrian camels may be crossed (Bactrian male crossed with Arabian female), the resultant mule having the single hump of the Arabian camel and the long hair of the Bactrian. In some respects, the mule is considered superior to the purebred animals, but it is less common.

Llama · *Lama peruana (glama)* · Camelidae

WHAT the Bactrian and Arabian camels are to Asia and Africa, the llamas, alpacas, guanacos, and vicuñas are to South America. Some of the South American animals live in both the wild and the domesticated states. On this page and the next we shall consider the llama, *Lama peruana (glama)*, and the alpaca, *Lama pacos,* both of which are domesticated; and the vicuña, *Vicugna vicugna,* and the guanaco, *Lama guanacoe,* both of which may be wild or semidomesticated.

The llama, *Lama glama,* shown above, is a domesticated animal used primarily as a beast of burden in southern and western South America. It can carry burdens at elevations of 12,000–16,000 feet, where other beasts of burden cannot function. Llamas are the largest of this group of animals. They stand 4 feet at the shoulder, are 4 feet long, have a 6-inch tail and a 23-inch neck. They are brown to black or even white. The hair on the neck, head, and limbs is shorter than that elsewhere on the animals. The body has long, dense, fine wool. These animals have 3-chambered stomachs like the camels, and while they do not need to go without water, their stomachs could serve as reservoirs as is the case in the camels. This may indicate a common origin.

Male llamas are used as beasts of burden and can carry to 200 pounds to 15 miles a day over rugged terrain. At the time of the Spanish Conquest, as many as 300,000 llamas were used to carry silver ore from the mines. They are still handled sometimes in droves of 1,000.

Vicuñas are shy, alert animals living in Ecuador, Peru, Bolivia, and Chile, in the high Andes in the tropics. They are a tawny brown with a white or a yellowish-red bib. While their coat is not abundant, it produces highest-quality fiber from

271

which the fabric called *cumpi* is made. Vicuñas stand from 2½–3 feet at the shoulder. In the wild, they run in herds of about 1 male and a dozen females.

Wild guanacos are found in herds of 100 or more from Peru through Bolivia, Patagonia, Argentina, and Chile. They stand to 4 feet high at the shoulder but can hold their heads to 5 feet above the ground. They take to water readily and may drink salt water. They are a woolly, yellow brown, with a gray head. The adults mate in August and September; 10–11 months later 1 young is born, which is nursed from 6–12 weeks and then weaned. Immediately after birth the young can run with surprising endurance. The hide of the kid is sold as *guanaquito* and is used in making beautiful robes.

While the males are used as beasts of burden, the females are used for breeding, for milk, and for flesh and hides. Mating takes place about November, when there may be a national festival celebrating the event. Males fight one another for dominance. Females may bear young in May or June every alternate year. As the young males develop, they are eventually driven from the herd by the united action of the females of the herd.

Alpaca · *Lama pacos* · Camelidae

ALPACAS are domesticated for their wool, which is in either a fine or a coarse grade. The hair is to 2 feet long and may nearly reach the ground. One alpaca yields to 15 pounds of wool a year.

Alpacas stand to 3 feet at the shoulder, are to 4½ feet long, with a 6-inch tail, and can hold heads to 5 feet above the ground. They are essentially animals of the hills, but are driven down from the hills for shearing. The color is dark brown to black. They may live to 12 years. A cross between an alpaca and a llama produces a sterile mule called a *machurga*.

Pecora or True Ruminants

THE remaining families in this book are the Cervidae, deer, pages 273–278; the Giraffidae, page 279; the Antilocapridae, pronghorns, page 280; and the Bovidae, cattle, goats, and sheep, pages 281–313. In all of these animals there are 4 pairs of incisorlike teeth on the lower jaw in front, and none on the upper.

The six deer considered on pages 273–278 all bear antlers, which develop as shown on page 274, and are shed each year. Normally the antlers are borne only by the bucks, except in the case of the caribou; in that species they normally occur in both sexes.

Wapiti or Elk · *Cervus canadensis* · Cervidae

Cow Bull

Trail

Skull

Dung

Alpaca

THE wapiti or elk ranges from New Mexico and Arizona to British Columbia. It has a length of to 9 feet and stands more than 5½ feet at the shoulder. Bucks weigh to 750 pounds, but average 700 pounds; cows (hinds), 500 pounds. Color is grayish brown, with dark chestnut along the back and mane. There is a gray rump patch. Cows are lighter in color than the bulls.

Wapiti bucks shed the rack of antlers about March, and a new set begins to grow immediately. Antlers may increase in size by 33% over a 10-year period; they are to 5 feet long.

In November, the bulls fight to win a harem of cows. From 210–262 days after mating, 1–3 calves, weighing to 30 pounds, are born. Calf has a spotted coat. It stands quickly, follows cow in 3 days, grazes in 4 weeks, is weaned and loses spotted coat in October, but follows cow until following spring. Young cow breeds at 3 years. Life expectancy, to 22 years.

Many wapiti bulls have been killed for their canine teeth alone, which are used as insignia by a fraternal order. Often the carcass used to be left to rot after the teeth were taken. Teeth are: I 0/4, C 1/0, P 3/3, M 3/3. Tracks are: F 3½ x 4½, 2; H 3¼ x 4, 2. Wapitis may leap to 10 feet high. From one track to the next track of the same foot of a speeding elk may measure 7 feet.

273

Black-tailed Deer

Odocoileus hemionus columbianus · Cervidae

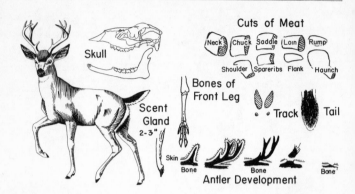

Skull

Cuts of Meat

Neck | Chuck | Saddle | Loin | Rump

Shoulder | Spareribs | Flank | Haunch

Bones of Front Leg

Scent Gland 2-3"

Track

Tail

Skin | Bone | Bone | Bone | Bone

Antler Development

BLACK-TAILED deer are found from the western slopes of the Sierra and the Cascade Mountains to the sea in the three Pacific states, and on into southern British Columbia and southeastern Alaska. They favor wooded areas.

The black-tailed deer is now considered a subspecies and not a distinct species. The essential differences, indicated in the drawing of the black-tailed, include a shorter scent gland on the inside of the leg, and a tail that almost wholly black above rather than black-tipped. The tracks and droppings are essentially alike. Teeth are: I 0/4, C 0/0, P 3/3, M 3/3. Tracks are: F 2½ x 3, 2; H 2¼ x 2¾, 2; L 150.

Some study should be made of the sketch above showing the growth and development of an antler, and this should be compared with the sketch of comparable structures of the pronghorn, page 280, and of cattle, page 292.

For those interested in hunting deer and possibly in cutting up a carcass, the standard names for the different cuts are given above.

The droppings of all deer, like the droppings of most other animals, vary greatly through the year and depend largely on the nature of the food eaten. Animals that have fed on evergreen browse and hardwood twigs yield smaller, drier pellets than those that have fed on fresh green stuffs.

Buck black-tails weigh to more than 300 pounds and have a length of to 7 feet. Height, 3½ feet. Does are smaller by roughly one third.

The ears of both the black-tailed deer and the mule deer are rather conspicuously larger than those of the white-tailed deer. Those of the black-tail are white lined. The tail is bushier than that of the mule deer. It droops when at rest, instead of being held close to the body, and when the animal speeds or is excited the black-tail may hold its tail erect as does the white-tail.

274

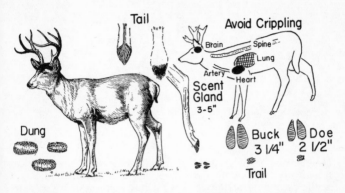

THE mule deer ranges from central Mexico to northern Manitoba and west to the coast, except in parts of western Washington, Oregon and California. The essential points in which it differs from the black-tailed deer were discussed on the previous page or appear in the cuts on pages 274–276. As the word "mule" implies, the ears are unusually large, and the tail is ropelike rather than expanded and hairy, as in the other deer. Note that only the tip of the upper part of the tail is black and that the animal does not carry the tail erect even when speeding. Also note the excessively large scent glands on the legs, as contrasted with those on the black-tail and white-tail.

Mule deer are about one fifth heavier than are the black-tails and are the largest of this group of deer. Buck mule deer weigh up to 400 pounds, while the white-tail weighing 300 pounds is the exception. The teeth and antlers of the black-tailed and mule deers are essentially the same, as are the tracks and droppings.

Mule deer and black-tails are in rut in November. At any time in the rut season they are likely to be untrustworthy. The buck, by fighting other bucks, wins himself a harem of does. The following May or June the does give birth to 1–3 fawns. These remain hidden for 6–8 weeks, are nursed by the does, and follow them during the summer and first winter. Some fawns may follow the does for 2 years. The life span is presumably about 7 years, if accidents do not happen, and unfortunately they do happen in abundance.

Coyotes, bear, cougars, and sportsmen are the deer's worst enemies, in addition to feral dogs that get the habit of running them when the snow is deep. Uncontrolled, deer would destroy their own food supply and face starvation. In addition, they might destroy the plant cover that anchors the soil to the hills. Deer become attractions in public parks, and if treated intelligently may be most useful.

275

White-tailed Deer or Virginia Deer

Odocoileus virginianus · Cervidae

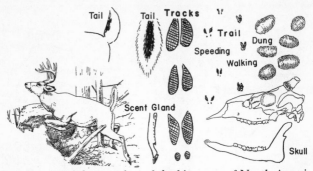

HERE is one of the grandest of the big game of North America. Practically nonexistent over great parts of the United States at the beginning of the century, it has recovered its numbers and in some areas has become a menace to crops, orchards, traffic, and other things. Its management requires intelligent understanding of the balance in nature and recognition of local situations by technicians, politicians, and landowners.

White-tailed deer, as shown above and on the preceding 2 pages, differ from mule deer and black-tails in the forward curvature of the antlers, the erect position of the tail when in motion, and the white border on the top of the tail; in having the smallest scent glands on the inside of the legs; and in their range, which is largely different from that of the other North American deer. At present they range through North America south of the Gulf of St. Lawrence and James Bay, west to the Rockies and parts of Oregon and northeast California.

White-tailed deer are 7 feet long, standing 4 feet at the shoulder. They weigh to 300 pounds. They are red chestnut or gray above to white beneath. They can speed at 40 m.p.h., jump 8 feet high or 30 feet on the horizontal. They require about 1 square mile of territory per individual. They feed largely on browse, will eat rye, but prefer weeds to timothy or bluegrass. They "yard," or mill around in herds in winter, to keep the snow down, but will starve in great numbers. Temperature, 100°–101° F. Tracks are: F 2 x 3½, 2; H 2 x 3, 2.

White-tailed bucks fight rival bucks for the does in fall. The winner forms a herd with 2–3 does and breeds in November. In June or later, from 6½–9 months, but more commonly in 210 days after mating, 1–4 fawns are born, each weighing at birth about 3¾ pounds. Young are hidden but nursed every 4 hours, and by 4–5 weeks follow the mother. At first they are spotted, but by 4 months they lose spots and are weaned. Young does may follow mother 2 years. Sometimes breed the first year. Bucks follow mother 1 year. One buck and 3 does in 11 years actually made a herd of 250 deer. Two bucks and 4 does in 5 years made a herd of 160. Life span, to 15 years.

Moose · *Alces americana* · Cervidae

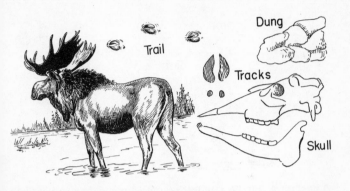

MOOSE range from New Brunswick and Maine across Canada to Wyoming, British Columbia, and Alaska. They have disappeared from much of their original range in the northern United States.

Moose are living exaggerations. Their broad "rocking-chair" antlers spread to 6 feet. They are to 10 feet long, including a 3-inch tail. They weigh to 1,800 pounds, according to some authorities. The cow is about three fourths the size of the bull and lacks the antlers, the great mane on the neck, and the "bell" at the throat. The forequarters are much heavier than the hindquarters. Teeth are: I 0/4, C 0/0, P 3/3, M 3/3. Tracks are: F 5 x 7, 2; H 5 x 7, 2. Temperature, 102° F.

Moose feed on browse from hardwood, but enjoy the underwater parts of water lilies and other succulent water plants. An aggregation of moose is called a herd, and a family of a bull, a cow, and some calves may stay together through the winter. They may live entire lives within a 10-mile radius. Can trot at 15 m.p.h.; speed to 22 m.p.h.

Rutting season is in the fall, and the animals are probably polygamous, but less so than most deer. In May, 242–246 days after the mating, 1–3 calves are born. They are not spotted, like many other young deer, but are a dull reddish brown. They begin to run with the cow when about 10 days old, and at that time stand 3 feet high. They may remain with the mother for 2 years. The cow is receptive to the bull over a 30-day period, but the bull may be in a breeding mood for twice that time. Cows call and bulls bellow. Animals 2 years old may breed. Life span, probably about 20 years, if accidents can be avoided.

In earlier days moose furnished food, leather, and bones for the industry and art of primitive Americans. They now provide a rugged sport which means much to men glad to escape from the cities.

277

Reindeer or Caribou · *Rangifer caribou* · Cervidae

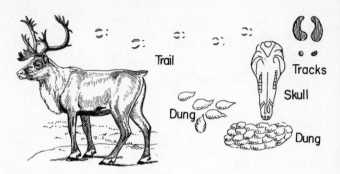

Trail

Tracks

Skull

Dung

Dung

A poet once said, "A reindeer is another name we give a caribou that's tame," and from this we may assume that most of us gained our original ideas of these animals from Santa's mythical and seasonally omnipresent team. The same writer tells us, "The mother caribou is queer and not like other kinds of deer. She has a set of antlers, too, just like the old bull caribou." This might be said more succinctly but hardly more effectively.

Reindeer are domesticated Old World caribou that were introduced into Alaska from Siberia after 1891. They are smaller, darker, and shorter-legged than our caribou, and have dish-faced profiles.

Woodland caribou bucks of most of southern Canada weigh to 700 pounds, stand to 4 feet at the shoulder, have a bounding gait, and antlers oval in cross section. Does weigh to 350 pounds. Barren-ground caribou bucks of northern Canada weigh to 400 pounds, stand to 3½ feet at shoulder, have a running or loping gait, and antlers with bases round in cross section.

Teeth are: I 0/4, C 1/0, P 3/3, M 3/3. Tracks are: F 3 x 5, 2; H 3 x 5, 2; L 80 plus.

A saddled reindeer can carry 150 pounds. It can pack a load weighing 90 pounds; or haul over snow, on a sled, 450 pounds for 40 miles a day; or rush 250 pounds 1 mile in 3 minutes. Reindeer swim at 5 m.p.h.; can travel 100 miles a day. Temperature, 100°–104° F.

An aggregation of caribou is called a herd. Herds make annual migration over established trails to 4 yards wide or wider. They are polygamous. In October, bulls fight viciously to build a harem of 30–40 cows. Rut lasts about 2 weeks. Bulls lose antlers in early winter but cows do not. One–2 young born 7 months, 7 days after the mating, or in May. Young walk in 2 hours, nurse more than 2 months, then join herd in migration. Does or cows shed antlers in spring. Reindeer breed earlier in season than New World caribou. Life span, to 15 years.

Giraffe · *Giraffa camelopardalis* · Giraffidae

IT seems absurd but is true that there is an animal that, standing on all 4 feet, holds its head 19 feet above the ground. Of course this is the giraffe, so well known in books and movies. Giraffes formerly roamed over most of Africa, but are now limited to central and southern Africa. Live in areas that are waterless a part of the year.

Giraffes have 2, 3, or 4 short, blunt, hornlike structures on the top of the head. Males have a stiff mane on back of long neck. Feet are large and heavy, with divided hoofs. Giraffes are yellowish white with large, squarish, black spots on body, neck, and upper parts of legs. Females are duller in coloring.

Giraffes feed largely on woody plants, such as acacias and mimosas, graze with difficulty, drink little, are usually quiet. They run in a trot or gallop, with forward-stretched neck and tail raised over back. With a good start they can outrun a horse.

There are at least 2 recognized kinds of giraffes, the blotched giraffe, *Giraffa camelopardalis,* of western Africa south of the Sahara, and the more attractive netted giraffe, *G. reticulata,* of East Africa. The latter has 4-sided liver-colored spots outlined in white. The bulls weigh to 2 tons. Height to top of head, to 19 feet. Cows are to 2 feet shorter than the bulls and weigh to 1,200 pounds. Giraffes are usually found in herds of to 15 animals, with 1 bull heading the herd. The herds can go without water for a month or more. Giraffes commonly sleep standing, but may lie down to do so. Pulse, 66.

Giraffe calves are born about 15 months after the mating in March or April. They are gentle animals which can stand on their wobbly legs 20 minutes after being born. They nurse for 9 months. Some young giraffes can be taught to eat in captivity, but many refuse to eat, and die. In captivity, giraffes have lived 28 years.

Pronghorn Antelope

Antilocapra americana · Antilocapridae

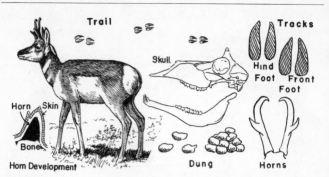

MANY of us get our first glimpse of a pronghorn in what seems like a telegraphic Morse-code signal of light spots that go on and off as we cross the western United States or southwestern Canada by train, car, or plane. As the pronghorns run, their white rumps are alternately exposed and covered, producing the telegraphic effect, but it is doubtful if any message is sent other than advice to the observer that the pronghorn is "getting out of there, and fast."

Pronghorns must depend largely on their speed to defend themselves, and some authorities claim that they have a speed of to 50 m.p.h., making them easily the fastest of North American mammals that run over the ground. They can leap a 5-foot fence easily and travel 20 miles a day on their annual migrations, or under hunting pressures.

Pronghorns stand 3 feet at the shoulder and 4 feet to the top of the head. They are more than 4 feet long and have a 3-inch tail. Bucks may weigh to 140 pounds; does, to 105 pounds. The horns, found in both sexes, are to 20 inches long, are divided, and hollow over a bony core, as are the horns of goats. Like deer, they shed their horns each year, the pronghorns doing so in October. Also like deer, the pronghorns have 4 teats and a woolly underhair. They are tan and white, with the does lighter than the bucks, and all have showy white rump patches. Teeth are: I 0/4, C 0/0, P 3/3, M 3/3. Tracks are: F 3½ x 2½, 2; H 3 x 2, 2; L 50, in slow running. Unfortunately for their own good, pronghorns have a great curiosity and may be induced to approach death from hunters because of this. Where there were once some 40 million pronghorns in the country, the number now is probably between 100 and 200 thousand. Both sexes are horned, so selective harvest is more difficult.

By fighting in early fall, bucks get harems of does. In 8 months, or in June, 2–3 scentless kids are born, which are able to walk, and in 10 days can outrun a dog. Mature at 5 years, aged at 15 years.

Zebu

ZEBUS were introduced into the United States in 1853 and in 1906, and are now established in the Gulf states.

They are representative of the humped cattle of India. They are a different species from domestic cattle but mate with them, producing valuable hybrids. Domestic cattle belong to the species *Bos taurus* and are discussed in immediately following pages.

Zebus vary in size from that of a small donkey to animals larger than the average domestic cattle. They have 1 or 2 large fatty lumps over the shoulders and a large dewlap that makes the neck unusually large. They have long ears that do not stand erect. They are pale fawn colored, black, bay, or iron gray, and darker forward. They are nervous animals and are often difficult to handle.

African breeds of zebus have unusually large horns. Indian breeds have small horns, or none. Their important points are that they are immune to ticks that carry Texas fever, and crossed with domestic cattle, produce tick-resistant animals. Similarly, they produce heat-resistant animals, which is important in the warmer regions. The cross also produces a better flesh than is normally found in the zebu.

The life history is essentially that of domestic cattle, outlined on page 283.

In India, zebus are considered to be sacred animals by the Hindus, who do not allow them to be killed. They serve as draft animals, however, for working fields, and in harness may haul a carriage 30 miles in a day. With a saddle, a zebu may carry a man at 6 m.p.h. for 15 hours. Zebus are not popular for direct beef production because of the large proportion of cheap meat. They have been domesticated since about 4,000 B.C.

281

The Cattle · The genus *Bos* · Bovidae

DETAILED help in understanding breeds and species appears in the sketches. General information appears in the text on the pages listed below:

Breeds. Dual-purpose, 282–285; dairy, 286–289; beef, 290–293; other types, 294–296.

Parts of Cattle. Cuts of meat, 283; horns, 292; leg bones, 293; parts, 289; skeleton, 290; skull, 291; stomach, 282; teeth, and determination of age through teeth, 284–288.

General Aspects. Ancestry, 285; food, 289; life history, 283; management, 291; myths and religions, 293; uses, 287.

The diagram below shows a typical ruminant's stomach, such as is found in cattle, and illustrates the path taken by food and the formation of the cud. In the camel, the ruminant stomach is 3-chambered instead of 4-chambered, and water is stored in cells in the walls of the rumen.

Polled Durham Cattle · *Bos taurus* · Bovidae

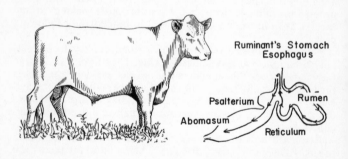

Ruminant's Stomach
Esophagus
Psalterium
Rumen
Abomasum
Reticulum

POLLED Durham cattle ("polled" = without horns) are dual-purpose, and 2 types are recognized. The double-standard polled Durham may be entered for judging in either the short-horned or the polled cattle group. The single-standard may be entered only with the polled Durhams. This is an agreed judging practice.

The breed originated in the United States and is much like the shorthorn, but the polled Durham is a much better milk producer than the regular shorthorn, which is more a beef type of animal. Polled Durhams are heavy for the milker type, but are better milkers than the average cattle of beef type. They are quiet creatures and are popular with those who understand their needs.

Red-polled Cattle · *Bos taurus* · Bovidae

Cuts of Beef

Chuck Rib Loin Round
Plate Flank

THIS breed came to America when a shipload of supplies was sent to Ireland following the famine in 1874. In appreciation for the gift, a red-polled heifer was sent to those who sent the relief supplies. The animal contributed to the improvement of our cattle and helped develop a line once known as Jamestown cattle.

This breed of dual-purpose cattle ranks high in the production of milk and butter and is good in beef production. Bulls weigh to 2,000 pounds and cows to 1,500 pounds. They occur in 2 types, the Norfolk red polled, in which the beef qualities are best developed, and the Suffolk, in which the dairy qualities have been emphasized.

These cattle produce a superior quality of beef as well as an excellent amount of dairy products.

Polled cattle have been known in England for a long time and may well have appeared shortly after the Roman occupation.

Life History of Cattle

A *calf* is born to a *cow* from 9–10 months after she is mated to a *bull*. During second year it is a *yearling;* in third year, a *2-year-old*. A young female is a *heifer,* but if twin with a male, a *freemartin*. Calves can run together until 4 months old, when sexes should be separated. Males with testicles removed when young are *steers;* if removed when mature, *oxen*. A good heifer may be bred at 18 months and continue to 12 years as a breeder. In heat 2–4 days every 3 weeks, unless bred. When a calf is born, the cow *comes in,* and when milk begins to flow she *freshens*. Cows not producing milk are *dry*. Bulls used for breeding are *service bulls;* cows nursing another's calf are *nurse cows*. Sperm from bulls of proven value in producing calves is collected and used artificially to impregnate cows. In artificial insemination 1 bull fertilizes to 200 cows at one service and may father 6,000 calves a year instead of the normal 30. This improves herds rapidly. Pulse, 40–100. Temperature, 102° F. Life span, to 20 years.

Shorthorn Cattle · *Bos taurus* · Bovidae

Teeth at 1 year

SHORTHORN cattle are popular in the corn belt area in the United States and on the range to the west. Commonly the western cattle are brought to the corn belt to be fattened before being slaughtered. Shorthorns fatten efficiently on corn. Breed might well be called Durham with safety.

Shorthorn cattle are red, red and white, or white and roan. They have broad backs, deep bodies, and mild dispositions. Cows have good-sized udders, and good average annual milk production is about 8,445 pounds of milk with 333 pounds of butterfat. An Australian shorthorn record was for 32,522 pounds of milk with 1,614 pounds of butterfat.

Shorthorn cattle have also been used as oxen, providing draft power on farms and elsewhere before the advent of the now more widely used farm tractors and road machines. Many a professional man nurses the ambition of retiring and having a ranch with a fine herd of shorthorns or Herefords on it, but comparatively few who have traded farm life for urban life return to the rugged existence of a cattle raiser.

Brown Swiss Cattle · *Bos taurus* · Bovidae

THIS is possibly the oldest of present-day breeds, and was developed in Switzerland on its mountain pastures. It is definitely of the dual-purpose type essential on farms, where both dairy products and beef are needed for firsthand use. The breed was introduced into America in 1869 and later in 1882 and 1889. Because of danger of disease from European animals, most direct importations have been suspended in recent years.

Brown Swiss bulls weigh to 1,900 pounds; cows, to 1,300 pounds. The animals are slightly lighter in weight than are Holsteins. Calves at birth weigh to 100 pounds and are unusually strong, as would be expected of animals developed in

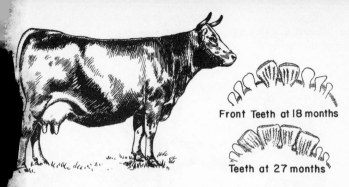

Front Teeth at 18 months

Teeth at 27 months

rugged territory. Color is mostly mouse color with a light stripe down the back. Nose, switch, tongue, and horn tips always black.

A good brown Swiss cow may average 6,000 pounds of milk a year, but registered, mature stock yields about 13,700 pounds, with 547 pounds of butterfat.

Ancestry of Domestic Cattle

PROBABLY domestic cattle evolved along 5 lines: 1. The Taurine group, which produced our domestic cattle of the beef and dairy types and the humped cattle of Africa and Asia, *Bos indicus* and *B. taurus* (pages 281–293). 2. The Bibovine group of southern Asia that produced the banteng *B. sondaicus,* the gayal *B. frontalis,* and the 6-foot gaur *B. gaurus.* 3. The Bisontine group, which yielded the American bison (page 297) and the Asiatic yak (page 296). 4. The Leptobovine group, represented only by fossils from India, Italy, and France. 5. The Bubaline group, represented by the water buffalo or carabao of India (page 294) and the Cape buffalo of Africa (page 295). The direct ancestors may have been the extinct Indian ox, *Bos namadicus,* associated with men of the Stone Age, the great ox *Bos primigenius,* which stood 6 feet at the withers and was used in bullfights before 1500 B.C., and the Celtic shorthorn, *Bos longifrons,* of western Europe and the British Isles. Cattle were domesticated as early as 2100 B.C.

Of course, over the world there are many kinds of breeds of cattle not considered here. Examples of these might include, of the beef type, the solid red Sussex, which resembles the Hereford but lacks the white face; the West Highland, which is variably colored, has long hair on poll and forehead, and large, long horns with spreading points; and the hornless Galloways, with long, rough coats. To the dairy group might be added the conspicuous Dutch Belted cattle, which are black with white belts. To the dual-purpose type might be added the bright red Devons, which have black-tipped horns.

285

Jersey Cattle · *Bos taurus* · Bovidae

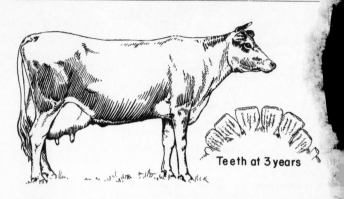

Teeth at 3 years

JERSEY cattle were developed in the Isle of Jersey in the British Channel, off the coast of France. The 7-by-12-mile island has a mild climate, and supports more than 50,000 inhabitants. No breed of cattle other than Jerseys is allowed on the island. The breed was introduced into the United States in the nineteenth century.

There was a time when Jersey milk was rated as tops. It still is by some, but it is too rich for many, and the production of greater volume, even at somewhat lower butterfat content, seems to be more popular and more profitable these days.

Jerseys are bred definitely for the production of milk of high butterfat content. The milk may test to 5% butterfat. One cow in 1 year produced 20,616 pounds of milk, and another 1,141 pounds of butterfat a year. Of course there is value in milk of high butterfat content, if butterfat is the dairy product wanted, and there always will be places where that is the case. Jersey bulls weigh to 1,400 pounds; cows, to 1,000 pounds. Bulls unreliable and dangerous.

These cattle are yellow or fawn with black nose, tongue, and switch.

Ayrshire Cattle · *Bos taurus* · Bovidae

ANOTHER relatively popular dairy cow came from southwestern Scotland, where it was developed in the middle of the eighteenth century. It was introduced into the United States in the nineteenth century. The Ayrshire is red and white or brown and white, with the white predominating and without the colors blending. Among the most conspicuous features are the long, slender horns, which curve upward, outward, and back. The backward-pointing section is remarkably straight. The bulls weigh to 2,000 pounds, the cows to 1,000 pounds. The animals are ideal milkers and long-lived.

Teeth at 4 Years

...he milk is high in quality and in quantity. An average cow ...ld produce to 7,000 pounds of milk a year with to 4% but-...at. Some cows 20 years old have produced to 10,000 pounds ...ilk a year.

The Uses of Domestic Cattle

...is surprising how many uses men make of cattle. Some of ...ese uses are dependent on the animal's remaining alive and in ...cellent health—the better the health, the better the product. ...thers necessitate killing the animals and using their bodies. ...Among the uses made of living cattle are these:

...Formerly much of the heavy labor on farms was performed ...oxen and other cattle. This sometimes involved riding the ...als under varying conditions. Men still ride or try to ride ...e in rodeos, much to the excitement of the onlookers. ...merly cattle were used in bullfights and in fights with dogs, ..., and other animals. The bull ring is still popular in some ...of the world.

...ides furnishing us with butter, cheese, and other dairy ...ucts, cattle also give us medicines, bones for fertilizers, ...re for enriching the soil, fat for lubricants, glue for ad-...es, soap, sandpaper, hair, and many other useful ma-...ls.

...From the hides of cattle we get a great variety of leathers ... use in making shoes, coats, traveling bags, gloves, hats, and ...her wearing apparel, particularly valuable when protection from wind is desired. From the hoofs we get a slow-drying oil useful in keeping leathers and fabrics flexible. From the intestines we get sandpaper, materials essential to some plastics, strings for musical instruments, and many more things.

The companionship of cattle is valuable to some people, particularly those whose neighbors are few. Boys and girls who rear calves in competition become greatly attached to their charges and regret having to close the books on the relationship.

Holstein-Friesian Cattle · *Bos taurus* · Bovidae

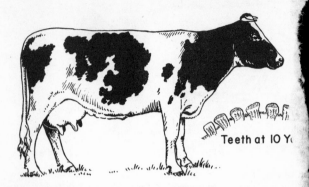

Teeth at 10 Y[...]

THIS breed was developed in Holland and Friesland a[...] been generally popular over agricultural Europe. It was [...] duced into America about 1795 and was followed by oth[...] portations through the next century.

These are the large, contented black-and-white cows s[...] quently identified with advertisements for milk pro[...] Occasionally there are red individuals. The bulls weigh [...] than a ton; cows average about 1,200 pounds. The cow[...] characterized by an unusually large udder and large body [...] by their usually philosophical attitude.

In one year, a Holstein cow produced 33,464 pound[...] milk with a butterfat content of 1,349 pounds. There ar[...] ords of many cows producing more than 1,000 pounds [...] terfat a year. That is a record that is hard to beat.

With the introduction of artificial insemination, it h[...] possible to improve the quality of herds tremendous[...] economically. Much of this has been because of the [...] standing of genetics and the identification of a relativ[...] bulls that have produced astonishing improvements i[...]

Guernsey Cattle · *Bos taurus* · Bovidae

OUR fourth dairy-type cattle breed is the Guernsey, wh[...] developed on the Island of Guernsey in the English Chann[...] the French coast. The island is only 24 square miles in a[...] but it has long been famous for success in producing a hig[...] grade dairy animal. Guernseys have been on American farm[...] since 1831, owing to a number of substantial importatio[...] over the years.

Guernseys are medium-sized animals, larger than Jersey [...] the cows weighing about 1,000 pounds. The animals are yellow[...] or fawn colored and never gray or buff, except for the nose,

Parts of Cattle

Head · Back · Neck Poll
Rump · Loin · Shoulder · Ear
Ribs Chops · Face
Muzzle
Chest · Dewlap
Fore · Breast
Hind Flank · Brisket
Flank · Shin

n is buff. Tongue and tail switch are generally white. nseys have a record of producing a good quantity of high- milk, but never the volume produced by a Holstein or the butter content of a Jersey. One Guernsey cow is recorded ving produced in 1 year 28,008 pounds of milk with a but- content of 1,098 pounds. In connection with this milk uction, it may be significant to mention that a cow nor- needs to produce only 1½ gallons of milk a day to main- its calf, yet through careful breeding cows have been oped that produce more than 11 gallons a day.

Cattle and the Problem of Food

TLE normally graze 8 hours out of the 24, and no more, ing the rest of the time resting and chewing the cud. grazing, the tongue is wrapped around the grass, which ed or cut by pushing front teeth of lower jaw against the jaw. Grass about 4–5 inches tall is eaten most rapidly. urs, a cow with 2½ inch spread of teeth cuts about 150 of green grass, which equals a pile 3 feet high and 6 diameter. Will not eat grass grown from fresh cow gs, but will eat grass grown from droppings of horses p. Stabled cattle are regularly fed roughage and grain y morning and late afternoon. Hay or silage is fed at nd water given twice a day. Exclusive of plant require-, from 15–30 tons of water are needed to produce 1 pound eef. To produce 9 gallons of milk, a cow must drink 22 allons of water. Milking is done at 12-hour intervals. A cow's respiration is 10–30; its temperature, 101.5° F. As shown on age 282, a cow has 4 chambers in its stomach, including the aunch or *rumen*, 80% of total; the *reticulum* or honeycomb; he *omasum, psalterium,* or *manyplies,* which is absent in some uminants; and the *abomasum,* or true stomach. The diagram shows the return of the food as a cud, and the second swallowing.

Hereford or White-faced Cattle · *Bos taurus* · Bovidae

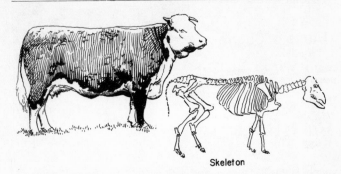

Skeleton

THE cattle presented on pages 290–294 are those raised primarily for beef. Of these the Angus and Herefords are the most popular in the northern cattle-raising country, and the longhorn and Santa Gertrudis the most popular to the south.

Herefords were developed in England in the valleys of the Severn and Wye rivers. They are large, chunky animals with white faces and white markings on the legs and under parts. They have heavy forequarters which made them popular as draft animals. They are tough and hardy in severe weather. They have a mild disposition. They are poor milkers, but you cannot expect everything of one animal. About 55% of a living Hereford steer is beef, as contrasted with 35%–50% in ordinary cattle.

The ability of Herefords to put on flesh rapidly has made them popular in the corn belt area, where fattening is an art and a profession. The usual system is to round up calves on the Western ranges and ship them to the Middle West, where they are fattened prior to being shipped to the slaughtering houses in the larger cities. Most of the animals slaughtered are steers—the cows having been left on the range to produce other calves for other years.

Aberdeen Angus or Angus Cattle · *Bos taurus* · Bovidae

THERE should be no difficulty in recognizing these hornless, wholly black, stocky beef cattle, which are relatively small but tremendously solid. The carcass of Angus steers may be 65% of marketable high-grade beef. Probably no other breed matches this record.

Angus cattle probably descended from a wild, hornless breed and were developed and improved in Scotland in Aberdeen, Kincardine, and Forfar counties. They have gained a rapid popularity in the United States in recent years.

Skull

In the Angus beef the fat is evenly distributed. In addition, no other breed can match the result attained by high-pressure feeding Angus cattle to bring about rapid production of baby beef, which commands the top prices in the market. In Scotland, the animals are rather affectionately known as "doddies."

Properly managed, the cows produce a good flow of milk that is better than that expected from a beef type of cow. The animals are quiet and do well in confined quarters and in the fields with most other domestic animals, such as sheep and goats.

Management of Cattle

ON page 289 were given some suggestions relative to management of cattle through feeding practices. Other aspects should be considered.

In the broad sense, cattle may be thought of as machines for turning grass into beef and dairy products. Incidentally, in the process they may enrich the soil through their manures. On many farms the cattle are fed grain raised off the premises, and the wastes from this grain enrich the soil of the farm on which the cattle live. The management of the manure pile must be considered in a close economy, so as to guarantee that its wealth is not washed away and lost, but rather spread where and when it may be most needed. Such manures, mixed with "green manures" from plowed-under living plants, add to the probable returns from the plants grown on the soil.

Many breeds of cattle are inefficient at certain times of the year because of the annoyance of insects. Milk production and beef production may be reduced by insect disturbance. Some insects, such as the warble flies, may drive cattle frantic so that they may injure themselves. The larvae of these flies eventually eat their way through the hides of the cattle at the shoulders, cutting holes in the best part for the production of leather. Ordinarily these flies do not molest cattle standing in the shade as much as they do animals exposed to the sun. Management, then, calls for the provision of shade.

Cattle may suffer or yield inferior products, of course, through eating some plants, such as some lupines, white snakeroot, St.-John's-wort, and the locoweeds.

291

Longhorn Cattle or Texas Longhorns

Bos taurus · Bovidae

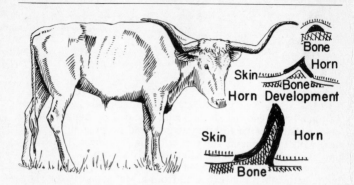

Bone
Horn
Skin
Bone
Horn Development

Skin
Horn
Bone

Most of us know our longhorns only through the movies or through seeing some of them at rodeos. In the southwestern part of the United States, where they were once abundant, they have almost completely disappeared.

The beef produced by longhorn cattle is rather coarse. The animals mature slowly. However, they do seem to be able to exist in territory which is impossible for better breeds.

Longhorns were once considered as producers of good milk for cheese making, but the better milk they gave, the poorer beef they produced, and other breeds can better the longhorns in both beef and dairy production. None can beat them, however, for picturesqueness, and they will survive on the rodeo circuit long after they have disappeared from the wide-open spaces.

The back is normally broad, the ribs deep, and the hindquarters rather well developed. Color may be either a red or a brindle, but usually there is a white stripe down the spine.

Because of the magnificent development of the horns of longhorns, it seemed appropriate to show here how horns in cattle are produced. Contrast the sketch above with the similar sketch on page 274, which shows how antlers are produced.

Santa Gertrudis Cattle · *Bos taurus* · Bovidae

The southwestern United States east of the mountains may be rugged country. It may be too hot, too dry, too badly infested with troublesome ticks and insects for ordinary cattle to accept. The Mexican cattle of longhorn stock that did exist there did not produce good milk or beef. Herefords and shorthorns were introduced to grade up the stock, but this did not prove to be the right combination.

Finally the King Ranch in Texas mated zebu bulls with the stock that evolved from Texas longhorns, Herefords, and short-

292

Leg Bones

horns. Fifty-two Brahma or zebu bulls and 2,500 shorthorn cows were involved in the program, which finally produced a breed in which a bull, Monkey by name, had the qualities desired. Before he died in 1932, he had produced 150 useful bulls for establishing the Santa Gertrudis breed. The breed gained official recognition in 1940.

The present Santa Gertrudis stock produces bulls that weigh to 1,800 pounds; cows, to 1,200 pounds, and 4-year steers to 1,400 pounds. These animals are a solid red with short, sleek hair. They have a heavy navel lap, large dewlap, and loose, stretchy skin, and the bulls have a neck crest. Santa Gertrudis cattle are mild-tempered, good rustlers, take rain or drought well, are good mothers, make large gains on grass, can walk long distances with little water, are highly tick resistant, and stand insects remarkably well. Best of all, their carcasses may dress out to nearly 72% of valuable meat.

Cattle in Myths and Religion

CATTLE have long been so closely identified with man's interests that it is not surprising that they have entered his mores, his mythology, and his religion.

In many parts of the world today cattle are considered as sacred, and, as such, cannot be killed, even though they may be worked. Some people think of them as the earthly residences of mythological beings, or as beings inhabited by the souls of departed men and women, who can eventually regain their human form in Paradise. If you thought of a cow as your grandmother or Martha Washington, you might treat her differently than if you regarded her as a mere milk producer. Bulls have probably been worshiped more than have cows. Also, they have been more frequently sacrificed to the gods. Warriors have drunk their blood to acquire the strength and courage of the bulls, and thus heighten their prowess in battle. Bulls have been kept in enclosures guarded by as many as 200 priests, who had no other duties. Not a bad life for a bull.

293

Water Buffalo, Carabao, or Indian Buffalo

Bos bubalus · Bovidae

Two representatives of the Bubaline group of cattle are shown above and on page 295. One, the water buffalo, is Asiatic; the other, the Cape buffalo, is African. While the Indian buffalo, in its native jungle as a wild animal, is savage, powerful, unreliable, and extremely dangerous, as a domesticated animal it is docile, uncomplaining, and can be handled even by children in doing useful work.

Water buffaloes, Indian or Asiatic buffaloes, or carabaos, are to 10 feet long, including a 2-foot tail, and stand to 6 feet high at the shoulder. Horns are heavy at the base and curve backward and inward to sharp tips. They are somewhat flattened and marked with cross wrinkles. The distance from tip to tip along the curve of the 2 horns is up to 12 feet. Head is longer and the ears shorter than in the Cape buffalo. Tail ends in a brush of stiff hairs. The color is dark ash gray to black.

These animals are found wild in India, the Philippines, Malaya, and Ceylon. Domesticated, they are used as draft animals through most of the warmer parts of the Orient. In the wild, the animals often live in herds. About 10 months after the mating, 1 to 2 calves are born.

Indian buffaloes are bothered by great clouds of insects. To protect themselves they spend much time in the water, or coat their bodies with a thick layer of mud through which the insects cannot bite.

Domestic carabaos give a goodly amount of extremely rich milk. From it the natives make a butter called *ghee,* which is most popular in India. The hide makes a superior leather, but the flesh is not superior in any way.

In the wild state, the animals are found from sea level to elevations of 6,000 feet in the mountains, but almost invariably near watercourses. Wild carabaos are a match for tigers.

Cape Buffalo · *Bos caffer* · Bovidae

Skull

THERE are plenty of men versed by firsthand experience in the dangers associated with powerful wild animals. A majority of those informed on the habits of the Cape buffalo are inclined to feel that it is one of the most dangerous of all wild creatures.

Bulls of this species may weigh more than 1,500 pounds and stand 5 feet high at the shoulder. Some contend that the Cape buffalo weighs to 4,000 pounds. The head and body have a total length of 7 feet; tail is to 4 feet long. Ears are larger than those of the water buffalo. The most conspicuous difference between these 2 buffaloes is in the horns, as shown in the illustrations.

In the Cape or African buffalo, the horns are broad and heavy at the base, nearly joining each other there. They curve backward to points. Each horn may be more than 3 feet long. Cape buffaloes have a gray skin and a black nose. In their prime, they have sparse black hair. Old bulls have little if any hair. Young calves may have considerable hair, but it is reddish instead of black, changing at about the end of the third year.

Cape buffaloes live in herds of 1,000 animals, and can move through brushy country with surprising silence. Mating takes place in January and the young are born about 11 months later. The herd takes remarkable care of its members, and few if any animals dare challenge it. Lions would be no match for even a small herd. The animals feed during the first half of the night, after having satisfied the thirst caused by the heat of the day. Usually they rest and chew their cuds during the latter half of the night, and after a morning drink, take it easy in the shade during the day. They suffer severely from the rinderpest, which has at times completely wiped out the animals in large areas. Normal life expectancy, more than 16 years.

295

Yak or Grunting Ox · *Bos gruniens* · Bovidae

MOUNTAINOUS central Asia, particularly in the Tibet region, is a forbidding territory, where many animals could not live. Forage may be sparse and the winters severe. Yaks, which look like longhaired cattle with humps like bison and long, spreading horns that are remarkably slender, thrive in that part of the world. They cannot survive in the lower and warmer parts of Asia.

Yaks are larger than most domestic cattle and are more solidly built. Long hair grows like a fringe on the tail, flanks, and legs, practically reaching to the ground, and there is a conspicuous tuft of hair on the chest. They are blackish brown in the wild, but domestic yaks may be brown, red, mottled, or all black.

Yaks usually feed in the morning and evening, resting and chewing their cuds between times. They can get along on little food if necessary.

They make excellent pack animals because of their surefootedness, and while they travel less rapidly than horses, they nevertheless move more surely where the going is tough.

Yaks are important to the natives. They provide transportation either as pack animals or as saddle animals. Cloth is made from their hair and leather from their hides. The cows give a rich milk from which butter and cheese for human consumption may be made. Their tails are used as ornaments and as fly brushes, and water bags are made from their bladders.

While yaks normally seem to be quiet, rather bored creatures, the cows will most actively and effectively protect their calves. The calves are born from 8½–10 months after the mating takes place. As they are born in the autumn, unless they were hardy animals from the start, they could not survive that first bitter winter which comes to them so early in life. Yaks are to the mountains of Asia what carabao are to wet, tropical lowlands, what camels are to the desert, and what horses are to less extreme climates. Life span, to 32 years.

Bison or Buffalo · *Bison bison* · Bovidae

Track

Trail

Skeleton

Skull

Skull

ONE of the tragedies of American natural history is the disappearance of the great herds of bison that once roamed the plains. One of the bright spots in American conservation is the survival and partial restoration of the remnants of those herds. In 1889 there were only 541 bison in the United States, and in 1900 probably only 250 of the darker wood bison in Canada. The numbers are now large enough to guarantee survival and permit a controlled harvest of surplus—a victory for conservation.

Bison are members of the family Bovidae, or hollow-horned ruminants. The horns (page 292) are paired, unbranched, usually borne by both sexes, grow slowly and continuously over bony cores, and are not shed as antlers are. There is a 4-chambered stomach (page 289). Teeth are: I 0/4, C 0/0, P 3/3, M 3/3. Tracks are: F 5/5, 2; H 5/5, 2. Temperature, 102° F.

Bison bulls are to 11 feet long, including a 2-foot tail. They stand 6 feet at the shoulder and weigh more than 3,000 pounds. They are dark brown, but lighter to the rear. They have shaggy hair over their heavy shoulders, their forelegs, and head. Horns are sharp, short, upward curving, and unbranched. Speed is to 40 m.p.h. The animals are grazers, and small family herds are led by an old cow.

Bison are probably monogamous, although bulls fight one another in August–September in the breeding season. One calf born 9½ months after the mating, birth lasting 1 hour. Calf stands in 3–4 days, is protected by bull and cow. Calf stays 3 years with cow, when the calf breeds and becomes independent. Cow may bear a calf every year for 30 years.

Bison provided the Indians with such essentials for survival as flesh, hide, horn, hair, bones, and fuel in the form of dried "chips," or dung. Many tribes were able to find bison almost anywhere in their country, and prospered in a bison-based society, depending on the animals for food, raiment, tools, and other things.

Mountain Goat · *Oreamnos americanus* · Bovidae

Skull

Track

Dung

Trail

THE Rocky Mountains and coast ranges in the United States and north to Alaska support this beautiful animal. In the United States, it is now practically limited to the various parks and sanctuaries. During the summer months it is found in the high mountainous pastures, but in winter it may come down to the lower levels.

Mountain goats are about 5½ feet long, including the 6½ inch tail. Their small backward-curving horns are black and about 1 foot long. Ears are shorter than the horns. The males weigh to 300 pounds; females, to 250 pounds. Color is all white the year round. Hair is long and relatively coarse. It is particularly heavy above the knees, and there is a conspicuous beard. The sexes and the young are colored alike. Teeth are: I 0/4, C 0/0, P 3/3, M 3/3. Tracks are: F 2¾ x 2¾, 2; H 2½ x 2½, 2. The points of the toes are rather narrow and are somewhat spreading. Temperature, 100° F.

As their habitat suggests, these goats feed on almost any green plant material available to them. They are not found in large herds, as are sheep and caribou, but in small groups that may be family units. They are preyed on by wolves, foxes, and bears when they are young. As adults their greatest enemy, of course, is man.

Mountain goats are probably monogamous. The male, female, and young live together through the summer. Young are born 6 months after the mating. The kids can stand in 10 minutes, nurse in 20 minutes, jump in 30 minutes, and at 2 days stand 13½ inches high and weigh to 7 pounds. The mother will defend her kid to the best of her ability, even if it means risking her own life. The ease with which these animals scale a steep wall of rock and avoid falling after phenomenal leaps is nothing short of miraculous.

It is quite possible that mountain goats may carry some diseases which may affect cattle or man, but they rarely come into contact with either of these creatures, so their influence can hardly be great.

Brindled Gnu or Wildebeest

Connochaetes taurinus · Bovidae

AFRICA is the home of these grotesque animals that seem to be a combination of a horse, a cow, and some unnamed beast. The mane and hindquarters look much like those of a horse. Much of the head and shoulders suggests a cow, or a bison.

Gnus live in large herds. They seem to have a trait of curiosity which often leads them to misfortune. They can run with the speed of a horse, and have great endurance, and yet they are caught by lions, which could not possibly overtake them in a long run in the open.

Gnus stand to 4 feet at the shoulder and exclusive of the tail are about 7 feet long. The face looks somewhat like that of a buffalo, is yellowish gray and blackish on the sides. Horns are borne by both sexes. The weight is about 500 pounds. There are dark stripes across the withers.

Gnus mate in June or thereabouts, and 8½ months later 1 or rarely 2 young are born. The cows and bulls then form separate herds.

Gnus are the favored food of many of the large flesh eaters of their environment. The natives also find that their flesh is delicious and that their hides make good leather. Since they compete for forage with more useful domestic animals, it is quite likely that eventually they will disappear from all areas not set aside as wildlife sanctuaries. While the animals have excellent sight and good ability to smell things, not only does their unusual inquisitiveness often lead to their death, but they are frequently stampeded by the behavior of certain members of the herd. Life span, to 16 years.

Chamois or Gems · *Rupicapra rupicapra* · Bovidae

THESE beautiful animals are found in the Alps, Apennines, Carpathians, and other mountains of Europe and the Asia Minor area. Most of us know the chamois from its skin, which for many, many years has been used for cleaning glass. Now, "chamois" usually comes from goats.

Chamois are to nearly 4 feet long, stand to 32 inches high at the shoulder, and weigh to 90 pounds, although these figures are above the average. Average bucks weigh 65 pounds; average does, 45 pounds. Chamois are dark brown to black in winter, a lighter, tawny brown in summer. Horns rise vertically from the top of the head for about 10 inches, curve backward and downward, and end in sharp points. They are borne by both sexes. Greatest horn growth is in the second, first, and third years, in that order. The hair is close and long, with thick, woolly underfur.

The chamois are considered as excellent game animals, and for that purpose have been introduced into New Zealand, where they have established themselves. The flesh is good as food and the hides make fine leather. Chamois have remarkably sensitive sight and hearing. They can leap a distance of 23 feet on the horizontal, and over a 13-foot wall.

Chamois kids, numbering 1–3, are born in May or June and are able to follow the mother almost immediately. In the wild, the kids will follow the mother for a half year or more, and show unusual concern if she is killed. They improve rapidly in their leaping ability during the first few days. Kids may be tamed if caught young. The animals will breed in captivity. Old animals may become vicious and may attack man and other animals vigorously, using their horns most effectively.

Ibex or Wild Goat · *Capra ibex* · Bovidae

THE relatively common wild goat of Asia, North Africa, and Europe is the ibex. Among the allies of *Capra ibex* are the Himalayan ibex, *C. siberica;* the Arabian ibex, *C. sinaitica;* and the Abyssinian ibex, *C. walie.* For the most part all live in the highest, most rugged country available to them. Some, living near homes of man, may become relatively tame.

Ibexes begin grazing in late afternoon and may feed through the night, retreating to wooded areas at sunrise and resting most of the day. They serve as good food and game animals, and while they may be tamed they are not reliable pets and are given to violent butting.

Ibexes stand 3 feet high at the shoulder and are to 5 feet long. Bucks are larger than the does and weigh to 200 pounds. Horns are heavy, backward-curving structures that curve obliquely, are to 56 inches long, and weigh to 30 pounds. They are borne by both sexes. The fur is rough. In the bucks there is a mane on the back of the neck and a short beard on the chin.

Mating time is October, when the herds of bucks join the does. During most of the year the bucks live more by themselves and at higher altitudes. In June or July, 1–2 kids are born. A few hours later, the kids may follow their mother over surprisingly rough terrain. The doe protects her young by fighting directly or by decoying potential enemies away from where the youngsters are. Of course the wild goats' worst enemy is man, but bears, wolves, and eagles also take their toll from the annual crop of kids and from the animals that are not alert. Life span, to 10 years.

Angora Goat · *Capra angorensis* · Bovidae

Lower Jaw
1st year
All Milk Teeth

2nd Year
1 Pair Permanent Teeth
3 Pairs Milk Teeth

3rd Year
2 Pairs Permanent
2 Pairs Milk Teeth

4th Year
3 Pairs Permanent
1 Pair Milk Teeth

DOMESTIC goats are of great value to man. In one breed or another, they provide hair useful in making cloth, flesh and milk suitable as food, and hides useful as leather. They even serve as draft animals, pulling small carts, and operate small treadmills. In addition they act as useful leaders to herds of sheep, which may well be stampeded to their death if such guidance is not available.

The age of goats may be determined by observation of the lower front teeth. Study of the diagrams on this and the following page will help.

Angora goats are raised in considerable numbers in the South and Southwest of the United States, but more ambitiously in the Old World. The names of these breeds—Cashmere (2 feet high), Tibet, Syrian (long-eared), Sudan, and Egyptian—indicate the regions where they were developed. Normally goats can exist on any land that will support sheep, and on land that will not support horses or cattle.

Goats are clipped twice a year for their hair. The hair is sorted according to its fineness and made into mohair cloth. Trained sorters can recognize 13 diameters between 0.003 and 0.0067 inch and can sort 500 pounds in 1 day. Only about 1 in 10,000 men has this ability, and to do the work effectively requires at least 3 years of preliminary training.

Hair goats must have water in both summer and winter to grow good coats. They are usually kept in herds of to 1,200 animals.

On the range, kidding time is most important. Since the newly born kid cannot stand and may well be trampled to death by the herd, it is a common practice to toggle the expectant doe so that she cannot move with her kid. Thus the mother is kept away from the herd. After 2 weeks the doe and the kids are allowed to graze in special pastures. To prevent too many kids being born at once, 1 buck is allowed to serve about 50 does, thus spreading the birth of the young over a considerable period. Pulse, 70–135.

Milch Goat · *Capra hircus* · Bovidae

Lower Jaw at 5th Year All Permanent Teeth

Track

Dung

MILCH goats are of Persian origin. Goats' milk is frequently recommended for the diet of persons with dietary troubles. Some cities maintain goat dairies to supply the special needs in this respect. A healthy milch doe can give milk from 7–10 months after her kid is born.

These goats are common in Europe, where in some sections 75% of the rural folk maintain them. Frequently in American cities, persons of European extraction living in suburban sections maintain goats on tiny bits of land.

Milch goats have long bodies with large hindquarters. The mouth is wide and the udder full but not tight. The hairs of the body are smooth, fine, and bristling. Many of the breeds do not have horns. In most cases the bucks have a decidedly unpleasant odor. Years before I moved to my boyhood home, a shed there had been used to house a billy goat. Until it was torn down 20 years later, it never lost its characteristic odor.

The 2–4 kids are born 147–155 days after the mating. Kids are well developed at birth, follow mother in 4–5 days, mature in 8–12 months, and are old at 6 years. Life span, to 18 years. Castrated males are known as *wethers*. Such animals are commonly slaughtered for their flesh, which is sold as "venison."

Goats make fairly good pets and to some degree can be taught to work in harness. Even domestic goats do not seem to lose the desire of the wild animals to seek a high point on which to stand, and which they do not like to be forced to leave.

Muskox · *Ovibos moschatus* · Bovidae

Skull

Track

Trail

Dung

IN Asia, Europe, and North America fossil forms of muskox have been found associated with the earliest of the men living in those areas. It is not stretching the imagination too much to suggest that in the not-too-distant future the animals, aside from their fossil remains, will be known only from man-made records.

Muskox are now limited to northern Canada and Greenland, the herds of Europe and Asia having completely disappeared. In the areas where they most recently disappeared, they were given protection which it was thought might be adequate. Obviously, to survive they need more protection than they have had in the past.

Muskox are to 8 feet long, including a 4-inch tail. They stand to 6 feet high at the shoulder and weigh to 700 pounds. The sexes are essentially alike except that the cow is smaller than the bull. They are shaggy animals with long hair. The recurved horns are much like those of the Cape buffalo, at least at the base, and spread to 2 feet. The head and body are deep brown, front and underparts black, the legs dirty white. They have a strong musky scent. Teeth are: 1 0/4, C 0/0, P 3/3, M 3/3. Tracks are: F 5 x 5, 2; H 5 x 5, 2; Sp 10.

As a great potential source of excellent food for those living in the Arctic, no other animal compares with the muskox. Once spotted, the animals are killed relatively easily, as they stand to be shot rather than try to escape once they have come to grips with man.

Bulls fight to gain mastery over a herd of cows, giving off scent in the fight. August breeding results in 1 calf per cow in late May. Calf weighs to 16 pounds at birth, stands 18 inches high at shoulder, and follows cow in 1–2 hours. A 4-day calf weighs 25 pounds and stands 20 inches high at shoulder. A 22-month calf stands 3 feet 2 inches high at shoulder. Cows are bred every alternate year.

Mountain Sheep or Bighorn · *Ovis canadensis* · Bovidae

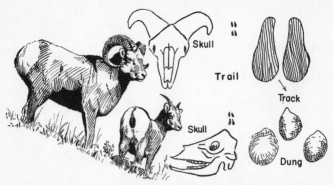

From the mountains of northern Mexico and western Texas to North Dakota, west to southwest Alberta, north across the Arctic Circle in Alaska, and west to the Pacific Coast, except for isolated areas, are the native homes of a group of splendid wild animals, the mountain sheep. They have suffered from heavy hunting, competition with domestic stock for food, the advance of civilization, and from their natural enemies, but they are still with us, and in not inconsiderable numbers in some areas.

Ram mountain sheep are nearly 7 feet long, including a 5-inch tail. They stand to 3½ feet high at the shoulder and weigh to 320 pounds. The horns of the rams may measure 4 feet along the curve. The ewes weigh to 175 pounds and have much shorter and straighter horns. Mountain sheep are brownish gray above, brownish on the sides, yellowish white beneath, and darkest on the back and upper neck. There is a conspicuous light-colored rump in each sex. Teeth are: I 0/4, C 0/0, P 3/3, M 3/3. Tracks are: F 2¾ x 2¾, 2; H 2¾ x 2¾, 2.

Mountain sheep have exceptional sight but a poor sense of smell. They must have access to water daily and must be able to reach salt at intervals. Normally mountain sheep feed at the higher pastures in the summer months and come down to the lower levels in the winter. They can survive for considerable periods on little vegetation.

In November the rams fight each other for mastery over a harem of ewes. From 1–2 lambs are born 150 days after the mating. The lambs can run and skip within 2 hours, but tend to hide until 3 days old, when they are strong enough to follow the mother. They are preyed on at first by eagles, coyotes, and other often abundant enemies. By the time rams have become 8 years old they have passed their prime, as is shown by the annual rings on their horns. Life span, about 15 years.

Domestic Sheep
Romney Sheep · *Ovis aries* · Bovidae

Dung

SHEEP live in varied places and serve so many uses to man that it is natural that they have been bred to suit many special needs. Romney sheep are of a general type, at their best in lowlands, where there is rich grazing. It seems just as important to select animals that do well where food and water are abundant as it is to select those that can flourish under difficult circumstances.

Romney sheep are possibly the largest of the lowland sheep. Wethers kept to 3 years weigh to 240 pounds. (Wethers are castrated males.) Ewes weigh to 150 pounds. They may be crowded together in rich pasture and thrive. They were developed in Kent and Sussex counties, England, and are popular where conditions are similar. They are rarely given extra food and shelter in winter in their homelands.

Romneys have white faces and usually a forelock. The wool is fine, lustrous, and of good quality, the average fleece weighing 9 pounds. They are prolific, 20%–30% of the lambs being twins. Lambs are born in March and April. The mutton from Romneys is good, and the fleece is one of the closest of the long-wool type.

Rambouillet Sheep · *Ovis aries* · Bovidae

RAMBOUILLET sheep are sometimes called French Merino sheep. The breed was introduced into America in 1840. The rams weigh from 175–285 pounds; ewes, from 160–260 pounds. Rambouillet sheep are definitely of the wool-producing type, and have fleece that may be 3 inches long. A ram yields to 15 pounds of fleece; a ewe, to 10 pounds. This does not rank with the fleece of Merinos ordinarily.

The Rambouillet rams usually have large spiral horns, but

these may be entirely lacking; ewes are always hornless. The ewes are recognized as good mothers and are highly prolific.

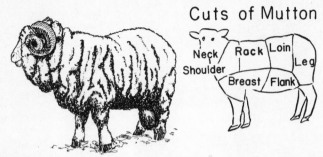

Cuts of Mutton

The lambs are hardy, reach maturity relatively early, and eventually yield a fair grade of mutton. The breed has been used extensively in Australia, New Zealand, and the Argentine to improve the wool-producing qualities of local breeds.

The Chief Uses of Sheep

SHEEP, of course, are the basis of the wool industry, and wool has long been basic to much of the clothing worn by man. It is possible that with the development of synthetic fibers, the demand for wool may decrease to the detriment of the sheep-raising business. The great centers for wool production are the western United States, western Asia and Australia, and New Zealand.

While we may dispense with sheep as producers of wool, it is unlikely that we shall ever discontinue using them as food. We get our lamb chops from lambs, our tender "hogget" mutton from year-old rams or wethers, and our regular mutton from mature sheep. In addition, we get some fats from sheep, and Roquefort cheese is made from their milk. Some breeds are popular because of their ability to produce many lambs that will develop early and economically. As with cattle, some breeds of sheep produce carcasses that are superior to others.

Sheep must be recognized as serious factors in soil erosion. Their competition with cattle for food has raised well-known conflicts between sheepherders and cattlemen. Sheep are sometimes difficult to raise because of the ease with which they are killed or stampeded by dogs, coyotes, bears, and other animals. As suggested earlier, it is sometimes customary on sheep ranges to have sheep share pasture with goats, as they are not so easily stampeded. It has also been found that sheep being pastured with Angus cattle are not so likely to be bothered by dogs, because the cattle drive off the dogs and incidentally protect the sheep.

307

Merino Sheep · *Ovis aries* · Bovidae

Lamb
All Milk Teeth

Yearling
I Pair Permanent Teeth
3 Pairs Milk Teeth

2nd Year
2 Pairs Milk Teeth

MERINO sheep are bred almost wholly for the production of a high quality and quantity of wool. Merino rams weigh to 140 pounds; ewes, to 100 pounds. The wool covers the head, obscuring the eyes, but the ears and muzzle are woolless. The skin is pink.

A ram may yield to 30 pounds of fleece; a ewe to 24 pounds, although the averages are lower than these figures. Different grades are recognized—a low-grade fleece weighing 18 pounds and an A-grade weighing 30 pounds. The fine wool hairs have a diameter of from $\frac{1}{1000}$ to $\frac{1}{1800}$ of an inch. This compares with a measurement of $\frac{1}{875}$ of an inch for the hair of the wool of a Southdown sheep (page 310). The wool of Merino sheep has a rather heavy oil protection, which makes the outside collect dirt so that the animals look dirty, although the wool beneath may be quite different.

Merino sheep do not fatten readily and so are not too popular as producers of mutton. They are used rather extensively in crossbreeding to improve the quality of wool of other breeds.

American Merinos were developed from the Merinos, which originally came from Spain.

Shropshire Sheep · *Ovis aries* · Bovidae

THIS breed was introduced into America in 1855. It was developed on Shropshire Downs and in Staffordshire County, England.

Shropshire sheep are of the general-purpose type, raised for both their wool and their flesh. They are characterized by having dark brown faces and legs. Rams weigh from 225–275 pounds; ewes, from 175–225 pounds. In general, these sheep are 15% heavier than are Southdowns (page 310). They are probably more fully covered than any other breed, as only the tip of the nose, the ears, feet, and eyes are woolless. Shropshires have squarely built bodies borne on straight, stout legs.

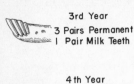

3rd Year
3 Pairs Permanent
1 Pair Milk Teeth

Sheep

4th Year
All Permanent Teeth

The wool of Shropshire sheep averages 8–10 pounds in weight. It is dense, fine, of medium length, growing to 6 inches in a year. The mutton of Shropshire sheep is of a good second quality.

Shropshires mature early, fatten quickly, and, more important, have a high birth rate. They are quite docile and easily handled.

The Life History of Sheep

IN management of sheep, it is a common practice to mate 1 *ram*, the male, to from 35–50 *ewes*, the females. Ewes should be 1½ years old before they are first bred. Ewes are in heat for 1–2 days and the mating act is phenomenally short. From 1–2 lambs are born 146 days after the mating.

Normally ewes need 16 square feet of floor space if kept indoors. Between the mating act and the lambing, ewes may increase their weight by 25 pounds.

Within 2 hours after birth the lambs begin to nurse. At 2 weeks they are able to nibble hay. At 2 months they are weaned, and at 4 months they are normally of marketable age. Usually the tails of lambs are cut when they are 2 weeks old. At the same time, the male lambs are castrated. Sheep from 2–15 months of age are called *hoggets, hogs,* or *tags,* names which are sometimes also applied to some other domestic animals when they are 1 year old. Hogget mutton is considered more tasty than mutton from older animals. Temperature, 100°–105° F.

As with many other domestic animals and some wild ones, a sheep's age may be told by examining the teeth. The diagrams on pages 308–309 will help in making such an examination. The sketches refer to the front teeth on the lower jaw. It should be noted that the first permanent teeth are those in the center and to the front. Milk teeth are replaced in a regular order, beginning with the front ones and progressing regularly backward.

Cheviot Sheep · *Ovis aries* · Bovidae

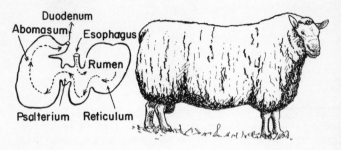

THE Cheviot sheep, a breed that is hardy, came from the mountainous areas of Scotland. It was rumored that they swam ashore with the sinking of the Spanish Armada. The face, nose, legs, and erect ears are covered with short white hair. The fleece is dense, fairly fine, and soft to the touch. There is a marked ruff at the neck. The tail is long, rough, and is usually cut. The fleece of a Cheviot ram weighs to 12 pounds, but that of the ewe is about 3½ pounds.

Cheviots are not phenomenal in production of wool or flesh. However, they do well on land too poor to support the better breeds, and need little more than grass to develop satisfactorily. They stand travel on foot well. They are not always easily herded, because they have a tendency to scatter unexpectedly. They are hardy under difficult conditions.

Wethers weigh to 200 pounds; fattened ewes weigh to 150 pounds. Authorities differ as to the quality of the mutton, but this may be owing to different feeding programs.

Southdown Sheep · *Ovis aries* · Bovidae

SOUTHDOWN sheep originated as a breed late in the eighteenth century. A record has been kept of the breed for about 200 years. It was introduced into America before 1803. It has been a popular Midwestern and Eastern breed but has never been favored in the Far West.

The animals are among the smallest of the mutton type. Rams weigh to 190 pounds; wethers, to 150 pounds normally, but may be fattened to 280 pounds; the ewes weigh to 130 pounds.

Southdown sheep are hornless. The ears are small and wide apart. The face is brown or gray. The limbs are short. The rump is broad. The feet are subject to foot rot.

310

Track

Lambs weigh 60–90 pounds in 1–6 months. The fleece of the ewes weighs 6–8 pounds, that of the rams, to 12 pounds. The average fleece weighs 7 pounds. The wool is short, close, fine, and grows 3–4 inches in a year. It ranks high in quality. The grade of the mutton is rather good, particularly if the animals are not too fat. The carcass dresses out little offal.

Southdown sheep are peaceful animals, and in the past were used rather extensively to graze the lawns of huge estates. With the passing of the large-estate period in our civilization, and the development of power mowers, the sheep are no longer useful in this connection.

Sheep and Their Food

SHEEP are completely vegetarian. Ordinarily they thrive best on vegetation that is short and cropped close to the ground. Clover mixed with grass is better than grass alone. Sheltered sheep are fed legume hay and grain mixtures, such as 4 parts of the roughage by weight, 4 parts of oats, and 2 parts of linseed or cottonseed cake. Salt and water should be constantly available. Pregnant ewes each day need 1–2 pounds of silage, 2–3 pounds of hay, and 1½ gallons of water.

Alfalfa is recommended as sheep forage. Bluegrass pasture does not provide adequate food during the warm summer months.

Following the weaning, larger ewes may require milking by hand at least once every day or so, until milk production has ceased.

The food needs of different breeds of sheep vary considerably, as suggested in the specific accounts. This variation makes it possible for sheep to make valuable contributions to man's needs from many types of places, high or low, damp or dry, lush or with poor vegetation cover.

Dorset Sheep · *Ovis aries* · Bovidae

WE have shown how sheep may be bred to produce superior fleece and high-grade meat, and to yield good quantities of both. We have seen how some prosper in the mountains and some in the lowlands.

Dorset sheep were developed in Dorset and Somerset counties, England. The Dorset sheep would have a hard time fitting into the pattern so far developed. Their fleece is poor, relatively speaking, both in quality and in quantity. The fleece of a ram Dorset sheep averages 7 pounds, while that of the ewe usually weighs about 6 pounds. In weight, the animals are between the Shropshire and the Southdown. In fleece value, they are also between these. You might suppose from all this that there would be no sense in raising Dorset sheep. But there you would be wrong.

Dorset rams weigh about 200 pounds; the ewes about 160 pounds. The face and legs of Dorsets are white. The nose is usually flesh-colored. They breed unusually early in the season. They produce large numbers of lambs, which are born early. The ewes give an abundance of milk, and the lambs grow rapidly. As a result, about 10 weeks after a Dorset lamb is born it may be ready for the market, and early spring lambs bring a better price than do those that come later in the season. Thus the Dorset sheep have a valuable characteristic that the other breeds do not have, and therefore they are worth raising. Their permanence in the whole general scheme of sheep husbandry is assured. Their possibilities have not been exhausted. They thrive in close quarters, and the time may come when living space on the world may be one of the most important of things.

Corriedale Sheep · *Ovis aries* · Bovidae

Dung

So far, in our discussions of sheep, we have left out one consideration. A breed may be most successful in one area and a failure in another. One of the major mistakes men have made in handling animals is in assuming that because an animal does well in one place, it will be sure to do equally well elsewhere. The secret of success in this game seems to be combining the known qualities of different breeds in such a way that the resultant animals will fit the environment where one finds himself living.

An example of this is the story of the Corriedale sheep, which was developed originally as a dual-purpose animal, in part from Merino stock. In New Zealand it now ranks second only to the Romney in total number of purebred animals raised.

Toward the end of the nineteenth century, after some discouragement, sheepbreeders in New Zealand found that Merinos were successful in the lowlands but not near the mountaintops. It was found that a cross of Merinos with Corriedales solved the problem in the South Island, while a somewhat similar combination, using Romney sheep instead of Corriedales, brought success in the North Island. Since nearly half of the total land area of New Zealand is devoted to sheep raising, this discovery was most important to the country. And since New Zealand contributed considerably to the economy of England, the "mother country," it was also important in the relations between the two parts of the British Commonwealth.

Here, once again, it may be seen that this business of man and his associated mammals has wide implications. Who can say that this or that mammal is the more important? Perhaps this book may have helped you to understand how varied are the services given to man by his associated mammals, and may have suggested ways in which that relationship may be made mutually more satisfactory. I hope that such has been the case.

INDEX

Other Books by
E. LAURENCE PALMER

Fieldbook of Nature Study
Aids to Knowing Natural Science
Fieldbook of Natural History
Fieldbook of Mammals

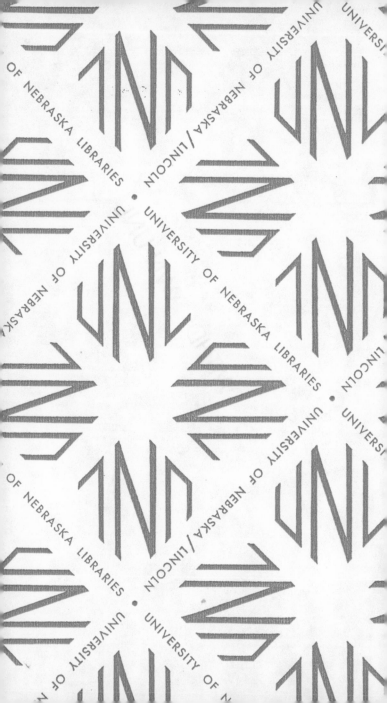